Women in A

G000141309

INTIMATE
KNOWLEDGE

ents

Plates

Figure, tables and map

Figure

Tables

Map

Acknowledgments

I am indebted to a large number of people without whom this study would not have been possible. Foremost, I wish to thank the people of Ban Srisaket (a pseudonym) for their hospitality and patience. Grandmother Bun let us stay in her house with her and shared her life with us. The Bencharoon family was always there with smiles and assistance. I wish to thank all my grandmothers, aunts, mothers and sisters of Ban Srisaket who shared their knowledge and experiences with me. I also wish to thank the women in the various villages in Roi Et and Khon Kaen provinces where I have conducted more recent research.

I am grateful to the District Head, Village Headmen and other district officials who facilitated my stay, as well as the staff of the Village Health Station in Ban Srisaket and the District Hospital and District Public Health Office. More recently, I wish to thank the Head of the Khon Kaen Provincial Health Office, Dr Kamron Chaisiri for his assistance and the public health staff in the various Districts in Khon Kaen and Roi Et where I have conducted research.

During my work in the North-east, I have enjoyed the support of Khon Kaen University. In particular, I wish to thank the staff of the Faculty of Nursing, Khon Kaen University, especially Dean Kalaya Patanasri, Former Dean Darunee Riykorakarn and Professor Rutja Phipaibul. I thank Associate Dean Siriporn Chirawatkul for her continuing friendship, support and advice. The staff of the Faculty of Public Health, in particular Professor Aroon Chirawatkul have also been very helpful throughout my research. In this regard I also wish to thank Dr David Elkins and Dr Melissa Haswell-Elkins and their staff for their assistance. I also appreciate the assistance extended to me by the staff of Srinagarind Hospital, Khon Kaen.

Many other people in Khon Kaen supported and sustained my husband and me with their hospitality and friendship. I owe a debt of gratitude to Sriubol Prachoomchit, Teranit Prachoomchit, and their children, Ron McMahon and Josie Ryan and their children, Lori Pomerenke as well as Sasithorn Inthayung, Dr Aree Pramote and John Bryant.

There were a number of organisations who supported the research. The National Research Council of Thailand gave permission to conduct the research. Funding was provided through an Australian Postgraduate Research Award and Australian Award for Research in Asia, The Walter and Eliza Hall

Travelling Fellowship, 1990, and a Vacation Scholarship to the National Thai Studies Centre, The Australian National University. My more recent research was funded by an Australian Research Council Postdoctoral Fellowship at the Gender Relations Project, The Australian National University. Some material presented in this book has previously appeared elsewhere. Sections of chapter 2 appear in *Thai Sexuality and Modernity*, edited by Peter Jackson and Nerida Cook, published by Silkworm Books, Chiang Mai (1999). Likewise, some material used in chapter 4 are my extracts from *Maternity and Reproductive Health in Asian Societies* edited by Pranee Liamputtong Rice and Lenore Manderson (published by Harwood Academic Publishers, (c)1996 OPA (Overseas Publishers Association) Amsterdam B.V). Chapter 5 is a revised version of my paper in *Asian Studies Review* (1996) and Chapter 6 is a revised version of my paper in *Medical Anthropology* (c)1999 OPA (Overseas Publishers Association) Amsterdam B.V.

Various people have also worked with me as research assistants both during my fieldwork in 1991-93 and more recently in 1997. My thanks to Kwanjai Hengsawat, Champhen Bencharoon and Yupin and especially Somjai Lomarath who lived in Ban Srisaket for two months with me and continues to help with her friendship, detailed knowledge and sound advice. Chulaphon Sangoentongullaya and Jaruwan Panta-armart assisted with my interview survey in 1997 and Amornrat Sricamsuk acted as my research assistant for four months in 1997. She and her family provided a wealth of assistance and friendship.

In Australia, I wish to thank the staff of the Tropical Health Program, ACITHN, University of Queensland. In particular, I would like to express my appreciation to Professor Lenore Manderson as my supervisor, mentor and friend, for her continued enthusiasm and support for my work. I also wish to thank Dr Margaret Jolly, and Ms Annegret Schemberg of the Gender Relations Project, Australian National University for their encouragement and assistance. Dr Shelley Mallett of the Gender Relations Project and Roger Averill sustained me with their friendship. Finally, I am grateful to the Series Editor, Dr Louise Edwards of the Australian Catholic University who encouraged me to persist with this book and provided much helpful advice and outstanding support.

I wish to thank my family for their continued support throughout the years and dedicate this book to my parents who always encouraged me in my studies. Finally, I want to thank Bruce Missingham for accompanying me to Ban Srisaket and for his love, support and intellectual companionship.

1 Introduction: Fevers of poverty

White smoke curls from each house. The sticky rice is being steamed upon charcoal fires. *Bok, bok, bok*, women crush chillies in their mortars, preparing the morning meal. In the cool of dawn, women complete the household tasks, sweeping the floors and yard, feeding scrawny chickens, leaving for the fields to collect mulberry leaves for the voracious silkworms. Other villagers have already left for the fields to water dry-season crops. Muddy men scoop up fish with circular nets from the almost-dry dams in the paddy fields.

From the fields, Ban Srisaket seems an oasis of green trees, contrasting with the surrounding flat, brown rice fields. Beneath this canopy of trees houses clump together, a collection of weathered wood, bamboo matting and rough carpentry. Most houses stand on stilts. Some have a buffalo pen underneath and a rice barn in one corner of the yard. Large concrete jars are assembled under the eaves, to collect rain water for drinking. Around the houses mango trees, kapok, bananas, tamarind trees, jackfruit trees and areca palms cluster, whilst in the gardens betel leaf vines, basil, chillies, lemon grass, and jasmine grow. It is a thoroughly humanised, cultured landscape.

The sticky rice is cooked, rolled into large balls, and placed inside the rice baskets, hot and fragrant; a special portion has been put aside for the monks. By now old villagers have already started to file to the temple. Other people stand outside their homes, chatting to their neighbours. As the line of saffron-robed monks files past, women kneel and bring their hands together to *wai* them, showing respect as they carefully place lumps of sticky rice into the monks' bowls. Mothers wash young children, who squeal at the cold water being splashed over their heads. Older children have already led the buffaloes out to the fields to graze.

The morning meal is ready and straw mats are laid out in a cool place for everyone to sit in a circle around sticky rice baskets and dishes of fish paste and greens. Small balls of rice are kneaded between the fingers and then dipped into the side dishes. Family and friends share news and laughter and

1

discuss the day's work. Some people are going to the provincial capital today—they have already left on the rumbling trucks that pass through the village and slowly wind through other villages along the 60-kilometre journey. The dust rises up from the village paths and drifts down on everything and everyone. *Shoo!* A man swears at a chicken stealing food from his plate.

Children walk to school through the dust, their white shirts glowing in the bright light. Their friends totter along riding oversized bicycles. Young women put away the food, sweep the floor again, and collect water for washing clothes and bodies. Hungry pigs grunt and squeal as rice mash is poured into their troughs. Old people have settled in the shade of a mango tree.

Plate 1.1 Grandmother Bun weaves silk.

Trying to be a conscientious researcher, I have been going from house to house in the heat asking people about any illnesses or chronic conditions they have experienced within the household in the last two weeks. This morning I visit Aunt Joy. She sits under her house weaving silk, chatting to a neighbour playing with her infant. I am impressed by her gnarled hands deftly controlling the loom. Silk thread shimmers as it runs into the cloth. Clod, clap. Clod, clap. Strand by strand the cloth is woven on the loom, revealing an intricate pattern thread by thread in purple and gold. We chat for a while as she weaves. We talk a little about her family and mine. She is bemused as I explain my survey. I ask her: 'Is anyone in the household sick this week?'

She smiles, 'Oh yes! I have *khai bor mi ngen*[1], the fever of poverty' she answers.

***

I came to Ban Srisaket to learn about the lives and health of people of North-east Thailand. As a study on health this book concentrates upon the intimacies of women's bodies. But as Aunt Joy reminds us, the experience of health and illness within North-east Thailand is embedded within a broader social and economic context. Throughout this book women relate their health to the demands of physical labour in domestic chores, in the fields and in the factories of Bangkok. They tell of the added burdens of childbirth and family planning, all of which combine to make it difficult to maintain good health. They speak of the constraints of poverty and their position as women. Poverty is related to the illnesses they suffer and hinders their access to care. Furthermore, illness jeopardises people's ability to maintain an income. Just as poverty causes illness, illness causes poverty. The insidious fevers of poverty are chronic and not easily cured.

Medical anthropology is fundamentally concerned with the nexus between the body as a physiological entity and as a social entity in relationship with other bodies/society. My intention in this work is twofold: to present North-east Thai women's knowledge and experiences of their bodies, health and illness, and to situate their descriptions within a broader analytic framework of the political and social context of the developing Thai state. For health is not merely a biological state, but socially constructed by political and economic processes. At one level, this work aims to describe the cultural context of health and healing as it applies to women in North-east Thailand. But at a second level, I propose that notions of tradition and modernity are key components in the meanings surrounding health practices, strategic fields for the production and negotiation of meanings about the world and one's place in it. An emergent theme through the various chapters is the location of knowledge and practices of the body within discourses of national development and modernity in Thailand and the ways in which representations of tradition align poverty and underdevelopment with ethnic and cultural difference. The negotiation and alignment of these discourses of modernity and tradition is explored with reference to the health of women.

Living on the margins: North-east Thailand

North-east Thailand is known colloquially as Isan, a Pali-Sanskrit term meaning North-east. This term implicitly reflects the marginal orientation of the region in relation to the social and economic centre of Thailand, the Central Plains and Bangkok. Despite constituting 31 per cent of the Thai population, people of the North-east remain marginalised economically, socially and culturally (Keyes 1989). The majority of the population are ethnically distinct, Lao-speaking people who express a collective identity based upon domestic language, cultural practices and regional history distinct from Central Thai people. The region is the least developed and poorest region of Thailand, with the highest incidence of poverty, calculated at 36.3 per cent of the population in 1988 (Krongkaew 1993:412-13, 431-34). Rice farming is the principal productive activity.

The relationship between the North-east and the Thai state has been characterised as one of internal colonialism involving systematic neglect and extraction (Brown 1994:173). Bangkok remains the 'primate city' of Thailand, the primary urban centre where political power and economic resources are concentrated (London 1980). Indicators of health status also reflect the marginality of the North-east. The North-east region has the highest incidence of diarrhoeal diseases, and the highest case fatality ratio from diarrhoeal diseases in the country (Thongkrajai, Thongkrajai, & Stoeckl n.d.). It also has the highest incidence of deaths from obstetric and perinatal causes, malaria and haemorrhagic fever in the country (Kanchanaraksa 1987:23). The cause of highest morbidity in the North-east is infectious diseases. In contrast, in more developed parts of Thailand, the causes of highest morbidity are diseases of the circulatory system, diseases of the nervous systems and endocrine disturbance (Kanchanaraksa 1987:12). Whereas the trend in Thailand is towards more of the 'lifestyle diseases' such as cardiovascular diseases and neoplasms, the North-east still shows high incidences of nutritional deficiencies, acute respiratory tract infections, and parasitic infections, associated with low socio-economic status.

Representations of Isan

Central Thai culture is defined by the state as the 'elite' culture of Thailand, both for Central Thais and Isan people. An important theme of this book is the way in which Central Thai identity is also associated with modernity and urban elite values and aspirations differentiated from rural peasant traditions. The discourses that constitute ethnicity are important as they are one basis by which the nation-state assigns resources and the ways in which people are categorised and treated by members of the dominant group. Essentially, they reflect and shape the relations of power between a group of people and the nation state. Theories of cultural politics pose questions of who controls the institutions and mechanisms of cultural production and distribution, which cultural representations and practices are produced, reproduced, sanctioned and valued by dominant interest groups, how these representations are 'consumed' or challenged by other groups and how social inequalities are legitimated through culture (Jordan & Weedon 1995:5). Cultural representations and practices are a 'site of contestation', open to resistance, reinterpretation and challenge by other social groups.

The elite culture emanates from and is reproduced by the state and mass media through the rhetoric of state officials, via the bureaucracy and public education. It is transmitted nightly into the flickering television screens of villagers. In these dominant forms of cultural production, the extension of state authority and capitalism are equated with national 'development', 'progress' and 'prosperity'. Pervasive imagery contrasts the social and economic comforts of 'modern life' to rural poverty and the practice of 'traditional ways'.

This contrast between tradition and modernity is captured in the use of the terms *samai kau, samai korn* (old times, past times) and *samai mai* (new times). This language is employed by people at all levels of Thai society in reference to perceived differences both between the present and the past but also between the status and prestige of images and practices which originate in the dominant culture of the urban-based middle and upper classes, and the customs and beliefs associated with life in rural communities and among regional minorities. These concepts provide a common ideological framework for explaining ongoing disparities in the distribution of wealth and power as matters of having (or lacking) knowledge and experience of 'modern' ways rather than as inequalities of class, gender, ethnicity and/or regional underdevelopment (Mills 1993).

Public discourses on Isan reinforced daily in the mass media draw upon a range of stereotypical images and narratives. Urban, modern, educated, wealthy and progressive Central Thais (usually from Bangkok) are commonly contrasted with rural, traditional, ignorant, poor and backward Lao/Isan villagers. Through such representations, the moral authority of change and modernity mediates ethnicity and class position, aligning inequalities, exploitation and underdevelopment with Lao-ness and a failure of peasants to adapt to modern times. This alignment of values runs as a subtext throughout this book. Through it, Isan villagers are constituted as subjects of 'development', and education.

As Hobart has argued, a central theme to such development discourses is the 'attribution of ignorance' to members of the subordinate group (1993:6). People's attachment to 'tradition', local practices and rituals, are constructed as obstacles to change and responsible for the continuation of ignorance and underdevelopment. Isan villagers are subjected to a 'project of enlightenment' revolving around the acquisition of appropriate knowledge in agricultural practices, in schooling and health (see Ram 1998).

Such public definitions of Isan culture affect health service providers' perception of their clients and community practices. The practices and policies operating in health care settings often revolve around assumptions of ignorance mediating the subordinate economic and ethnic status of villagers. For example, the tensions which exist between local traditional healers and the Thai public health system, several aspects of nutrition such as changing eating habits regarding raw fish, difference in cultural ideas concerning hygiene, water supply and rituals, and attitudes based on local wisdom are informed by notions of ethnicity. The mediation of Isan/Lao ethnicity thus runs as a subtext throughout this book. Women's corporeal experiences of their health, the choices they make, the options available to them and the ways in which they are treated are saturated with power relations pertaining to gender, class and ethnic difference, discernible through a contest between 'tradition' and 'modernity' (see Jolly 1998).

As I argue throughout this book, the meanings and values attributed to *samai mai* and *samai korn* are neither fixed nor uncontested, but women tend to encounter these disjunctures as personal dilemmas—decisions about new practices of birthing and post-partum, new contraceptive technologies, whether or not to breastfeed. At times women embrace new modern technologies of the body—as with family planning, at others, they contest the assumptions and practices of biomedicine. At all times their decisions are constrained by their marginal social status and their poverty.

'Politics of reproduction'

Ginsburg and Rapp (1991) have drawn attention to the 'politics of reproduction', the fundamental linkages between local level actions and broader social ideologies and practices. As a number of recent edited collections testify, colonialism, state-making, capitalist transformations of economic markets and globalisation all have their effects upon the intimacies of reproduction (see Ginsburg & Rapp 1991; Greenhalgh 1995c; Ram & Jolly 1998). Varied approaches to menstruation, contraception, antenatal care, birth, lactation, menopause, infertility, reproductive tract infections and the ways in which women care for their bodies and that of their infants are positioned within the colonial and postcolonial narratives of states, the economic and social forces that mould state institutions and state imperatives. The multiple variations health practices display across different settings demonstrate the particular ways in which ethnic, gender and class categories are imposed upon and construct social and individual bodies and the consequences of these upon health behaviours and access to care. The effects of these processes however, are not uncontested, and, as this book illustrates, spaces remain for resistance. The recognition of the agency of women in negotiating their identities as women, mothers and wives underlies this work, and is revealed in the choices that the Isan women of this study make in the modes of healing they use, their use of family planning services or their decisions about post-partum care. Such acts are read throughout this study not only as practical health behaviours but also as markers of identity and, in some cases, struggles over cultural meanings and autonomy.

Approaching the body: discourses, institutions, corporeality

Much of the literature that takes the body as the focus of analysis has concentrated on the way in which the body is 'constituted in the intersection of . . . institutions, discourses and corporeality' (Frank 1991:49, his emphasis). Foucault identified 'discourses' as historically situated ways of specifying knowledge and truth. Through the production of knowledge or 'truths', discourses constitute power and are institutionalised as a set of practices. Foucault describes the network of power relations as a 'dense web that passes through apparatuses and institutions, without being exactly located in them' (Foucault 1984:96). In this way, 'discourses can be both an instrument of and an effect of power' (1984:101) through constituting and expressing certain forms of knowledge as 'truth'. Practices within institutions mediate the dissemination of knowledge and, in doing so, exercise power that subjugates those who interact with the institution. In his genealogies of prisons, madness and medicine, Foucault was concerned to explore how particular practices and knowledges appropriated and regulated the body within a network of institutions. For example, in The Birth of the Clinic (1973), Foucault described how medical knowledge and practice functioned at the micro-level to establish medical power. His studies of prisons (1977) and sexuality (1984) were similarly concerned with the ways in which bodies are managed and disciplined.

A number of feminists have applied Foucault's ideas to examine women's bodies as politically inscribed entities, with their physiology shaped, managed and controlled through practices and discourses (see discussion in Bordo 1993). Emily Martin focuses on the representation of the body in medical and popular discourse, drawing attention to the ways in which technological society tends to see the body in terms of economic metaphors of energy and production, birthing in terms of implicit economics and labour (1987). Similarly, this book explores the discourses and discursive practices related to public health, biomedicine, and modernisation and development, which constitute male and female bodies in sometimes complementary, sometimes contradictory ways.

The institutions in which I am primarily interested are those of the health system: village health stations, hospitals, public health programs. These are institutions which promote or suppress certain discourses concerning village women's bodies. The institutions themselves are constituted through discourses concerning development and modernisation.

One aspect of the institutions explored in this work is their position as sites which manage and discipline women's bodies. The analysis of the disciplining of bodies and populations emerges from both Foucault's concept of 'bio-power' and from feminist theories of women's bodies as the sites and expression of power relations (Bailey 1993:102).[2] In this book, I am interested to explore bio-power not only in terms of the institutions that create discourses but also the sites at which these discourses are enacted, resisted or transformed, that is, the bodies of women. Bio-politics includes the overt regulation of the population through family planning programs, or the illegal status of abortion, but also the indirect forms of self-government and through disciplinary regimens which align personal behaviour and self-management with political and economic objectives of the state.

The surveillance and regulation of women and women's sexuality in antenatal clinics, family planning programs and abortion legislation, draws attention to the ways the female body is governed through medical discourse and practice. This is not to say that these practices always constitute oppressive or negative outcomes. As the women in this study frequently state, the changes to their lives that have come through the advent of contraception and the decrease in maternal mortality have been embraced by women in Ban Srisaket. This provides a perfect example of the Foucauldian alternative view of power as not only producing negative repressive effects, but positive enabling effects (Foucault 1980).

Embodiment

More recently, theorists have struggled to develop an analytical framework that encompasses both the representations and constructions of the body through discourses and institutions, but also recognises that bodies are lived experiences. Through their concept of the mindful body, Lock and Scheper-Hughes argue for a recognition of the body as an entity which carries a range of meanings and aspects. The body is assumed to be 'simultaneously a physical and symbolic artifact, as both naturally and culturally produced, and as securely anchored in a particular historical moment' (Scheper-Hughes & Lock 1987:7). Their approach derives from a recognition that the Western intellectual tradition has been based upon the Cartesian postulate of the mind/body dichotomy and seeks to set up a foundation for comparative work without a reliance on universalist definitions of mind or body (see discussion in Strathern 1996). They describe three perspectives from which we may explore the various relationships, representations and practices. First, there is the individual body, the sense of the embodied self as experienced apart from other bodies. The constituent parts of the individual body/mind/self and the ways in which the body is experienced in health and sickness are highly variable cross-culturally. At this level, medical anthropology is concerned to describe cross-cultural differences in body imagery, disease aetiology and treatments, and cultural differences in the conception of the self. The second level of analysis is that of the 'social body', a natural symbol for thinking about relationships between nature, society and culture (Scheper-Hughes & Lock 1987:6). At this level the anthropologist is concerned with the symbolic uses of the body as a metaphor of society and social relations. The third level of embodiment considered is that of the body politic, referring to the regulation and control of individual and social bodies (1987:8). This level of analysis elucidates the power relations between particular social groups, or individuals and groups, and the processes of socialisation, regulation and conformity to the social and political order.

My approach within this book attempts to incorporate these various levels of analysis through an understanding of the body as the site of representations and interventions. But I wish to move further in exploring the means through which cultural practices play a central role in constituting our sense of ourselves through the enculturated body. In doing so, I do not wish to objectify women's bodies as though they are devoid of intentionality and subjectivity, but explore *embodiment* as both representation and as the means through which we engage with the world, understand ourselves, and create culture (Csordas 1994).[3] I am interested in the ways in which bodily practices of healing, of contraception and ways of birthing create and mediate understandings of who Isan people are, their place in wider Thai society, and the experiences of the 'modern' woman. Thus this book is not just about how the intimacies of the body are constituted in discourse and in the institutions of the Thai state, but also how they are *experienced* and contribute to female subjectivity. Throughout this book, corporeality, the actual bodily processes of women—menstruation, abortion, birth—are fundamental. My interest is in the ways in which these processes are culturally constructed, elaborated, and inform women's understandings of themselves.

From this perspective then, this work poses some basic questions. How are particular bodily practices institutionalised? In what ways do the lived bodily experiences of women conform to institutionalised power and authority, or alternatively subvert or contest it? How do bodily practices mediate ideas about modernity and tradition and women's identity?

Resistance

In doing so, this work crosses onto territories long traversed in anthropology by engaging with fundamental questions of agency and structure. Throughout the book, women make pragmatic choices about health services, birthing, abortion and contraception. In turn, through their practices and the relationships they entail, women enact and create identities. But these choices and women's diverse motivations are constrained by pre-existing medical discourses, power hierarchies and at times the overt interventions of the state.

An important consideration is the extent to which women are able to resist. The exercise of power is not absolute: 'discourse transmits and produces power; it reinforces it, but also undermines and exposes it, renders it fragile and makes it possible to thwart it' (Foucault 1984:101). The possibility of resistance draws attention to the agency of individuals and the ways in which they may actively fashion their identities (Petersen 1993:121). As Bordo writes, 'even the most subordinated subjects are therefore continually confronted with opportunities for resistance, for making meanings that oppose or evade the dominant ideology' (Bordo 1993:193).

However, some writers suggest that we need to re-evaluate our attributions of resistance; that 'resistance is rapidly becoming a word that covers anything, defines itself, and may be said to exist because we insist that it do so' (Lewin 1998:164). As Brodwin warns, there is a tendency among anthropologists to produce 'heroic representations of people usually marginalised in global politics', which at the same time 'delegitimises peoples' literal (and often more circumscribed) accounts of body/self experiences' (see also Abu-Lughod 1990; Brodwin 1996:197). Abu-Lughod speaks of the theoretical dilemmas that arise in anthropological efforts to cast 'everyday' behaviour as resistance, particularly in relation to our notions of agency and consciousness and the presumed opposition between resistance and accommodation. Kielmann summarises the issues thus: '[H]ow does one investigate the ways in which women's bodily knowledge and practices are limited through asymmetrical power structures, and at the same time treat women as knowledgeable actors in the constitution of social life?' (1998:135).

She calls for a more nuanced and reflexive analysis of body action. In her study of infertile women in Tanzania, Kielmann argues that:

women derive and articulate different sometimes opposing possibilities
for meaning and conduct *on the margins* of dominant discourses
regulating their bodies. It is this position that allows them to defend their
knowledge of the body, to mediate between social orders, and to invent
new forms of knowledge (1998:138).

Isan women also occupy the margins of dominant discourses in their movements between conflicting sites and bodies of knowledge as they manage their reproductive health. At times their actions resist the dominant rhetoric, subvert or comply with it. Throughout this book, women respond pragmatically to their personal dilemmas and experiences. But whatever their intent, their acts either implicitly or explicitly comply with, accommodate, or contest institutional authority and forge their identity. For example, the discussion of abortion in the final chapter is an excellent example of pragmatic acts which may both ratify and subvert social ideas concerning the body, femininity, moral order and religious identity.

On occasion, women state their conscious awareness of their bodies as sites of mediation; how the symptoms they suffer form part of wider oppression and subordination. They talk of the linkages between work conditions, poverty and their illness, their lack of access to expensive doctors. They are aware of the denigration of traditional sources of healing power by biomedical practitioners and the local struggles over moral authority and healing power. At these times they articulate a sophisticated understanding of the mediation between their bodily experiences and the wider social forces which are fragmenting rural society. As discussed earlier, often their explanations are phrased in terms of differences between the past and the present, between modern life and past tradition.

Women's health

Women's health has become the subject of renewed interest in recent years.[4] Public health programs for women have traditionally placed emphasis upon maternal and child health (MCH), concentrating upon pregnant women and their children and neglecting other women's health issues (Winikoff 1988:197). However, despite several decades of maternal and child health programs, women throughout the developing world continue to suffer poor health. There is increased concern about the high rates of cancer of the reproductive system among women in developing countries, the substantial morbidity and social consequences of a variety of reproductive tract infections and the threat of HIV infection. Experience in health centres in developing countries suggests that while the incidence of reproductive tract infections (RTIs) and other troublesome conditions is substantial, many women do not seek treatment from the formal health sector for these problems, or else postpone treatment until the condition is acute. A culture of silence reigns over vaginal discharge, pain during intercourse, and chronic pelvic pain along with other reproductive health problems, such as menstrual difficulties, contraceptive side effects, miscarriages, stillbirths, and potentially life-threatening clandestine abortions (Dixon-Mueller & Wasserheit 1991:11). As many women in this study state, such problems are endured as *pokati,* the 'normal' and inevitable consequences of being female. The chronic results of these conditions, such as pain, malodorous discharge, discomfort during intercourse, itching and painful urination, receive little acknowledgment by health care providers, but may affect the social, economic and psychological quality of women's lives (Cook 1993).

Anthropological perspectives contribute to understanding the specific local cultural encodings, responses, and practices surrounding these issues. In parallel with public health interest in maternal and child health, early ethnographic studies drew attention to the diverse ways of managing pregnancy, childbirth and mothering (Jordan 1993 [1978]; Kay 1982; MacCormack 1982). Other studies brought attention to the cross-cultural management of breastfeeding and infant care (Hull & Simpson 1985) or menstruation (Buckley & Gottlieb 1988; Chu 1993) and menopause (Chirawatkul 1993). Emily Martin's (1987) study in the United States was one of the first studies to forego the artificial partitioning of women's experience by bringing together the multiple facets of reproductive health in examining menstruation, childbirth, lactation and menopause as aspects of ongoing

embodied female experience. Similarly, Sobo's (1993) study of Jamaican
ethnophysiology explores how the body and culturally constructed idioms of
health and sickness serve as metaphors for the social and moral order. More
recent editions not only reinstated a holistic approach to the varied facets of
women's health, but have explored these within broader social, historical and
economic processes (Ginsburg & Rapp 1995a; Greenhalgh 1995c; Ram &
Jolly 1998; Rice & Manderson 1996).

However, there remain few studies which fully contextualise women's
health within a single cultural setting. This book provides a more completely
grounded ethnography in which women's experiences take centre stage. This
provides an opportunity to unravel some of the complex political and
economic processes interweaving through their experience.

Previous studies on women's health in Thailand

The majority of studies on women's health in Thailand have been
demographic studies and surveys on reproduction and contraceptive use
stimulated by Thailand's successful family planning program. Likewise, the
majority of anthropological studies of women's health have concentrated on
birthing, with little discussion of other aspects of women's reproductive
health. Phya Anuman Radjadhon's work on *Customs Connected with Birth
and Rearing of Children*, originally published in Thai in 1949 and in English
in 1961, continues to be quoted as a classic reference on 'tradition' by scholars
(Anuman 1961). As part of the longitudinal Cornell Thailand Project, Hanks
(1963) documented the beliefs and rituals surrounding maternity. Now over 45
years-old, her work serves as an historical marker of practices in Central
Thailand. Other early works on birth include Pedersen's (1968) descriptive
ethnography which concentrated upon the Lao Song Dam in Ratburi and
Mougne's (1978) ethnography of reproduction in a Northern village, based on
research carried out in the 1970s. Later works on reproduction include
Poulsen's longitudinal study (1983). It follows changes in birthing practices
over a 20-year period in a North-east village from 1961 to 1978. Although not
well-known, this study provides a wealth of information about North-eastern
practices and changes over time. Most of these researchers have been content
to describe rituals and practices without situating these within the broader
context of social change or within a theoretical framework. Muecke's (1976;
1984) work on birth among urban Northern Thai women is significant in this
respect in that it describes health practices as part of a broader world view in
which women aspire to a range of markers of modernity. Van Esterik's (1985)
work on breastfeeding reflects the public health concern with the decline of
breastfeeding. Her work also situates health within the broader context of
women's lives and the conditions of their changing economic roles. Irvine's
(1982) thesis is one of the first to approach health within a broader framework

of the conceptions of the person and self, and the politics of the nation-state. Within his work is a section devoted to the intimate link between reproductive health practices and indigenous notions of mental health.

A range of recent studies have broadened the picture of Thai women and their health and will be drawn upon in this work. They represent the growth of medical anthropology within Thailand and a growing interest in women's health issues. Siriporn Chirawatkul (1993) studied the construction of menopause in North-east Thailand within the context of the shift from traditional social mores to those of the modern Thai state and the increased adoption of a Western biomedical construction of menopause as a disease. Pimpawun Boonmongkhon's work on infertility (1997), and more recently on reproductive tract infections (1998), explores women's feelings on subjects rarely discussed in Thailand and provides a baseline for public health interventions. Warunee Fongkaew's (1997) work on female sexuality and reproductive health represents an intimate description of the secret worlds of women, detailing young women's knowledge of their bodies, their naivety in sexual negotiations and their risks of infection with HIV.

Academic writings on women and gender in Thailand

These works form part of a growing literature on women and gender in Thailand. Early writings on gender relations in Thailand proposed ideals of gender complementarity and the relatively equal status of men and women (Hanks & Hanks 1963). These writings usually made implicit comparisons between the status of Thai women and women in other areas of Asia. A 1963 article by Hanks and Hanks entitled 'Thailand: equality between the sexes' stresses the equal but complementary and relatively undifferentiated roles of men and women, based on observations in Central Thailand. They described men and women in rural village life as jointly cooperating in domestic and agricultural tasks and sharing household decision-making and resources. The customary female inheritance of land, the practice of a marriage payment from the groom to the bride's family (rather than dowry), as well as the preference for post-marital residence with the wife's parents were all cited as evidence of the high status of Thai women. Hanks and Hanks (1963) suggested that this high status was under threat with increased westernisation and commercialisation.

This image of the high status of Thai women was continued in a series of studies which focused upon the extent to which women provide the structural links in Northern Thai society (Davis 1984a; Hale 1979; 1984; Potter 1977; Turton 1972; Wijeyewardene 1984). This research was indicative of the movement occurring throughout the social sciences to address the paucity of studies on women. These writings emphasised the matrilateral bias in the Northern Thai kinship system, documenting practices such as the inheritance of land and houses by daughters, and the discovery of matrilineally organised spirit cults. An example is Potter's ethnography which was entirely woman-focused and explored the 'structural dominance of women . . . [but] an ideological dominance of men' in Northern Thailand (1977:11).

Opponents of this 'equal but different' school point to a range of other social indicators to argue for the subordinate status of women in Thailand. They argue that despite women's higher participation in the labour force than men, very few employed women work as administrative, executive or managerial workers, or in the professional or technical fields. On average Thai women still receive lower wages than men for similar tasks (Tantiwiramanond & Pandey 1997). Thai women continue to lack political and economic power and remain largely under-represented in government and higher levels of the public service. High reported female literacy rates often fail to reveal that many women have received only four years of schooling (Phongpaichit 1980:13). In addition, there is a lack of legal protection for women, especially regarding Thai laws on divorce, rape, property, and abortion (Prukpongsawalee 1982; Rathanamongkolmas 1983; Somswasdi 1987:13).

The most conspicuous image that pervades literature on sexual inequality in Thailand is that of the prostitute. There is an enormous literature on female prostitution in Thailand (although very little on male prostitution). Researchers argue over the numbers of prostitutes in Thailand, with estimates ranging from 120 000 to 700 000.[5] Although there is some debate as to the extent to which Thai men in rural areas use the services of prostitutes (Lyttleton 1994a), it is recognised that a significant proportion of Thai men patronise commercial sex workers and that discourses of Thai masculinity regard sexual adventure, including the use of prostitutes, as a normal and necessary activity for men (Fordham 1995; Hantrakul 1988). The sex industry ranges from village-based prostitution and women working at cattle markets to the Chinese tea-houses specialising in young virgins, to brothels, coffee shops and massage parlours and women working from hotels, to the men, women and children working with foreigners in tourist centres and the international trade in mail-order brides, domestic workers and escorts.[6] It is important to recognise the diversity of women in the sex industry and the complexity of their lives. Clearly, the experience of sex workers varies greatly according to whether they are discretionary sex workers who can choose their clients or are bonded workers who are forced to accept clients. Other factors which affect the degree of control sex workers have in their sexual encounters include their age, ethnicity, citizenship, dependents, health, place of work, mobility and drug dependency. Across the literature, regardless of the circumstances of the women involved, prostitution serves as a symbol of a misogynist and unequal society (see further discussion in Chapter 4).

Adding to this complex picture of the status of Thai women, other authors have looked at the role of Buddhism in informing gender ideologies. These studies emphasise the importance of Theravada Buddhism in Thai society and debate the extent to which it influences and is responsible for the status of women in Thailand. At times these largely textual analyses reduce the complexity of gender relations in Thailand to crude religious determinism rather than ethnographic engagement. In a 1975 paper Kirsch argued that the large preponderance of women in economic-entrepreneurial activities and the lack of women in political/bureaucratic roles could be explained by Buddhist principles. He suggests that the high levels of female participation in economic fields in Thailand is not a sign of high female status but, rather, reflects their subordinate spiritual status in Buddhism (Kirsch 1975). Kirsch argues that in Buddhism 'women's merit mobility is tied to a role in the world, that of wife and mother, and thus to particular relationships' (Kirsch 1982:27) as opposed to men who are associated with 'Other worldliness'. He suggested that when Thai women are seen to be engaged in economic pursuits (which they dominate) Westerners see this as a sign of their equality with men. However, he interprets this as being conditioned by a Buddhist devaluation of economic 'this worldly' activity in general.

Several other authors also document the subordination of Buddhist women across religious texts and in Buddhist practice (Tantiwiramanond & Pandey 1987; Thitsa 1980). In her work on Buddhist nuns, spirit mediums and prostitutes, Khin Thitsa argues that Thai women are considered subordinate to men. She sees Buddhist norms as being the basis for the exploitation and subordination of women in Thai society. She argues that Buddhist ideology represents women as inferior to men and negatively values female sexuality. Male control of women's sexuality is understood as a sign of their superior spiritual power and hence allows the continued exploitation of women within the sex industry (Thitsa 1980:85). The subordinate and ambivalent role assigned to female Buddhist nuns (*mae chi*) is taken as further proof of Buddhist misogyny. As a category *mae chi* are not admired or respected, but remain an anomalous and ambiguous group (Muecke 1989; Thitsa 1980).

Van Esterik (1982b) and Keyes (1984) also analyse Buddhist texts and practice, but continue to argue for women's complementary gender status. They acknowledge men's greater access to spiritual and moral power and prestige through the monkhood and men's domination in the bureaucracy. However, they argue that women enjoy a parallel prestige through their roles as mothers and nurturers. Women nurture their children and the Buddhist religion through their offerings to monks and by producing sons who will ordain as monks. Van Esterik argues that Buddhist values of attachment and detachment are associated with both male and female roles. Although there is no institutionalised role for women to be detached as monks, this does not mean that they are denied this goal (1982b). However, the concerns with textual interpretation and the popular images of monks, mothers and mistresses utilised in these works do little to explain the construction of gender as lived in day-to-day experience.

More recently, the types of questions asked about gender relations have changed. Localised accounts of different groups of women have deepened the understanding of gender ideologies, differences in power relations and the processes through which gender/sex systems are constructed, sustained and transformed. These studies were in response to a call for a reorientation in gender studies beyond debates on 'women's status' and subordination. These studies include Pasuk Phongpaichit's (1982b) study on rural women migrants working as prostitutes, Muecke's (1984) ethnography of lower-class urban women in the North and John Van Esterik's study of women meditation teachers (Van Esterik 1982a). Eberhardt's edited volume on women from minority populations in Thailand, the Akha, Yunnanese Chinese and the Shan explored the moral power of gender ideologies and how violations of the gender system are experienced as disturbing transgressions of social order (Eberhardt 1988; see alsoVan Esterik & Van Esterik 1992)[7].

Very few ethnographies exist of rural Thai women. Exceptions include Mill's study of young North-east village migrant women (1993) and Gray's thesis on young women in 'dormitory villages' surrounding Chiang Mai (1990). Both explore the experiences of village women as they migrate for work in the city and the new forms of status, prestige and gender relations involved in their transitions. Gray argues that young women are at the forefront of agrarian class differentiation. Education and other strategic resources determine young women's incorporation into the capitalist workforce and subsequent social mobility. This is increasing the differences between women and their households and changing the status markers within the community (1990). This observation has also been made by Muecke (1981; 1984) who argues that migration and smaller family sizes have separated women from traditional sources of status and that education and wealth have come to be seen as the predominant status markers for men and women. With their concern for the transformations occurring in rural society from modernisation, these studies foreshadow the perspectives on women and change that underlies my discussion of health and bodies.

Outline of the book

This book is the result of long-term ethnographic fieldwork in North-east Thailand. In 1991–93 I lived in North-east Thailand for eighteen months, spending over ten months of that time in living with my husband in the village of Ban Srisaket, conducting interviews, undertaking various surveys and observing (see Appendix 1 for methods). That village ethnography forms the basis of this book. The rest of my time in the North-east has been spent in a variety of other rural village settings in Khon Kaen and Roi Et provinces, most recently for eight months in 1996–97. Material collected during these visits is also incorporated into this book. The task of writing this text is problematic, as

I reduce to a few paragraphs the long time spent talking and chatting to people, the wasted efforts, the dances around the village at ordinations, the lies, laughs, and meals in between.

The themes of each chapter follow from the stories of women and cover a range of issues. The book is structured into discrete chapters, each of which explores certain health experiences, forcing divisions upon processes which are not lived as discrete events, but form part of embodied experience and identity.

Chapter 2 introduces the community of Ban Srisaket, and the changing construction of gender in Isan and the transformations taking place in the context of economic and social change associated with 'modernity'. Changing relationships between production and reproduction, changing priorities and the capitalist transformation of the village economy have all had repercussions in women's lives and the ways in which they view and experience their bodies. The changed needs of production, waged labour, migration, and smaller families have shifted the sources of status for women away from reproduction towards production. This chapter thus provides the context surrounding the tensions women negotiate in their decisions to work, to migrate, in the ways in which they order their lives and construct their identities.

The next chapter focuses upon understandings of the body in Isan. Bodily balance is manipulated and restored by domestic treatments with locally available medicines, the balancing of body humors through diet, or attention to the spiritual and social realm. These understandings of the body inform the decisions people make when they suffer illness or misfortune. Chapter 3 also introduces the ways in which discursive distinctions are made between the 'modern' and 'traditional' healing powers available to Isan people. 'Tradition' includes local knowledge and practices of health care and healing, and the guardians of that knowledge who remain largely excluded from state definitions of legitimacy. Local forms of knowledge as forms of 'cultural capital' are displaced by scientific biomedical knowledge in official discourses, practices and institutions: in public health education, hospital and primary health care services, university hospital training of doctors and nurses, and in the mass media. The meanings of illness may thus become contested as the patient moves between and negotiates the discursive frameworks and practices of biomedicine and traditional healers. The act of healing thus 'powerfully reinforce[s] the validity of meanings drawn from the dominant forms of knowledge in the wider culture' (Comaroff 1981:369). Yet the forms of knowledge themselves may be contested. Illnesses provide the occasion for the reinforcement and justification of cultural, social and political meanings. For Isan people these meanings relate to their cultural identity and relationship to the Thai state.

The meanings of women's bodies and the significance of processes of menstruation and humoral flows to concepts of health and strength are examined in Chapter 4. It introduces fundamental ethnogynaecological knowledge of the interrelationships between menstruation, vaginal discharge and women's strength and fertility. Women's ability to bear and nurture children successfully remains important to women's identity in Isan, as highlighted in women's stories of their attempts to conceive and carry a child. This chapter relates women's perceptions and experience of reproductive tract infections including sexually transmitted diseases. HIV/AIDS exposes the sexual contradictions and gender conflicts in Thai society and the inequalities which leave women in Ban Srisaket vulnerable to infection. In their declarations of the linkages between poor health and poverty, hard work and pain, and their lack of resources to secure a cure, women articulate their subordinate economic position within the Thai nation-state.

Chapter 5 grapples with issues surrounding the highly successful Thai family planning program. While the objectives of the state family planning program coincides with the desires of women to control their fertility, in their interactions with service providers, women are made participants in a process of medicalisation, regulation and surveillance with class and ethnic specific dimensions. Isan women are faced with discursive oppositions in health care as they become participants in a process where their bodies are constituted as the sites of reform and modernisation, just as their village society is the site of similar reforms and development by the state.

Chapter 6 explores birth and the post-partum period and the changes wrought by the introduction of Western biomedical practice. It analyses the power relations involved in representations of traditional birthing practices and the contested legitimacy of differing sources of knowledge. As the practice of birthing within the village declines, the authority of traditional knowledge and practices is being increasingly subordinated by 'modern' medical expertise regulated and promoted by the state. In essence, what I describe is a cultural contest involving different versions of knowledge and ascriptions of agency. In conflicts between traditional healers and government health officials, what is at stake is legitimacy of different systems of knowledge and a contest over the control of cultural capital. The continuation of traditional post-partum practices, despite knowledge of disapproval by biomedical doctors of these practices, can not only be read as practical health behaviours but also as ways in which people make meanings and assert identities that ignore or evade the dominant. Such resistance often involves the assertion of Isan ethnic identity through the maintenance of distinctive rituals and practices.

The question of abortion highlights the complexities of women's reproductive decision-making and the ways in which it entails relations of power. Despite the illegalities, the dangers to their health and the moral opprobrium attached to abortion, women assert their agency in seeking abortions in defiance of the state. The stories of women seeking abortions reveal the complexities of the context surrounding decisions to abort. It also calls for a nuanced approach to their actions, one which recognises that while having an abortion constitutes a resistance to the state's legitimacy to regulate women's reproductive bodies, at the same time women may consent to the dominant ideologies surrounding abortion and motherhood. This problematises the easy characterisation of women's actions.

This book situates reproductive health within the context of gender and sexuality as it is experienced in the lives of women, not as a construct separate and divorced from the broader issues affecting them. To this end, the stories and voices of women feature prominently throughout the text, informing the reader in their own words of their experiences and concerns.

2 Women of Isan

Grandmother Thau

Grandmother Thau sits on a bamboo platform at her home chewing betel nut. She is the oldest woman in Ban Srisaket, now eighty-six years of age. Although her memory is fading she can remember some events vividly. She recalls helping labouring in the fields, growing rice, growing cotton on the high ground, raising silkworms and making silk when she was young:

> I think of my mother. In those times living was hard; now things are easier. In those times you had to husk rice by hand; now we have machines to husk the rice. In those days everyone used buffaloes to plough the fields; now you can use machines . . .

Her education was limited as the only school in the village was run by the monks at the temple. She was from a prominent family in the village, and married a teacher when she was twenty-five. Her bride-price was 30 baht, which was very expensive, but as her husband earned wages of 12 baht a month, the elders decided he could afford it. She gave birth easily at home to a daughter. Her husband died soon after the birth, coughing up blood (probably from tuberculosis). Later she remarried Grandfather It, who became village headman and has since died. Her bride-price then was 9 baht. She gave birth to three sons. The youngest died after a severe headache which no local medicines could cure. Her daughter died as an adult after childbirth. Now she has six grandchildren. Grandmother Thau has lived in this house since her birth. Now she is looked after by one of her sons and his children.

Plate 2.1 Grandmother Thau remembers times past.

Wi

When she was nineteen years old Wi married a man from Ubol Ratchathani whom she met and lived with while she was working in Bangkok. He was twenty-three. Her bride-price was 17 000 baht and 1 baht weight of gold.[8]

Now she is twenty-one years old and gave birth to their first son ten months ago. When she was married she took the contraceptive pill for the first six months and then discontinued when they wanted a child. When she was three months pregnant, she travelled to Bangkok to find her husband who was working in a factory which produces plastic bags. She stayed in Bangkok throughout her pregnancy but returned when she was eight months pregnant to attend a merit-making ceremony for her dead father. Her husband returned to Bangkok soon after the birth. When her son was seven months old, she left him in the care of her mother and elder sister to return to work in Bangkok.

Plate 2.2 Wi nurses her baby.

She returned to Ban Srisaket after the baby started to become sick. Her husband sends 1000 baht each month. 'I think I will join him when the baby is a year old, as you can earn 2000 baht each month [A$125] and there is a place to stay at the factory.'

The stories of these two women summarise the enormous changes that have transformed the way of life of villagers in Ban Srisaket. The incorporation of North-east Thailand into the Thai state and the accompanying spread of capitalism have entailed physical and economic changes, but also altered the identity and expectations of men and women. Grandmother Thau's life has centred around marriage, children, land and subsistence agriculture. Mother Wi balances wage labour in Bangkok with her responsibilities to her family in the village. Her reproductive roles in caring for her child are separated from her economic activities. This chapter provides the background for the discussion of health and illness. It introduces the village of Ban Srisaket in North-east Thailand. Since the mid-nineteenth century the emerging institutions of the Thai nation-state, the development of industrial capitalism and engagement with the world economy have had a profound impact upon the social and economic organisation of village society[9]. As Giddens argues:

> The modes of life brought into being by modernity have swept us away from all traditional types of social order, in quite unprecedented fashion . . . the transformations involved in modernity are more profound than most sorts of change characteristic of prior periods . . . they have served to establish forms of social interconnection which span the globe; . . . they have come to alter some of the most intimate and personal features of our day to day existence (1990:4).

A number of theorists have described the emergence of multiple, fragmented or ambivalent selves under modern social orders, evidence of the extent to which modern discontinuities permeate intimate aspects of everyday experience and identification. An exploration of the culture of gender in Ban Srisaket reveals some of the alterations and changes in meanings that are affecting women as the bearers of tradition and modernity within the village. The first part will describe the traditional discourses of femininity within Isan, the practices and discipline that create the sexually appropriate gendered body, and the sexual patterning of production and reproduction within the community. The second part will describe the shifting representations of women within discourses of modernisation and the consequences for women as producers and reproducers. There is always a slippage in the ways in which people encounter and interpret dominant meanings in their everyday lives resulting in varied identities and responses which may differ from or even contest features of the dominant order. Women of Ban Srisaket experience the tensions between *samai mai* and *samai korn* ways of life as personal dilemmas as they negotiate decisions to migrate, desires for modern commodities and a different way of life (Mills 1993). Likewise, as later chapters describe, these same negotiations underlie women's decisions about their health, whether to use modern contraception or not, how to give birth, whether to continue post-partum practices. As such, this chapter examines a shift in the signification of women and their bodies, and provides a context for the later discussions of women's experiences of health and illness.

This chapter provides a brief background to the region and to the village of Ban Srisaket. This provides the context for a discussion of the place of women in Isan, the constraints and freedoms they experience which all have consequences for the later discussion of their health.

Map 2.1 Map of Thailand.

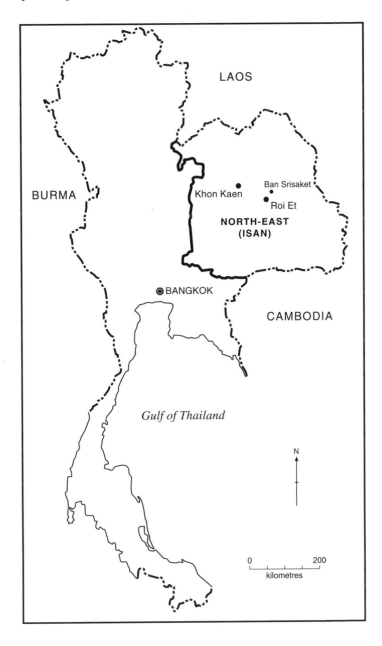

The village of Ban Srisaket

Ban Srisaket is located in the heartland of central Isan, in Roi Et Province. It is situated approximately 60 kilometres north of the provincial capital of Roi Et, near the border with Kalasin (see map 2.1). According to local oral history, Ban Srisaket was founded about two hundred years ago, by Lao migrants from the region of Suwannakhet in present-day Laos, escaping epidemics and political unrest in search of fertile land. In two hundred years the community they founded has grown to 740 households with a population of 3926 people. It is the largest community in the *tambon* (sub-district) and consists of six administrative *muban* with two temples, and on its outskirts are both a primary and secondary school, police station and health station.

Ask anyone of Ban Srisaket what they do as an occupation and they will answer *'het na het hai'* (I work rice paddies and high ground). The traditional strategy of farmers is to grow enough glutinous (sticky) rice to meet household consumption needs. Additional production is of non-glutinous rice for the market and other crops for sale.

Household land-holdings in Ban Srisaket are small, averaging 3 rai per head of population (1 rai is equivalent to 1600 square metres). In most cases, small land-holders no longer own enough to ensure a viable subsistence base and are forced to supplement subsistence rice production with day-labouring and migration.

The major constraint on rice production in Ban Srisaket is the often inadequate and unreliable rainfall patterns of the region. Without irrigation, the farmers of Ban Srisaket can only grow one rice crop each year from June to December. Anyone looking at the rice fields surrounding Ban Srisaket would be amazed to think that they can grow anything there. Infertile sandy soils and problems of salinity constrain production and force reliance on chemical fertilisers. In some fields the salt forms a glistening crust on the surface. Since the late 1960s all households have adopted new high-yield varieties of rice and associated chemical fertilisers and pesticides. Now farmers of Ban Srisaket must pay on average 250 baht per rai on chemical fertilisers, insecticides and other inputs in order to maintain yields (Thailand 1989b).

Apart from the yearly rice season, farmers of Ban Srisaket grow a variety of cash crops as well as dry-season vegetable crops for home consumption. Cassava is an important cash crop as it is well suited to the erratic rainfall patterns and poor soils of the area. Tobacco is planted under the supervision of private companies after the rice harvest but is of poor quality. In 1992 tomatoes were grown for their seeds under quotas to a Canadian agribusiness. In 1993, lucerne seed was cultivated also under a quota scheme for the Thai government. Decreasing soil fertility, smaller land-holdings and lower prices are increasingly limiting the productivity and income generated from cash crops.

In order to cover the input costs of fertiliser, pesticide and labour, most families obtain loans each year. Nearly all farming households in Ban Srisaket utilise credit from the Bank for Agriculture and Agricultural Cooperatives (BAAC) (*thanakhan phu'a kankaset le sahakorn*). The BAAC is considered one of the government's major financial commitments to rural development to allow small farmers access to credit. The case below represents a family earning close to the average agricultural income from diverse sources:

> This household consists of Phen, who is thirty-six years old, her husband Thorn, who is thirty-nine, and their two boys, now eleven and thirteen years old. Her husband is presently away with a group of other builders in Udorn Thani working on a temple building. He receives about 4000 baht for his work and takes such work whenever it is available. They have a little more than 5 rai of rice land which produced about 2000 kg of which they have already sold about 250 kg at 3.6 baht/kg, a total of 900 baht. The rest will be for their own consumption. Nearly 2 rai of land was planted with ordinary rice and produced almost 900 kg which they sold for 4000 baht. Through the dry season they grew tobacco on 1 rai for which they received 1300 baht after the company took out the production costs. They also grew 100kg of lucerne seed which sold for 4 000 baht but they are still waiting for payment. On their 1 rai of highland they grew cassava and produced almost 1250 kg which sold for 1000 baht. Their total income from agricultural sources was 11 200 baht (approx. A$700). They have a debt with the BAAC of 6000 baht (approx. A$375) for their input costs.

Detailed financial data from fifty-nine households in 1993 revealed that 88 per cent of these households were in debt, averaging 7525 baht/household. The majority of these were loans taken out with the BAAC annually to cover production costs. Loans are repaid by the farmer selling the harvest to the bank at a price per kilogram fixed by the bank. Ranging from 6 to 12 per cent/annum, the interest rates are preferable to the informal credit resources available within Ban Srisaket which have interest rates varying from 36 per cent/annum from the temple fund, to 120 per cent/annum from local money lenders. Each year the cycle is repeated, so that most families in Ban Srisaket are continually in debt. The average income from agricultural sources in Ban Srisaket in these same households in 1993 was calculated at 14 617 baht/household/annum (under A$1000).[10] Thus over half of the total agricultural income each year services the debt of production costs. Most households therefore are locked into a cycle of debt and chronic poverty.

Plate 2.3 Typical village housing.

As the stories at the beginning of this chapter document, the way of life for the women of Ban Srisaket has undergone massive change. The economy of north-eastern villages has shifted from one based on subsistence rice production to an economy dependent on cash crops and labour migration. The effect upon village communities has been that of rising income disparities, increased levels of debt and impoverishment. In the past, the production of subsistence rice was intimately intertwined with social relationships. Kinship patterns, land ownership, household formation and community cooperation all reflected the centrality of rice production. Through their inheritance of land, post-marital residence patterns and the importance of reproduction of a labour force, women were central mediators of the means of production. There was a high degree of congruence between women's perceptions of themselves and their position in production and distribution. This is changing with the extension of capitalist relations of production into daily village life, which has eroded many of the former bases of women's status in village communities, separated the reproductive sphere from the productive sphere, disrupted their links to land and matrilineal kin through migration, and exposed them to new, 'modern' values, practices and representations of women. Simultaneously, new status markers and meanings are evolving for women, yet often these are beyond the access of village women with low education and skills and few economic resources.

The following discussion examines how people in Ban Srisaket conceptualise gender distinctions as background to the later chapters which concentrate upon the female body and the subtle structuring of the body through discursive practices of modernity and tradition evident in health practices.

Gender ideology in Isan

mi hu'an bor mi fa	There is a house but no walls
mi na bor mi horng	There are ricefields but no channel for water
mi plorng bor mi fa at	There is a container but no lid
mi wat bor mi sang	There is a wat but no monks
mi thong bor mi porn hoi	There is a bag but no place to hang it upon
khong mu nan bor di	These things are no good

This Isan saying expounds many of the traditional discourses informing notions of gender in Isan (Komonkitiskun 1992:9, my translation). It speaks of the importance of female fertility and nurturance and the female association with land and homes, the differential relationship of men and women to Buddhism, and the need to constrain and protect female sexuality. At the broadest level, the saying emphasises the complementary roles of men and women within village society, each with their sphere of responsibility. Women occupy central positions as the mediators of land and household resources, while men dominate religious and public affairs.

The metaphor equating women with houses and ricefields in the traditional verse above reflects the tradition of matrilineal inheritance of land and houses. This tradition placed women in positions of structural importance. Traditionally the custom of post-marital residence with the wife's parents ensured that women were surrounded by their matrilineal kin who provided protection and support, especially at times of marital or economic crises. Women are also intimately linked to houses through the continuation of matrilineal spirit cults which strongly associate women with domestic space, and are nurtured by the female matrilineal kin who reside in the house. They govern female sexuality and the well-being of the house, causing sickness when wronged or neglected (Davis 1984a; Hale 1984; Turton 1972).

The complementarity of men and women's roles is reflected in the association of female potency with earth and rice, and male potency with water, which is a recurrent theme in Isan mythology. As Sparkes describes (1995:83), in Isan cosmology nature is anthropomorphised through both male and female spirits, both of which have their positive and auspicious incarnations and both of which can threaten the social order of the village.

Female spirits include *mae thorani* (mother earth) responsible for growth and unlimited fertility but requiring activation by the male sky spirit to cause rain. Another is *mae phosop* (mother rice) personifying the staple food of humans but dependent upon the action of the rain of the male sky spirit and protection of male rice field spirits. These spirits are linked to imagery of dormant fertility which, when activated, generates nurturing food (Sparkes 1995:66-68).[11] The traditional saying quoted above emphasises how without water the ricefields lay barren and infertile. This evokes the importance of fertility to women's identity in Isan society. Not only does having a large family affirm a woman's spiritual status through the merit gained from nurturing her children and through the children's deeds, but, in the past, large families were important to provide labour for rice production.

The description of the *wat* (temple) with no monks also refers to women's role in nurturing the Buddhist religion. Women are essential to the continuation of Buddhism as the mothers of sons who will ordain as monks, and as the providers of food for the monks (Van Esterik 1982b; 1986). Whereas women are oriented towards the domestic realm, men are expected to dominate public activity. Ordained as monks, men have access to an education in religious/ritual matters and are accorded the highest status in the village. In their monopoly over this cultural capital they are considered to be the upholders of the moral order. Men hold all formal and political appointments in Ban Srisaket and are considered the most powerful and knowledgeable ritual specialists (Tambiah 1970:127-134). As Davis states:

> Outside the domestic sphere, men clearly hold political and economic
> dominance . . . This dominance reinforces and is reinforced by the ritual
> ideology of male superiority. Men are 'natural' leaders because of the
> preeminence accorded them ritually, and this ritual ideology is partly
> maintained by the power of men in extradomestic politics and economy
> (1984a:68).

Finally, the verse above suggests that the social position of a woman in Isan is dependent upon her relationship to a male, just as containers are in need of the protection of a lid and bags require a place to be stored.[12] Female sexuality is understood as most appropriately constrained through marriage and motherhood. As Mills (1995) observes, outside of the control of husbands or fathers, female sexuality in Isan is associated with the shame of prostitutes and promiscuity. Female sexuality also carries potentially dangerous powers which must be appropriately restrained. If uncontrolled, female powers of fertility and generation are depicted as dangerous threats to social harmony, typified in mythical imagery of wandering, homeless, voracious *phi mae mai* (female widow ghosts) or female spirits hungry for human flesh and blood, such as *phi pob* and *phi phai* (Mills 1995). In such stories, the cultural ideal of disciplined, domestic, virtuous women is inverted into fearsome, sexually voracious beings.

The traditional ideological construction of appropriate male and female qualities, roles and relationships continues to influence expectations and practice within Ban Srisaket. But the image presented in the traditional saying is one of idealised consensual harmony effacing any suggestion of tension, contestation, or disagreement over what it means to be a man or woman in Isan society.

Gendered divisions in practice in Ban Srisaket

At first glance within Ban Srisaket an observer may be struck by the extent to which men and women in the village jointly share responsibility for many domestic tasks and farm work and the expectations that women as well as men will migrate to work, or will be involved in decisions. Other markers of social identity, such as seniority by age, relative wealth and kinship ties, often appear more important factors structuring everyday interactions. However, a longer stay will reveal a range of gendered divisions structuring daily life in the village. Whilst both men and women share multiple tasks around the household and fields, there are many activities which display a subtle gendered codification and division. It is this patterning of tasks which constitutes the daily acting out of gender in the village, the discursive practices of gender.

Women have primary responsibility for domestic tasks, the daily running of the home: cleaning, cooking, hand-washing clothes and child-care. In particular, unmarried daughters do most of the work pertaining to the reproduction of the household under the instruction of their mothers, aunts and older sisters. Men will occasionally help with such tasks, when for example a woman is confined to stay by the fire after childbirth, and men control the cooking of particular dishes, such as *lap*,[13] on special festive occasions. Other activities are largely structured by gender. Older women are involved in the labour-intensive nurturing of silkworms, and the production and weaving of silk cloth. The definition of the domestic extends to selling and buying food in the small local weekly village market and travelling with the sick to seek medical care. Daily feeding of the monks is also primarily a female activity on behalf of the household, as is the production of ritual banana leaf offerings.

Plate 2.4 Early Saturday morning at the village market.

If women are oriented towards the domestic realm, activities which are particularly associated with men are directed outside the household. Ploughing rice fields is a male task. Men are the only ones to hunt with guns in the fields and the only ones who throw fish-nets. Male activities around the house, particularly during the dry season, include repairing and maintaining the house, weaving fish nets and baskets. The production of rice whisky, drinking, smoking and attending cockfights are all considered male activities. Some women do drink in public, but with less frequency than men, and usually only on liminal festive occasions when many gender rules are inverted, for example, during *hae nak* (ordination processions) or during *bun bang fai* celebrations.[14] Finally, men are the ones most involved in public village politics. They hold all formal and political appointments in the village and are considered the most powerful and knowledgeable ritual specialists.

The most obvious sexual differentiation within the village is centred around religious activities at the temple. Buddhism is one of the principle institutions for the production of discourse and the maintenance of practices that reinforce male ritual authority and superior religious status. Women cannot be ordained, and can only be lay devotees.[15] Men perform all the public roles of Buddhism ordained as monks or as lay officiants, leading the chanting, conducting rituals, and as members of the *wat* committee. Strict spatial separation is

Plate 2.5 Villagers make merit by feeding the monks each morning.

meeting hall, the organisation of space and body position clearly denotes the differential moral status distinctions between monks and laypersons, elders and younger people and the divisions between men and women. Monks sit upon a raised platform above the congregation, denoting their higher status. Elderly men sit closest to them followed by younger men. Women, who outnumber the men attending, sit around the perimeter. The elderly men make merit by placing food in the monks' bowls first, followed by the younger men. Not until the youngest boy has made his offering will the most elderly woman lead the other women to make their offerings.

Such daily gendered routines constitute the lived experience of 'maleness' and 'femaleness' in the village. These differences in ways of acting and working are understood and legitimised in Isan culture through reference to cultural models of gender appropriateness. In part they are based on understandings of biological difference, but they also represent the bodily inscription of the ideological values structuring social, economic and moral relations within the village.

However, new gender relations and identities are emerging through the changes wrought with the capitalist transformation of the village economy. The following section explores this reworking of gender relations, in particular the position of women.

Changing economic roles: the effect of waged labour

The penetration of capitalist relations of production has restructured and transformed the economic roles of men and women. Whereas formerly agricultural labour was exchanged for rice or reciprocal labour, cash is now the currency of transaction and has replaced traditional patterns of social-based exchange.

The advent of wage labour has disadvantaged women. With the advent of wage labour into agricultural production the tasks conventionally done by men have come to be rewarded with higher wages. For example, during the planting season in 1993, men from Ban Srisaket earned 60 baht a day for the 'male' task of removing seedlings from the seedling beds and transporting them to the rice fields. In contrast, women earned 50 baht a day for the equally arduous 'female' task of planting the seedlings into the rice field. Even for the same tasks, such as planting cassava, women received 50 baht a day, whereas men received 60 baht a day. Aunt Man explained that this was because 'men are stronger, and so do heavier work and can do more than women'.

Under a system of common production, men and women shared the benefits of their combined labour in the fields and in the home. Under a system of wage labour, a large proportion of women's work in maintaining the household and caring for children is not paid and they are increasingly dependent upon male wage earners for support. Households with no male wage earner are the poorest in Ban Srisaket. Older people who can no longer work are reduced to total dependence upon their children's remittences.

Government development projects also have ignored women's contribution to agricultural production. Land ownership documents are generally registered in men's names, even though most land has been inherited by women. State development projects have also tended to exclude women from public roles in village development programs (Gordon & Sirisambhand 1987; Thomson 1990). For example, in Ban Srisaket membership in government-supported agricultural cooperatives and the registration of land as collateral for loans are usually taken out in the name of the male 'head' of the household, even if the land in question was inherited by a female family member.

Similarly, the state-initiated organisations set up in a top-down approach to village development reproduce an ideology of appropriate gender roles for men and women. Despite the important role of women in agricultural production, the membership of the 'Farmers' Group' (*klum kasetakorn*) is exclusively male. Women are allocated membership in the 'Housewives' Group' (*klum maeban*). In 1992, while the 'Farmers' Group' discussed farm prices and received training from the agricultural extension officer about new cash crops, the 'Housewives Group' was given lessons in cushion making from the District Office, meant to be a marketable skill appropriate for women, although the few cushions produced were distributed to friends and kin as no opportunities for sale existed.

More commonly, the 'Housewives' Group' is allocated a subordinate role, often being called upon to provide, prepare and serve food at public village functions. In these ways, state institutions produce and reproduce a particular modern, urban, middle-class discourse and practice of women as housewives and fail to recognise rural women's roles in agricultural production.

Changing inheritance patterns

The traditional pattern of female inheritance is slowly shifting towards bilateral inheritance, with both sons and daughters inheriting land and moveable property. Women stated this was because of small family landholdings. One woman described how her parents had worked 100 rai of land which they divided between their five daughters. Now she owns only 30 rai of land to divide between her five children. She said that now sons need to inherit some land in case they married women with only a small parcel of land. Another woman wondered how she would divide up 9 rai of land among her three daughters and one son. In another case, an older woman had already divided up her land. Each daughter received 3 rai of paddy land and 1 rai of high land, whilst each son received 1 rai of high land. The daughter who looks after her will inherit the house.

> Nowadays sons only get a little less than daughters, but the child who will stay with the parents will also get the parents' share of land when they die. Sometimes sons will sell their land to their sisters. (Grandmother Thong)

> Sons and daughters now all get equal shares and we will divide up the land and possessions and the last child or the person who looks after the mother will get her piece as well. Some people sell the house and divide the money between them. (Grandmother Sai)

These new arrangements represent a break from the peasant subsistence economy of the past. In the absence of sufficient land to divide amongst children, many young people are moving out of the village to pursue occupations other than farming, and some young people spoke of selling their inherited land to their siblings. Some young people say that their education is their inheritance which will allow them to secure well-paid employment. Without land, people may leave the village to seek a livelihood in Bangkok or other urban centres—as a landless generation reliant upon selling their labour instead of rice.

Migration

Each year after harvest the buses and trains to Bangkok are crowded with hopeful migrants from North-east Thailand and elsewhere, seeking employment through the dry season when there is little work to do on the farm. The village of Ban Srisaket is all but deserted, with only the elderly and mothers with young children remaining. Most able-bodied adults leave to sell their labour in the cities.

With the income from agricultural production insufficient to meet most household needs, migration is an essential strategy to supplement the household income. Official village statistics stated there were 466 people from Ban Srisaket who migrated in the years 1988–89 from a population of 3 926 people (Thailand, Dept. of Rural Development 1989b). A village survey I conducted during the dry season in 1992 suggests that these figures were probably underestimates, as 66 per cent of households surveyed had at least one member absent at the time of the survey, not including those members who were considered to have migrated permanently. In 1993 a second household survey revealed 81 per cent of households had at least one member who migrated for work, not including those people considered to have left the household permanently. My data is consistent with other studies in the North-east which confirm a long-established tradition of circular migration (Goldstein and Goldstein 1986).[16] Several families in Ban Srisaket are totally dependent upon wage labour for their income:

> Nine people live in this household. At present there is Grandfather Khai, Grandmother Oi and three grandchildren in the house; the rest are away. One 23-year-old daughter works in Bangkok with her husband. She works as a housemaid and earns 1500 baht/month and he works as a mechanic earning approximately 5000 baht/month. They have three children: two sons aged seven and five, and one daughter of twenty-one months, who have been left in Ban Srisaket in the care of their grandparents. Another son, who is eighteen, works with his sister's husband repairing cars and earns 3000 baht/month but does not send any money home. Another daughter, aged sixteen, works as a housemaid in Bangkok earning 1500 baht/month. She has worked there since she was thirteen. Her 14-year-old brother works as a gardener in the same house in Bangkok, earning 1000 baht/month. Between them they send 1500 baht/month back to their family in the village. This family works 7 rai of land, they plant 6 rai with sticky rice and 1 rai with ordinary rice, producing enough for their own consumption. They do not have official ownership of this land, as they do not wish to pay the land tax and are not members of the BAAC.

The majority of Ban Srisaket migrants work as unskilled workers in the construction industry, factories or in the service industries, for example as drivers or housemaids. Ban Srisaket is known as a cane-cutting village with large numbers leaving for the fields of Kanchanaburi in Central Thailand for one to three months each year to harvest sugar-cane by hand. Many young women from the village work as machinists in overcrowded clothes factories. Yet these generalisations mask the variety of experiences of migrants. The variety of jobs ranged from a small group of young women who worked as score keepers in pool halls (usually associated with discretionary sex work) to one woman who had worked in Russia for two years as the housemaid of a Thai diplomat. Despite the importance of international labour migration in some Isan communities, only two households of Ban Srisaket had members who had migrated to work in the Middle East. Both had well-built brick houses as a result and were considered wealthy by other villagers.

Ban Srisaket villagers were reluctant to state how much they received from migrant household members. Part of the difficulty is that rather than sending remittences every month, many migrants give their families money on their sporadic visits when they return for the harvest or festivals. This makes it difficult to calculate a total amount. It must also be recognised that just having members of the household supporting themselves represents an economic bonus for households. Villagers suggest that migrating daughters were far more reliable in sending money to their families than sons, who tended to *kin len* (eat, play) their wages on alcohol, women and entertainment. The 1988 Household Socio-Economic Survey found that 30.4 per cent of households in North-east Thailand reported receiving remittences (including cash and in-kind) each month averaging 795 baht (Thailand, National Statistical Office 1988:74). Tirasawat (1985:491) suggests that remittences constitute roughly 15 per cent of the annual income of the recipient households and that they are used for general consumption expenditures rather than investment (also Lightfoot, Fuller and Kamnuansilpa 1983). Many households, especially those of the elderly or disabled who are unable to be economically productive, are totally reliant for their cash income upon their sons' and daughters' wages. The collapse of the Thai economy in 1997 and shrinkage of the construction and service industries seriously threatens the availability of employment for many Isan migrants and with it the economic viability of many households in villages such as Ban Srisaket.

Migratory labour starts at a young age. It is common practice for children to leave the village after finishing compulsory schooling at age twelve or thirteen. In the sample studied by Larson et al. 35 per cent of girls and 30 per cent of boys had left the village for an extended period at least once by the age of fifteen (1993). Many young people enjoy the opportunity to travel and escape the village and parental control, swapping the heavy labour of the rice fields for tedious or heavy labour in often dangerous and overcrowded conditions in factories and construction sites.

My survey data from both surveys showed that overall, male migrants outnumbered women. A number of studies show similar sex distributions amongst migrants.[17] However, up to the age of twenty, young women (58.6 per cent) outnumber men (41.4 per cent) as migrants.[18] This reflects the greater employment opportunities for young unmarried women in places such as Bangkok, which was the overwhelming destination of most young women (93 per cent for young women, 85 per cent for all migrants). After marriage however, males outnumber female migrants (see also Bell 1992; Lightfoot et al. 1983:25).

The majority of these young women find work in the lower-paid service sector jobs, for example as housemaids, or in the manufacturing sector in garment factories. Such jobs are characterised by poor working conditions, exploitation, and low wages. As other case studies in Asia have documented, capitalism has intensified pre-existing gender divisions and positions women in the lower-paid, subordinate jobs (Elson & Pearson 1981; Mies 1986). Bell (1992) notes that the recent economic development of Thailand has been largely founded upon women. Thai export-led development has been based upon a subordination of women and the exploitation of a cheap young, female workforce, particularly in the export-oriented industries (textiles, garments and footwear) where up to 80 per cent of workers are women (Bell 1992:69). The penetration of capitalism into the rural agricultural sector has exacerbated inequalities of income distribution, leading to a further exodus of villagers, the majority of whom are young women entering into low-paid domestic or factory work. These jobs involve 'low wages, poor working conditions, considerable variability in employment, harsh and often arbitrary discipline and little opportunity to advance' (Thorbek 1987:61). As Elson and Pearson note (1981:150), jobs which are considered to be 'women's work' tend to be classified as 'unskilled' or 'semi-skilled' positions, whereas 'men's jobs' tend to be classified as 'skilled' positions, not through an objective definition of the skill required, but because women are pre-defined as 'inferior bearers of labour'. Capitalism thus intensifies, restructures and transforms pre-existing gender subordination.

Sex work

Sex work is a prime example of the relationship between gender subordination and capitalism, where women's bodies are the commodities sold, bought and made to produce profit. Local rumours and hearsay suggest several women from Ban Srisaket are involved in sex work, but it is difficult to confirm. Villagers are reluctant to acknowledge that local women work as commercial sex workers and are careful to maintain the reputation of local women and, by extension, the reputation of the community. However, a number of young women who work in Bangkok were described as score keepers in snooker halls, a job commonly associated with discretionary sex work. Women in particular consistently deny that their daughters and nieces might be involved in prostitution. For example, Grandmother Phong stated, 'My daughter is unmarried and she is now twenty-eight. She works in Patpong, but she's not a prostitute. She doesn't work like that!'. When we asked if there were any women in our village who worked in prostitution, Uncle Daeng laughed and said:

Oh, that's hard to answer! There isn't anyone in village 8 who works like that. There must be some women who work like that. One can only suppose who they are, as they don't like their parents to know—they are ashamed and so they lie. Some are married and have children two or three years-old and when they go to Bangkok they work as prostitutes. You know from the women who return wearing make-up and by what they wear. Some women wear lots of gold. You don't know for certain, but suppose that's how they got it.

Financial necessity is perceived to be the chief motivation for sex work and generally prostitutes were pitied, but not condemned. Local depictions of prostitutes range from an image of prostitutes as victims forced or tricked into brothels, to young women wishing to enjoy themselves, to women who had been jilted by a lover or left by a husband, to dutiful daughters suffering as prostitutes to support their families. For example, Aunt Im suggested: 'Women work as prostitutes because it is necessary. Some women [work that way] because they have a broken heart or their husbands leave them'. Aunt Mu'an preferred an image of prostitutes as 'good time girls' who 'won't have a smooth life because the money is easily come by and easily spent and they are teenagers who like to enjoy themselves'. Yet even 'bad' women may become legitimate through their success. Commercial sex work may be consistent with ideals of a woman as a dutiful daughter or nurturing mother whose work and sacrifice provides financial support and enhances the well-being of her family (Muecke 1992). As Aunt Thii suggested:

I sympathise with them . . . The difference between the North-east and Central people is that the people of the North-east don't look down on prostitutes. The prostitute that has got a lot of money, it is good that they can help their family, but in Central Thailand they are against that, they don't want their children to do that.

The comment of Aunt Thii suggests that attitudes towards prostitution in the North-east may be shifting towards opinions reported in Northern Thailand, where a prostitute is not condemned for her occupation if it is perceived that she has done so for the good of her family, not for personal pleasure. At least some of her demerit may be absolved through later meritorious behaviour such as merit-making, marriage and re-entry into village life.

Meanings of movement

The 'pull' of the city is not just for the short-term economic gains that may be made there. The movements of a migrant to and from the city also carry meanings from the perspective of the migrant herself and also in terms of how her community views her. Villagers jokingly refer to young migrants in the village as the *dek thep*, literally the 'children of Krungthep (Bangkok)' and/or 'child angels', and some are said to have returned as *khon thai* with the habits and speech of urban Thais. Young people talk of *pai au phiw*, going to the city 'to get a [white] skin'. Both men and women returned from Bangkok are said to be more attractive because their skin colour has lightened as they have not had to work outside in the sun. Gaining a whiter skin thus acts as a metonym for discarding the inferior status of peasant farmer and participating in modern urban values and lifestyle. Women migrants must reconcile the divergence between the traditional expectations of them and modern values and demands. As Mills describes, 'part of what draws young rural women into the city is an unspoken but powerful suggestion that there they can be at once beautiful, modern and mobile' (1997). Such images of modernity both contrast with and transform understandings of femininity in the village with its constraints on female mobility and close association of women with the domestic realm.

The conflicting nature of these discourses is evident in the contradictory roles women migrants assume. They are expected to uphold Lao community values of womanly nurturance, modesty, respect and support of parents and domestic responsibilities, and are valued as mothers and dutiful daughters, yet their economic roles are highly valued: as workers they are mobile, independent and economically productive. The female migrant is expected to move between these roles as readily as she sheds the village sarong for the Western clothes of the city.

Anxieties and ambivalence towards female migration resonate with the perceptions of social changes and the disruption of the social order. Female migratory labour provokes ambivalence as their mobility and wage-earning power challenges the economic and moral authority of parents. Within the village, the 'good' woman is one who fulfils her obligations as a daughter to support her family. This is consistent with the ideology of *bunkhun* relationships through which children must repay a debt of gratitude to their parents. Sons may repay this debt through their ordination as monks which makes merit for the parents, especially the mother. In the past, a daughter repaid her debt to her parents through her obedient labour and care of her parents in their old age. But now daughters fulfil their obligations through sending money home to support the family. Whereas through their migration young women fulfil one set of filial obligations, they jeopardise other values: virginity, modesty, and domesticity.

Mills' (1993; 1995; 1996; 1997) work on migration in a north-eastern village, explores how gender identities and meanings, particularly ideas about appropriate roles for women, have become the focus for the expression of tensions generated in the migration process. At the same time, cultural meanings of modernity and the experiences of migration are forcing the reworking of these existing gender understandings and identities. A struggle over cultural meanings, values and goals is taking place as village women negotiate shifts in space but also shifting identities and social relations. Mills argues that rural–urban migration not only provides an opportunity for economic accumulation, but is also an encounter with the meanings of modernity and tradition. Villagers experience these conflicts most sharply as contests over appropriate gender identities, roles and relations.

Codes of gender appropriateness in Isan draw clear associations between spatial mobility and sexual activity (Mills 1993). Female mobility is associated with unrestrained female sexuality as women move beyond male control. Hence female mobility through migration to the city challenges parental and community controls over female sexuality. Without the supervision of parents and kin, pre-marital virginity can no longer be guaranteed. Parents fear the sexual impropriety of their daughters in the absence of parental supervision and are aware of the possibility of their daughters becoming involved in the vast sexual services industry, yet they approve of their daughters working to help support their parents and siblings. The possible sexual experience of young migrant women (not men) is a source of anxiety and gossip amongst villagers. In the negotiation of marriage payments the fact that a young woman has migrated to work for a long period of time is often used to cast doubts as to her virginity.[19] For these reasons villagers prefer daughters to migrate in the company of a trusted friend or kin. Young women returning to the village from work in the city are careful of their clothes and demeanour, as wearing make-up, gold and expensive clothes may be read as signs that they have worked in the sex industry (see also Gray 1990). For villagers there is a fine line between modern images of glamorous, sexually attractive women, and sexual availability and prostitution.

The female migrant body is thus a site of contested meanings. Ways of dressing, walking, wearing make-up, haircut and decoration simultaneously convey aspirations of modernity and wealth, but when transposed onto the body of a Lao woman in the village may also be read as signs of ill-repute.

Women's bodies thus mediate the breakdown of traditional constraints on female sexuality and the growth of the sex industry, the decline in the importance of matrilineal kinship and authority of elders, and the pressures upon Lao ethnic culture to assimilate modern Central Thai elite values.

Separation from spouses, matrilineal kin and land

With the material changes of urbanisation and the separation of production from reproduction in industrial capitalism, women find themselves with lower status in their relationships with men and separated from their traditional sources of economic and social support.

Married migrant women also may find themselves more economically and socially dependent upon their husbands than is normally the case in the village. As Thorbeck notes in her study of Bangkok slum women, 'Many of the material interests which are the foundation of the importance of matrilineal descent up-country are eroded in city-life with the atrophy of inheritance and common production' (1987:117).

In the country, women control and regulate land and hence control the means of production. They also mediate future inheritance and usually administer the family income. In urban areas, women are often made dependent on their husbands because of the greater earning power of men in the city (Thorbek 1987:120-121). At the same time they are removed from the social and financial support of their matrilineal kin in times of social crisis or marital problems.

The movement of the younger generation away from the village and the smaller size of families is also jeopardising mechanisms for the support of the elderly. This is becoming an increasing source of anxiety for the elderly, as these women state:

> Mothers look after children, children look after their mothers. That's the way it should be. Look at Grandmother Mai, she has many sons, she has many daughters, but now she lives all alone. She has to eat and live by herself without company. (Grandmother Sim)

> When I divide my land my daughters will share the land and usually the youngest will get twice as much, as she will look after her parents in our old age. But now I'm not sure who will look after me. It isn't the same now as it used to be and I'm not sure who will look after me. (Aunty Dorn)

For married women, migration has consequences as well for their relationships with their husbands. The majority of married couples in Ban Srisaket have experienced extended periods of separation as one or both partners migrate for waged work. Whereas infidelity on the part of a man is considered a natural consequence of such separation, for a woman the double standard of appropriate behaviour requires her to be careful of her reputation while separated from her husband. Although traditional marriage relationships and support is disrupted, discourses of tradition continue to judge the actions of women.

Making money, not babies

Even the sacrosanct nurturing role of mothers has been subsumed to the practicalities of migration. The changed needs of production, waged labour, migration and smaller families are shifting the sources of status for women away from reproduction towards production as women choose to 'make money, not babies' (Muecke 1984). Facilitated by the new contraceptive technologies, most young women of Ban Srisaket delay marriage and childbearing so that they can continue to work in the city before returning to the village, as single women can find employment easier than married women. Women may return to the village for the birth and early nurturing of their child, but many young couples now leave their children in the care of matrilineal grandparents in the village while they pursue city employment. Young women's roles as producers are thus directly impinging on their roles as reproducers.

Conclusions

In village discourse, imagery of the feminine centres around procreation and nurturance, as opposed to imagery of threatening female sexuality in need of appropriate control. Village society sustains an ideology of the complementary domestic strength of women and the public strength of men through its organisation of production and reproduction and traditions involving female inheritance, post-marital residence and tutelary spirits. In particular, Buddhist ideology supports the public superiority and religious excellence of males.

The capitalist transformation of the Ban Srisaket economy is realigning the economic and social relationships between men and women. The experience in Ban Srisaket reveals two related consequences. First is the changed pattern of women's participation in production. In Ban Srisaket women are involved in more and greater varieties of productive activity than ever before and yet are being made increasingly economically vulnerable. Large-scale capitalist production has required spatial mobility and has intensified sexual divisions of labour as well as changed patterns of marriage, kinship, and reproduction, as increasing numbers of villagers are forced to abandon a subsistence agricultural lifestyle. The old patterns of social life in the village are being fundamentally changed as villagers adapt and accommodate to capitalist imperatives and the demands of modern times.

The second consequence is the way in which traditional gender ideologies are being renegotiated. Men and women are challenging traditional values and expectations through their migration to the city. Women's bodies in particular have been the sites of pluralistic discursive practices that transform and contrast with traditional village discourses. From the perspective of women, they are experiencing a disjuncture between the 'traditional' values and expectations and 'modern' practices. The meanings and values attributed to *samai mai* modernity and *samai korn* tradition are neither fixed nor uncontested, but women tend to encounter the disjunctures between them as personal dilemmas, in decisions about migration, work, desires for consumer goods, problems with inheritance. The following chapters explore the negotiation and alignments of these in practices where the body itself is the site of intervention, in practices of health and illness.

3 Contesting bodies of knowledge: Health and healing

Come khwan, oei!
Don't wander off *khwan*, come back here!
Don't go off into the forest, come back to rest on your bed here! Come and enter the body of this person here, not the people of the forest, they are spirits. This body isn't the same as those friends, they are spirits of the forest. You can't be friends with them!
Rise back into this body to give her strength!
Please come!
Taste the rice of this body, you can't say it is *meng sap*![20] When you eat the rice, you can't say it is bitter!
On the way to the high land, don't stay in the high grass!
On the way through the rice fields, don't stay in the rice stalks!
When you reach a tree, don't rest your head under it and go to sleep!
When you come back here, don't be afraid!
When you arrive come up and enter the house!
Don't go wandering in the forest! Those that live in the forest are different, they are forest spirits!
Come and return to the house where you used to live!
If you don't return this body will remain sick and without strength! *Oei*!

We move to make a clear path for the *khwan* (soul) between the family members and the village elders all sitting on the wooden floor. The string with the ball of sticky rice suspended from its end held in the left hand of the *mor oen khwan* (soul-calling doctor) remains very still. In her right hand Grandmother Pay holds the offering tray of two betel leaves, two small lumps of lime, four betel nuts, two steamed sticky rice and banana sweets, four green bananas, four small pieces of sugar-cane, two hand rolled cigarettes of tobacco, white flowers, a mirror and a comb, two candles, forty baht, white cotton thread and seven pieces of clothing. On top of all of this is a small tin plate with *khan ha* (five pairs of candles, five pairs of flowers and raw husked rice) which earlier she offered to the *thewada* (Buddhist angels) who now inhabit the used clothes of the patient. She starts singing again. Her voice is strained from the many repetitions: '*Oei, khwan, Oei!* Don't go out to play but come here to Grandmother who hasn't been well. Come and eat! The sweets are sweet! You have been away too long!'

Grandmother Mii kneels in front of the *mor oen khwan* with her hands raised in a *wai*. Close by sits one of her daughters fanning her mother's thin gnarled yellow face. The ball of sticky rice attached to the white string still does not move. 'Oh, it is taking so long. The *phan* offering tray is heavy!'

Other people in the room call out 'Come *khwan*, come. *Oei!*' One of the patient's young sons, with a bald head signifying that he had very recently left the monkhood, is told to go downstairs and call the *khwan* from there. He moves out and down the steep narrow stairs calling '*Oei!* Come *khwan*, come!' Several people laugh and smile at his call.

The ball of suspended sticky rice starts to sway back and forth. The *khwan* has come.

The *mor oen khwan* continues to sing as the ball of rice sways. Someone nudges the young man and says, 'Your call helped. You called well'. Grandmother Pay takes the hand of Grandmother Mii and rubs the ball of rice on the palm of her hand and then throws it towards an open window. She misses. Another person sitting nearby picks it up and throws it out of the window. Taking a piece of white cotton thread she ties a knot in it and then proceeds to tie it around the wrist of her patient. 'Live well and be happy! Be strong and well again!' She hands Grandmother Mii the mirror and comb and instructs her to comb her hair whilst looking in the mirror.

The white strings are passed around to everyone present. 'Tie a knot in it and then hang it over your ear as you wait.' I do as everyone else and wait my turn alongside Noi, my research assistant. First the elder men and Grandmother Mii's husband tie Grandmother Mii's wrists, wishing her to recover her strength and happiness. Next, members of her family, her sisters, daughters and grand-daughter come forward. Then all of us proceed on our knees to tie her wrists and wish her well. 'Go on. See, the foreigner has come to tie her wrist. Surely she will recover.'

'Live well and be happy,' I say to her, and I rub the string three times under her wrist and then tie three knots in it and *wai* her. She returns the *wai*. Grandmother Mii now has both wrists covered in white string from the thirty people crowded into the small open room. Some people begin to tie the wrists of other friends and family.

Steaming baskets of sticky rice are placed before the guests, who chatter loudly and form small circles. Men sit with men and women sit with other women. 'Come and eat rice!' the young female relatives call. There is a clatter of dishes as bowls of hot stew of pork bones, gourd and greens are served to the groups of people. Dishes of fermented fish with chilli are placed among the groups and several water containers with a glass on each are placed around the room. We share the sticky rice, taking small balls and dipping them into the dishes. The noise level increases as some men start to drink whisky.

Grandmother Pay, the *mor oen khwan*, takes the boiled egg from the offering tray and shells it. She takes a strand of her hair to slice it in half but is unable to and so asks Noi, my research assistant, for a strand of her long thick black hair. She slices the egg. The outside of the yolk is dark grey-green. 'The colour is no good,' she says. Inside the yolk of the egg is a red blood vessel. 'There is a worm in her liver which is causing her illness.' The close relatives discuss the signs quietly and then the parts of the egg not containing the red blood vessel are given to Grandmother Mii to eat. A small amount of the yolk is pasted onto each of her soles of her feet.

A few people are still sitting chatting when we offer to accompany Grandmother Pay back to her house. The son of Grandmother Mii accompanies us. Rain falls lightly as we thread our way in the darkness down the dirt paths between houses. Grandmother Mii's son, Long, says that his mother has been to many doctors but they have all said that she cannot be cured:

> They say she has *maleng met lu'at* [leukaemia]. She hasn't been sleeping
> but the day before yesterday we bought some *ya hak mai* [root medicine]
> which was ground and she drank it and slept well. Many people call
> Grandmother Pay to come and call the *khwan* because she is good.
> Usually men in our village do it, but we think that women are better at it.

Grandmother Pay says she will invite us again next time and she disappears up the stairs into her old wooden house.

Her sharp tongue, sense of humour, and fine memory make Grandmother Pay a popular healer among many in Ban Srisaket. The *oen khwan* ceremony described above, despite its idiosyncrasies, incorporates many of the themes important to this chapter. It was part of a series of ceremonies, medicines and doctors resorted to by Grandmother Mii and her family in an attempt to cure her deteriorating health. Treatments by biomedical doctors in hospitals, self-treatment, massage, a series of soul-tying rituals, herbal medicine, injection doctors and finally exorcism of a *phi fa* (sky spirit) by a monk were all undertaken before her eventual death. In the ritual described above Grandmother Mii and the healer were the central participants of the ritual, but they were supported by a crowd of concerned kin, friends and neighbours. With the fragrant sticky rice and sweets as supernatural bait, Buddhist angels, spirits and souls were all importuned to seek out and call back the errant soul of Grandmother Mii, whose absence contributed to her poor state of health. In a ritual process the *mor oen khwan* called Grandmother Mii's soul back to her body and then shifted her illness from her body into the ball of sticky rice which she then cast out of the house via the open window. Her soul was reflected and brushed back into her through the comb and mirror, and finally tied to her body through the now sacred *saisin* (thread) which acts as a barrier against the soul's further flight from her body. As each person tied threads onto her wrists she was re-incorporated into the social community, an act reaffirmed by the sharing of rice together. Although the ceremony was ostensibly for Grandmother Mii's benefit, many of the people present took the opportunity to tie the wrists of members of her family and their friends and kin, and others who had suffered ill-health recently or were very old.

This chapter explores the notions of the body in Ban Srisaket as informed by discourses about health. Descriptions or explanations of ill-health make explicit local understandings of the body, its processes and boundaries, and provide useful insights into the meanings of the body and person in Isan. Illness also draws in the need for therapy, and this chapter describes the variety of modes of healing available. These various modes of healing entail their own understandings of the body. In particular, I draw comparisons between two seemingly incompatible discourses of the body as implicit in traditional therapies and biomedical care. As such, this chapter provides an introduction to later discussions of women's health issues and their health-seeking behaviour. It also begins my account of the tensions between tradition and modernity that form part of the everyday experience of villagers.

'Medical pluralism' has been used by theorists to describe a number of different situations (Bhattacharyya 1983:947).[21] It refers to the social organisation of healing practitioners and the cultural organisation of their practice. It also addresses how people choose between competing therapies. Fundamentally, medical pluralism addresses the ways in which competing therapeutic discourses mediate bodily experience.

Early studies in medical pluralism attempted to categorise medical systems such as the relationships between 'professional', 'popular', 'folk' medical sectors (Kleinman 1980). But such attempts to categorise plural medical systems simply produced rigid functionalist typologies and divisions and no common vocabulary (Kundstadter 1978). As this chapter will show, such distinctions are not useful for a description of the varied health resources of Thailand, where the boundaries between formally sanctioned health care and other healing practices are not well defined but share techniques, medicines and even personnel. Such characterisations are also overly simplistic generalisations for the complexity of patient agency involved in making choices between differing therapies.

An alternative approach to medical pluralism that focuses upon practice respects the agency of people rather than seeing them as the repository of 'health beliefs'. Choices between therapies involves what Nichter has called 'taskology' rather than 'taxology' (Nichter & Nichter 1996:121). As he states, 'much popular knowledge of how the body functions is tacit, embodied, and practice-based as distinct from being objectified and abstract' (1996:1). From this perspective, medical pluralism is a social process and embodied action. Case studies throughout this book illustrate the multiple health strategies of villagers and their pragmatic negotiations with practitioners.

In rural Haiti, Brodwin describes the ways in which the 'contest for healing power' involves competing notions of affliction and a set of discourses and practices through which people negotiate their identity, and moral and religious status. Competing forms of healing offered by practitioners aligned with the Catholic Church, Protestant missionary denominations and Voudon traditions propose different accounts of the body, personal identity and morality. The healing practices also mediate between disorders in the body/self and the body politic (Brodwin 1996). His account firmly situates health strategies as social and political action, involving contests between different forms of medical knowledge in differing relations of power and as statements about personal identity.

Likewise, villagers of Ban Srisaket must negotiate and balance a number of factors in their decisions about health services. Riley and Sermsri (1974) describe the Thai medical system as one in which patients 'choose freely' among many alternatives. I argue that the 'quest for therapy' is not a simple exercise of choice but involves movement between discursive frameworks which co-exist in unequal relations of power (Ram 1998). My focus throughout this book is thus upon how notions of the body and choices of therapy are articulated with overarching material and ideological forces and on the contestation between different forms of medical knowledge (Brodwin 1996:16).

This chapter also continues to explore the sub-text throughout this work: tensions between 'modernity' and 'tradition'. My use of these terms is not accidental nor a remnant of romanticised nostalgia for lost authenticity. As noted in Chapter 1, I use the terms, modernity and tradition to gloss local understandings of *samai mai,* 'modern times' and *samai korn,* 'past times'— the altered and sometimes sharply fragmented differences between what people understand as the lifestyles and expectations of the previous generation and what is promoted in state discourse and popular media as the 'new generation'.

With reference to medical institutions, traditional practices are referred to as *phaen boran* (ancient types [of practice]) and practitioners as a groups are described as *mor boran* (ancient doctors). These terms in English, Thai and Lao imply a temporal relationship: tradition is something past, being replaced by modernity, something of the present and future. Yet, as seen throughout this book, both 'traditional' and 'modern' practices continue in the present. Rather, this temporal metaphor signals a differential power relation: a statement of what *should* be the case, (i.e. the 'dying' out of traditional practices) rather than what *is* the case.[22] As will be seen in this chapter, although biomedicine is a dominant form of therapy, it has not erased other non-biomedical therapies and alternative representations of the body, health and illness. Nor are there always firm boundaries between biomedicine and 'traditional' therapies. As this chapter describes, there exists a range of healers utilising a bricolage of techniques and explanatory models in their practice. Significantly such practitioners are described neither as 'modern' nor 'traditional' by villagers.

As Martin has demonstrated, the discourses and practices of biomedicine entail certain understandings of ourselves and our bodies, from the ways in which we visualise the interior of our bodies, to the transformation of intimate relations through technologies such as contraception (Martin 1987). The same may be said of traditional healing therapies, which also entail a particular understanding of the body. In theory the forms of knowledge of biomedicine and traditional healers seem incommensurable, yet the differences are transcended everyday in practice as people seek care and healing from various practitioners.

The first part of this chapter describes various dimensions of the body. This task is a difficult one, for the act of writing such a description of necessity formalises various explanatory models about how the body works into discrete systematic consistent sections, in a way far removed from the pragmatic utilisation of such theories when people experience illness. Informants usually offer only partial and sometimes contradictory explanations in response to questions about their action. These notions of the body are not discrete, rather as in the case of Grandmother Mii and her family, people take action based upon a number of dimensions simultaneously.

Concepts of the body/person: Flesh, spirit, flows and balance

Isan concepts of the body/person do not draw stark distinctions between self and society, mind and body as found in Western biomedical epistemology. Villagers perceive the 'person' not as an entity separate from the community, but rather a process of embodiment of spirits and flesh, karma and community. Informants differ on the details of the descriptions of the body according to their expertise or the emphasis they would place on the importance of some elements over others, but the description below draws upon the local beliefs in Ban Srisaket rather than the urban institutionalised forms of traditional Thai medicine. In any given case of ill-health or distress, a number of different dimensions of the person are said to be involved. These multiple dimensions are linked through an underlying representation of the person as an entity with porous boundaries or 'gates' between the inner world of the body and the outside world. Elemental humors, spirits and souls may pass between the boundaries of the body causing destabilisation. A healthy body is one whose various dimensions are in balance and equanimity.

Humoral balance

The human body is said to consist of four *that* (elements) derived from Ayurvedic medicine, namely *din* (earth), *fai* (fire), *nam* (water), and *lom* (wind).[23] These *that* are associated with various body substances, such as phlegm, bile and blood. Disequilibrium of one or more of these four elements will result in illness. The body itself, *tua,* is perceived as a cavity supported by bones, covered with skin and with a series of *sen* (channels such as blood vessels, tendons, nerves, muscles) through which circulates the *lu'at* (blood), several kinds of water including *nam khram* (waste water), and winds which push and circulate the other humors throughout the body, such as the *lom beng* (pushing wind) and *lom chawat* (pulling wind). Some winds may enter the body and cause illness, particularly after childbirth when the boundaries of a woman's body are most permeable. Some winds are poisonous *lom phit* (poison wind). The fiery element of the body is considered a common cause of illness. An excess of *fai* can cause fevers, a deficiency causes a cold state and weakness:

> If something is wrong with these, you are sick. If you get a fever there are healers who *aap nam lom fai* [wash people with water to reduce the fire element]. If you have too much wind in your body you will have weakness or be *win wiang* [dizzy]. (Grandmother Lek)

Dietary practices must also be considered as forms of therapy. The proportions of heating and cooling properties in the diet may be manipulated to influence the overall balance of these states. Thus there is little distinction between what is eaten as food and medicine (Mulholland 1979; Van Esterik 1988). The heating or cooling properties of foods—how *man* (fat) it is, whether it is 'itchy' food, or poisonous for one's present state—and the proportions eaten may all be considered in prophylactic and curative actions.[24] The taste and fragrance of foods also can influence the overall balance of these states and hence may influence a person's emotional states and behaviour (Manderson 1986b; Mulholland 1979).

Rice is fundamental among all foods. In Thai and Lao, the verb to eat is literally *gin khaw,* 'to eat rice'. Rice is neither hot nor cold but a neutral food that should be consumed at every meal as it is understood to be an essential part of the human body: 'man's body itself is rice, and eating rice renews the body directly . . .' (Hanks 1972:22). Most healing ceremonies in Isan involve sticky rice in various forms, both as food to entice and nurture supernatural beings and souls, and also as a metonym of the body onto which may be transferred illness and bad fortune. In the ceremony described at the beginning of the chapter, the illness was transferred onto a ball of sticky rice which was then thrown out the window.

The consumption of a distinctive type of rice, *khaw niow,* sticky rice, by Isan people in contrast to the ordinary rice *khaw jao,* eaten by Central Thai, is a fundamental signifier of the essential difference between Isan and Central Thai people. Isan people state that only *khaw niow* satisfies them and makes them strong enough for heavy work. Many Central Thai people state that they are constitutionally unable to eat sticky rice and associate the consumption of sticky rice with stolidness, sloth and sluggish thought (Moerman 1968). Villagers were amazed that as a foreigner I was physically able to eat sticky rice. The type of rice one chooses to eat can thus carry expressions of status and class aspirations as well as be a fundamental statement of affinity and identity as a person (see Manderson 1986b for a discussion of food symbolism).[25]

Environmental and climatic conditions may also influence the balance of the body; for example, I was warned that washing with cold water in the heat of the day may induce a humoral shock to the system, resulting in sickness. A cold wind from a draft may enter the body and cause a wind illness.

Just as external conditions may cause internal imbalances, so too internal thoughts and behaviours may cause internal imbalances in the humors. Eating the wrong food may upset the humoral balance of the body, as can working too hard, thinking too much, or being exposed to un-seasonal cold. In terms of bodily experience, these are in the same category. The body does not constitute a solid boundary between the external and internal; it is a porous membrane connecting worlds made up of the same elements and forces.

Binding fickle souls

Apart from these physical components, within a person also reside thirty-two *khwan* (souls) positioned in various organs of the body. These souls are entities understood to animate and vitalise the organs in which they reside. In this way the Isan body is understood as constituted by a multitude of beings. The *khwan* in Isan is frequently used in the collective sense, referring to all thirty-two *khwan.* It is often used by villagers as an equivalent term for the state of the mind-heart (*chit-jai*) of a person. A person who is easily startled—

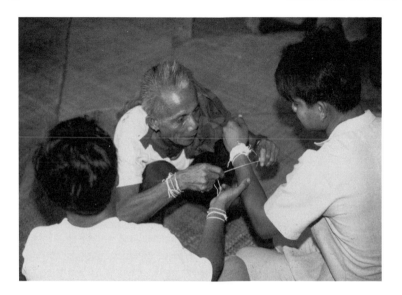

Plate 3.1 A young man has his wrists tied during a *phuk khaen* ritual.

tok jai ngai, (heart falls easily)—is one whose *khwan* flee from the body easily.

The *khwan* is central to much of Isan medicinal practice and belief. All thirty-two *khwan* must be correctly positioned for good health. Villagers informed me that the *khwan* positioned within the head is the most important and the most likely to flee or become dislocated from the body. If disturbed by any force the person will be ill due to the loss of this life essence (Heinze 1982; Tambiah 1970:224-27).

Ceremonies to call and secure the *khwan* to the body are held for people suffering from prolonged illness, or who have had an accident. In some instances, such as the case of Grandmother Mii described above, the soul of a sick person must be located and called back to the body before recuperation is possible. This requires the skills of a *mor waen khwan*[26] or a *mor oen khwan*.[27] All such ceremonies involve the calling of the *khwan* and the fastening of it to the body through the binding of the wrist (*phuk khaen*) with white thread (*fai mongkhon*). [28] In this way the *su khwan* ceremonies are both prophylactic and therapeutic, by preventing the *khwan* from fleeing the body at times of stress which may then result in ill health, and by restoring it to the body when it has obviously fled. Such ceremonies are also performed for the elderly to ensure a long life and at significant rites of passage throughout one's life, such as birth or pregnancy, ordination, travel from the community or return to the community after a long absence.

Tying to reinforce the body's strength is thus a central motif in Isan practices. With the ubiquitous *su khwan* ceremonies that accompany incidents of sickness, affliction and misfortune as well as all important life transitions, the person is tied into her relationships with kin and friends, with the ancestors and supernatural beings—an act which restores bodily as well as spiritual and social equilibrium, essential for well-being and happiness. As Devisch has noted for the Yaka people of Zaire, 'to become a person is to be connected, bonded and tied into, and with, those multiple forms of reproduction and exchange that give form to the Yaka universe' (1998:130). So among Isan people, the body/self is a porous interface subject to dangerous flows between self and non-self. Body boundaries are enforced through the tying and binding of the gates of the body with a knot of multiple relationships. As each person ties the sacred cotton threads they murmur wishes of health, happiness, strength, a long and good life.

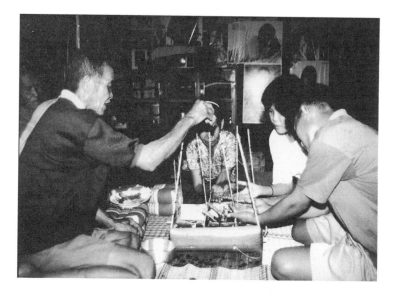

Plate 3.2 A *su khwan* ceremony conducted by Grandfather Muan.

Merit and karma

Apart from the fickle *khwan,* people have another type of soul: *winyan,* which is the essential spiritual essence which leaves the corporal body at death to undergo reincarnation (Irvine 1982; Tambiah 1970:57-9). Unlike the *khwan* which leave the body easily, the *winyan* only departs the body at death. The fate of this spirit essence is determined by the person's store of *bun* (Buddhist merit). The Buddhist concept of life as continuous cycles of suffering caused by karmic fate, underlies the beliefs concerning ultimate causes of disease. Whilst most health problems are believed to arise in response to imbalances in the natural, supernatural or social environment, or due to natural aging, actions from a previous incarnation are often blamed for chronic and permanent congenital conditions. For example, a woman I met in front of a provincial hospital with crippling arthritis in her hands and feet described how, after trying various traditional and modern remedies and massage, she now practised meditation. Whilst meditating she had a vision of a white clothed Brahman, who told her that her illness was caused by her breaking a promise and thus cheating someone in her former life. A promise, she explained, is something that binds your hands and feet and hence in this life she was afflicted at her hands and feet.

In this way a person's present life/self is understood as an expression of accumulated karma formed through the actions and consequences of a collectivity of previous beings in previous lives, even as non-human incarnations.

Plate 3.3 Grandfather Muan conducts a *sadorh khro* ceremony.

Efforts to improve one's store of Buddhist merit are, in effect, health practices to lessen one's experience of suffering in this life and the next and ensure physical and spiritual well-being. Ordinations and participation in temple activities are a means of ensuring well-being for oneself and family but also for dead relatives. For example, during the final stages of the terminal illness of Grandmother Mii, her son ordained as a monk for a short period. This is an act which brings great merit to one's parents. Often sons ordain, even for two nights, at the death of a parent to improve the karmic status of the deceased person's soul.

A person's store of positive merit assists in negating the influence of *khro*, vaguely described as an inauspicious malevolent force linked to astrological influence. *Khro* is used as an explanation to explain more minor misfortune, such as sickness, economic loss at the lottery, and disputes. The influence of *khro* is divined through inauspicious signs. For example, one family sought a *sadorh khro* ceremony from the local *mor taeng kae* to chase away misfortune after finding a dead bird in the house. As the young daughter of the house was in her first pregnancy, this was considered a bad sign for the unborn. The ceremony involved creating a box with effigies of the two young people of the house with offerings to entice the *khro* from their bodies. Another tray of offerings to the *thewada* (Buddhist angels) was prepared. The ceremony ended with a *su khwan* to strengthen the bodies' boundaries against further malevolent influence.

Ghosts, magic and restless spirits

The body can also be exposed to the actions of *phi* (spirits) and may be influenced by *saiyasat* (magic).[29] There are a range of rituals to cure illness, affliction, and alter destiny and misfortune, all of which are ultimately concerned with stabilising the relationship between the person, spirits and community, and reinforcing the boundaries between the human community and external forces.

A host of spirits connected to natural places and the dead inhabit the landscape of the village. *Phi* are usually described as formerly human, and like humans vary in their personality. Certain eminent ancestors may become powerful benevolent and disciplinary guardians of places, while people who have suffered a violent or unnatural death may become extremely vengeful malevolent spirits. These spirits may enter people and cause illness requiring the skills of a spirit doctor to persuade them to leave. In Ban Srisaket possession by spirits was no longer considered as common as in the past when *phi porp* and *phi phai* entered newly delivered mothers and their babies, causing death through haemorrhage, and *phi fa* and *phi su'a* caused illness and death in the vulnerable. Deforestation and the long period of settlement is considered to have removed the 'wild' places frequented by many types of spirits, yet, as one elder warned, 'Isan still has many spirits. They descend at night and are everywhere in the village and must be treated with respect.' Throughout the village, people are careful to close their shutters at night as barriers against roaming spirits.

An example of how the action of spirits are implicated in illness is provided by an account given by Grandmother Kaew. While cutting grass one day she encountered a man and a woman, dressed in shabby white clothes, who chatted with her. Feeling sorry for them she invited them to eat and drink at her house. But as she led them to her house they disappeared. 'I returned home and after a month I dreamed of these people asking to stay with me. I answered, "Yes, you can". Then I became very sick'. So Grandfather built a spirit house for them and invited them to stay in it. 'Each *wan phra* [holy day] I go and pay respect with flowers and rice and I got better.'

Grandmother Kaew's story highlights how explanations for the onset of illness may involve multiple aetiologies. She explained that for two years after this incident she had active tuberculosis for which she still takes medicine that she receives from a public health centre in Khon Kaen. Yet her explanation for why she was inflicted with tuberculosis involved her contact with these spirit figures. Once a home had been made for them in the form of a spirit house in a shady spot at the front of their house, these spirits left her and she recovered. The medicine for the tuberculosis may address the intermediate cause of illness, the action of a bacillus, yet only by addressing the reason for her vulnerability to this illness, the actions of the spirits, was she able to be fully cured.

Another prophylactic strategy is to utilise magical protection against the actions of spirits and humans. Such talismans strengthen the physical and spiritual boundaries of the wearer making them invulnerable to the action of spirits or magic. These may be small terracotta or copper amulets of the Lord Buddha or Buddhist scenes, Buddha images from particular wats, images of revered monks or Buddhist saints (*arahant*) or verses from the Buddhist cannon written on small pieces of paper or cloth rolled up in small cylinders on necklaces (see Tambiah 1984). Popular in Ban Srisaket were copper amulets from the oldest local temple, Wat Srisaket, which houses an auspicious Khmer Buddha image.

Holy water liberally splashed over the congregation at particular Buddhist ceremonies and temple rituals also has important curative properties. It is collected, drunk and splashed over the old and infirm whenever available to ensure health and contribute to the recipient's attainment of merit. *Mor nam mon* (holy water doctors) specialise in using this sacred water in the setting of broken bones.

The well-being of all village inhabitants, both human and animal, also depends on the correct observance of the *hit sipsorng, khlong sipsi,* the Isan cycle of rituals and laws.[30] These reassert good relationships between the gods, ancestral village spirits, those of dead relatives and the living, ensure the fertility of rice and animals, and celebrate Buddhist values. Much effort, time and financial resources are used to ensure the success of these ceremonies.

The mind-heart

Traditional Asian medical systems often merge the psychological and physiological domains, making it problematic to assume the cross-cultural validity of Western biomedical epistemology which separates the two (Adams 1992; Laderman 1992). Biomedicine makes distinctions between organic illness and psychosomatic events, the somatization of distress, whereas Thai and Isan theories of humoral and spiritual balance treat them as indistinct. Among Thai and Isan, the Cartesian mind/body dualism is transcended, as the physical body is the site of mental emotions. At the same time, the term *chit jai* (mind-heart) in both Central Thai and Isan distinguishes the mental-emotional mind as opposed to the flesh. The word *jai*, the mental-emotional heart (as opposed to *hua jai*, used for the physical heart) is used in a number of compound expressions such as *di jai* (good heart) to express emotional happiness, and in expressions that refer to states of mind, such as *jai noi* (small heart, irritable) or *khaw jai* (to enter the heart, to understand). The stability of the mind-heart is also precariously balanced. Some people are described as inherently more unstable than others, described as being *jai ron* (hot-hearted), people who are quick to show their emotions, especially anger, as opposed to people who display the culturally desirable qualities of being *jai yen* (cool-hearted).

Humoral imbalances of the body can affect the stability of the mind-heart as will be discussed later with reference to women and postpartum afflictions. Likewise the mental-emotional stability of the mind-heart is influenced by factors in the social, spiritual and astrological environment (Irvine 1982). Fundamentally, the concept of *chit jai* recognises that physical disorders are inextricably related to emotional and moral worlds.

Incorporation of biomedical concepts of the body and disease causation

The introduction of Western biomedicine into Isan has led to the incorporation of a variety of ideas, techniques and medicines into common usage. Representations of local medicinal practices as 'traditional' reifies practice and knowledge as somehow frozen in past times. Despite such representations by Isan people themselves, local medical theories of disease causation and techniques of healing show dynamic change and flexible embracing of other technologies. Notions of how the body works are not static, but are constantly changing and being revised partly in response to interpretations of how new medicines and technologies work. Sometimes interpretations draw upon established conceptual frameworks, such as humoral notions of hot/cold, or may extend analogies drawing upon new sources of knowledge and observations. Household health knowledge now includes substantial familiarity with different brands of Western medicines, the concept of germs, and an expectation of speedy recovery when treated with Western therapies. The legacy of a variety of public health programs makes its appearance in many hybrid forms. For example, in the ceremony described at the beginning of this chapter the egg yolk divined by Grandmother Pay was said to indicate the presence of a parasitic worm in Grandmother Mii's liver. Although the presence of worms and other creatures within the body exists in traditional aetiologies of disease causation,[31] the idea of parasites in the liver as a specific cause of liver disease clearly relates to the extensive public health campaigns concerning liver fluke infections of *Opisthorcis viverrini* associated with the high incidence of cholangiocarcinoma in the Isan population.[32] Local understandings of the liver as a source of illness and as a site of intervention have come to dominate descriptions of ailments within the village. Whilst liver cancer is one of the major causes of death in the Ban Srisaket, there is now a tendency to subsume all forms of jaundice and all cancer deaths in the village under the label of *rok tap* (liver disease) or *maleng tap* (liver cancer), which marks a change in the local perceptions of causality of terminal illness.

Older villagers romanticise that in the past traditional medicine was efficacious and adequate for the illnesses of the population. Modern forms of life are regarded as now requiring modern medicines to cure a range of new disease forms. For example, I was informed by one elder that 'in the past there was no cancer, there was just wind abscess [*fi lom*] in the stomach.' Another villager said that '*khai padong* [illness or fever and itchiness] was like what today they say is *rok tap* [liver disease] although back then they could heal it. They didn't die like today'.[33]

Similarly, germ theory is transmuted in villagers' understandings. *Chu'arok* (germs; literally, the source of disease) are said to carry illness. However, the actions of germs are understood to create ill-health if the balance of the body is disrupted, or a soul disturbed, thus leaving a person vulnerable to attack by natural or supernatural forces which catalyse these disease-inflicting agents. Significantly, where words have specific medical meanings there is considerable merging of concepts. For example, the term *aksaep* is used to mean infection in biomedical discourse, but may also mean inflammation, a condition recognised by villagers and attributed to an excess of heat. As will be discussed in Chapter 4, this difference has consequences for women's understandings of their reproductive health.

Embodying tradition: Traditional healers

My typology between traditional and modern healers is based upon the village perception of the diversity of therapies that co-exist in North-east Thailand. As mentioned earlier, however, such a typology is based upon a false reification of what are dynamic and blurred boundaries. Healing knowledge entails continuous transformations of meanings and sometimes even the 're-invention' of knowledge as 'tradition'. Villagers recognise one set of healers as *mor boran* (ancient doctors), who follow traditional modes of healing. They are sometimes referred to as *mor phu'n ban* (local doctors). Their authority is derived from the immediate community that they serve as 'locally sanctioned healers' in contrast to other 'officially sanctioned healers', such as government medical staff whose authority is based upon the institutions in which they work (Weisberg 1982).

Within Ban Srisaket there is a host of people recognised as *mor boran*. In addition, a network of massage doctors, spirit doctors and ritual specialists extends throughout the district. Four male specialist *mor su khwan* are regular practitioners at healing ceremonies and weddings involving the tying of *khwan* to the body. Three women and one transvestite man are *mor waen khwan*, who call the souls of people in rituals (as described above). The village *jam* cares for the village through being an intermediary of the village spirits and communicating their wishes. In addition two elder men are *mor tham* (*dharma* specialists) who use sacred Buddhist texts to heal sickness caused by magic spells and *phi*. Many other elder men who had been ordained in their youth practise the arts of *mor pau* (blowing doctors), who blow magic phrases over the heads of the ill. There are five men recognised as *mor nam man,* who use blessed coconut oil or sesame oil to set bones. There is one woman who is a *mor jap sen,* who specialises in massage. The local herbalist has died with no one to continue his skills, although many people have knowledge of herbal remedies and grow them in their home gardens. Finally, there are six women who are trained traditional birth attendants, of which only one was still actively assisting women give birth at home in 1992 (see Chapter 6).

In Thailand 'traditional' medicinal practices retain an ambivalent relationship with the state. In 1923, a Medical Practices Control Act made registration of traditional healers compulsory, and bureaucratic interference and harassment of healers led many practitioners to cease practising. The development of traditional medicine was further discouraged through legislative acts; Controlling the Practice of the Art of Healing (1939), the 1961 Medical Practice Act, and 1967 Drugs Act (Grand & Sri-ngernyuang 1989:14). In 1978, WHO suggested the promotion of the training of traditional practitioners, such as herbalists, bonesetters and traditional birth attendants (TBAs), the selection of essential traditional medicines and techniques for primary health care, basic and applied research, and development of traditional medicine (Grand & Sri-ngernyuang 1989:1). In response to this, the promotion of traditional medicine was introduced in the Thai National Health Care Program in the Fifth National Plan (1982–86) and the Primary Health Care system was instituted. These programs were initiated as a means by which the government health system could acquire some of the social closeness and accessibility of traditional healers through their selective

Plate 3.4 The village health station (*sathani anamai*).

incorporation into the government health system as part of rural primary health services.

The incorporation of traditional practices has been selective. Government attention has centred upon the training of traditional birth attendants (TBAs) and upon the promotion of herbal medicines, but little upon other traditional practitioners.[34] For example, in Ban Srisaket all currently practising traditional birth attendants have received government training. Women who were considered too old to be trained are no longer encouraged to practise (see Chapter 6). Brun and Schumacher suggest that 'traditional curers are being used to serve the spread of the Western medical tradition . . . this exploitation will hasten the disintegration and destruction of the traditional medical systems' (Brun & Shumacher 1994:238).

Certain forms of knowledge based on Western, rational science have been privileged over local wisdom. As Cohen notes, the history of the Thai medical profession is one of assertion of 'its dominance over other health practitioners by means of subordination or exclusion' (1989:160). What is at stake is the legitimacy of opposing systems of knowledge and a contest over the control of cultural capital.

Embodying modernity: Government health services and biomedical practitioners

Government health services first became widely available to Isan villagers as counter-insurgency measures. In the 1950s there was a growing fear of communist insurgency in the North-east. Under the military rule of General Sarit the North-east was defined as a security problem due to the activity of 'communist separatists' (Turton 1978). Through this period, the 'development' of the North-east was promoted as a counter-insurgency measure to alleviate the poverty which the government feared made the North-east vulnerable to the communist cause (Demaine 1986:98). Improvements in infrastructure, the expansion of communication, transport, and trading networks along with 'rural development' policies sought to both increase the productivity of the region through agricultural diversification and to increase living standards to reduce support for communist subversion (Brown 1994:200). For example, in 1976 a project to train villagers in Sakhon Nakhon (a stronghold of the communist insurgency) called the 'Village Health Volunteers Project' was administered under the Division of Internal Security and run by that division, the army, Red Cross and government health staff. Its stated objectives were to help and give service to villagers, prevent diseases and 'to guide the villagers in politics' (Thailand, Ministry of Public Health 1977:57). As I argue throughout this book, the linkages between state health services and state ideologies and development agendas remains, although less overtly than in the past. As a result of policies promulgated in several National Health Development Plans, health care facilities and services have been set up in almost all rural districts and sub-districts. Government health services are organised at several levels under the administration of both the Ministry of Public Health and the Ministry of Interior. At the local level, village health stations (*sathani anamai*) provide primary health care to each *tambon* or sub-district consisting of three to ten villages. In 1991, there were 8040 health stations in Thailand (JICA 1992). These are usually staffed by an auxiliary midwife and a junior sanitarian or technical nurse. The health station at Ban Srisaket is staffed by one technical nurse, an administrative officer/sanitarian and a technical nurse/midwife.[35] Such centres are responsible for antenatal, delivery and postnatal care, immunisation, nutrition and family planning services, water supply and sanitation activities. They also provide treatment for minor illnesses and emergencies, and provide referrals to district or provincial hospitals for complicated cases.

District community hospitals represent the next level in the government health system. They serve approximately 50 000 people per ten to thirty bed hospital. As of 1987 there were 558 such hospitals predominantly providing outpatient facilities and a limited range of in-patient care including maternity services (Sermsri 1988:18). In addition, they provide preventative and

Plate 3. 5 The local district hospital.

promotional health services, such as family planning and immunisation services. The local district hospital for Ban Srisaket has ten beds and is staffed by one medical doctor and nine nursing staff.

Provincial-level general hospitals have between 150 to 500 beds. These hospitals provide referrals to the specialist teaching hospitals, such as Srinagarind Hospital at Khon Kaen University and the large hospitals of Bangkok. These represent the highest level of the government health system and are the most prestigious hospitals, providing specialist services, research and teaching facilities.

These services are also supported by district and provincial-level health offices. The district health officer is responsible for supervising and providing technical and logistic support for the health stations as well as the collection of health data. The Provincial Health Office is responsible for the administration of both hospital services and public health including the collection of health data, focusing on the supervision of rural health facilities.

Private practice

Overlap between government services and private practice is common at all levels of the government health service. Strict distinctions between 'government' health services and 'private' health services are therefore not useful to describe the Thai health system, as the boundaries between the two are not discrete. Hospital doctors and health personnel usually operate private clinics outside of hospital hours. It is believed by villagers that the service received by a doctor in private practice is superior than if the same doctor was seen at the hospital.

Within Ban Srisaket Nurse Silaa runs her additional private clinic and drugstore, closely intertwining her roles as private practitioner and government official. Likewise, the doctor and several nurses at the local district hospital have private practices and pharmacies at which their government qualifications are prominently displayed.

Apart from the prolific private medical clinics, private hospitals are found in most larger district centres. Although out of the price range of most villagers, the private hospitals appeal to the wealthy middle class with promotions of more personalised service, more comfortable modern surroundings and access to high technology and elective surgery.

Most private medical services and drugs cost much more than government services or traditional healers, and yet are greatly utilised. For example, giving birth in a private hospital in Roi Et Province costs 1500 baht compared to 300 baht in government hospitals. The expense of a particular treatment and the distance involved in seeking it may not discourage patients, especially if the service has a good reputation. Indeed, expense and distance may add to the prestige of the healer and some villagers express a certain pride as they account the inconvenience and expense required to secure a cure.

Other medical entrepreneurs

The hybridisation of western biomedicine and traditional modes of healing is most evident in the practice of injection doctors (*mor chit ya*) (Reeler 1990). They are usually untrained people who have learned to give injections by trial and error and administer intravenous and intramuscular injections of Western medicines, usually antibiotics, vitamins, pain-killers and saline solutions, for a variety of ailments, from haemorrhoids to hangovers. They will also administer saline drips upon request. Injections or saline intravenous infusions remain one of the most popular forms of treatment. Injections are commonly understood as being *ya reng* (strong medicines), which are highly effective because of their direct mode of delivery.

Ban Srisaket has a number of injection doctors. All five village health volunteers moonlight as injection doctors and charge for the service even though only trained nurses and doctors are legally permitted to give intramuscular injections and intravenous injections (Riley & Sermsri 1974; Weisberg 1984). Neighbouring villages and district centres all have their own injection specialists—one old gentleman provides a mobile service as he rides through the village once a week beeping a horn on his bike offering both injections and haircuts.

Injection doctors are considered *mor phu'n ban* (local doctors), but are not considered *mor boran* (traditional/old doctors). They are part of the community, readily accessible to villagers and of similar social status. In many ways they acts as a 'broker', an easily accessible source of the most popular form of biomedicine: injections (Cunningham 1970). As will be seen in later chapters, they are an important source of antibiotic and tonic injections for women in the village suffering from gynaecological complaints. Although they use the equipment of Western medicine, the theories of disease causation are those of villagers, and so injections are usually combined with the murmuring of magic *khatha* (Pali phrases) over the site of the complaint. In marked contrast to consultations with biomedical doctors and nurses, injection doctors spend considerable time casually socialising with villagers, discussing a range of concerns with their patients and often sharing some food together.

Other medical entrepreneurs include salesmen of Buddhist images who travel through the villages, specifically asking about anyone who has recently been ill or had an accident. I was at the home of a man who had broken his foot in a motorcycle accident when such a salesman sold a set of three plaster images for 200 baht. These images were duly 'consecrated' by the salesman and placed at the head of the afflicted.

Self-medication

When referring to drugs, a broad distinction is made by people between *ya boran* (ancient medicine) and *ya farang/ya padjuban* (foreign medicine/contemporary medicine). Western medicines are considered more effective than traditional medicines for most conditions because of their rapid symptomatic relief. However, some long-term chronic conditions and certain traditional conditions can only be treated by traditional means. *Ya jin* or Chinese medicine refers to products sold by the many Chinese drug sellers and pharmacists who offer advice and medicines from the Chinese pharmacopoeia. In addition, there are various *ya samunphai* (herbal medicines) that are commonly recognised and grown by people in their gardens. Patent herbal medicines sold in stores or hawked by travelling medical salesmen are also referred to in the village as *ya samunphai*.

Drugs bought from local stores are an important health resource within the community. My data from a village health survey reveals self-medication as the most usual first step in treatment of illness (see Figure 3.1). This is consistent with national patterns (Krongkaew 1980; Osaka & Nanakorn 1995a; Osaka & Nanakorn 1995b). Self-medication is convenient, inexpensive and allows villagers to assert their agency in health care.

Figure 3. 1 First treatment choice reported by villagers when ill, Ban Srisaket, 1993.

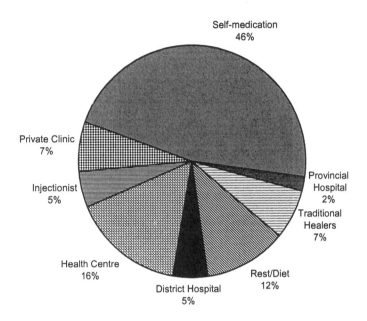

Self-medication
46%

Private Clinic
7%

Injectionist
5%

Provincial
Hospital
2%

Traditional
Healers
7%

Health Centre
16%

Rest/Diet
12%

District Hospital
5%

SOURCE: Household survey, 1993

A survey of medicines available for sale in six small general stores in Ban Srisaket in November 1992 revealed a total of 76 different brands of medicines available, as well as numerous different patent medicines (see Appendix 2). Of these, there were seven different brand-name forms of tetracycline for sale by the tablet, as well as sulphonamides and seven combination analgesics which combine aspirin, paracetamol and caffeine.[36] It is estimated that there are currently over 30 000 brands of drugs on the Thai market.[37] Over-consumption and the expense of drugs are major problems. In addition, there is widespread use of potentially harmful and addictive drugs, in particular analgesics, corticosteroids, antibiotics and *ya chut,* which are small packets of a mixture of unmarked drugs sold as universal remedies for a variety of complaints and often containing potentially harmful and potent medicines. Shopkeepers of Ban Srisaket were unsure of the use of many of the drugs they sold, and some drugs were poorly labelled as to their contents, indications for use, contra-indications or expiry dates. In Ban Srisaket, *ya*

Plate 3.6 Village stores sell a variety of patent medicines and pharmaceuticals over the counter.

chut were dispensed by the local injection doctors and remain freely available in village stores and at local district towns.

The mode of administration of medicine is an important means of reference and has consequences for the perceptions of its effectiveness.[38] It also means that villagers are rarely able to offer the name of the medicine they are taking, but rather refer to broad categories of types of medicine. Distinctions are commonly made between *ya kin* (oral medicines) and *ya chit* (injections). Herbal medicines are commonly identified as either *ya tom* (boiled medicines), *ya mor* ('pot' medicines), or *ya fon* (ground medicine). Further secondary identification of medicines is in terms of their actions. Thus antipyretics are *ya kae khai* (medicine to correct fever) and cough medicines and bronchial dilators are identified as *ya kae ai* (medicine to correct cough); all pain-killers are *ya kae puat* (medicine to correct pain). *Ya nam* may be any 'liquid medicine' and the term *ya bamrung* (strengthener) refers to vitamins, tonics or caffeine tablets. In this way, medicines are identified in terms of the symptoms they relieve, just as diseases are described symptomatically rather than in terms of their aetiology. The ingestion of medicines usually only continues until there has been a relief of symptoms, at which time a person is considered cured. Courses of antibiotics are rarely completely taken, and this practice is encouraged by the sale of antibiotics by the single tablet in pharmacies and village grocery stores.

Choice of medicine is usually based upon previous experience, or advice from kin, friends, the village drug fund and the shop owners. Certain trade names are very popular and heavily advertised through posters, sponsored movies, free samples and the media. Pain-killers and stimulants are the most heavily used drugs and are promoted as indispensable accompaniments to hard physical labour.

Within the village, drugs are usually sold by the tablet, which makes them affordable to villagers whose disposable funds are limited. To help ease the expense of medicines, Village Drug Funds have been set up in five of the six *muban* comprising Ban Srisaket but in 1992 only one was nominally operative. The village health volunteers are responsible for the administration of the fund which was implemented to supply villagers with affordable medicines from the National Essential Drug List.[39] Lack of funds, little support from the community due to the limited drugs available, difficulty in maintaining supply, and the time involved were all mentioned by the health volunteers as reasons for the failure of the funds. For the most part, villagers resort to the small general stores for drugs and the drug sellers and pharmacists in district towns and Roi Et.

Conclusions

When people fall ill or suffer misfortune, they must choose between multiple and competing systems of healing. In many ways, biomedicine and traditional healing involve incommensurable knowledge, based on fundamentally different metaphysics about the nature of the world and beings within it. Yet in practice, in the pragmatics of their quest for therapy, people routinely combine elements from diverse and even contradictory medical systems. Even the healers they consult may commonly combine in their therapy and in their conceptualising of the body a range of concepts of health and disease and a bricolage of elements borrowed from diverse traditions. Despite the apparent dominance of Western biomedicine in Thailand, institutionalised through the government health system, it has not erased other non-biomedical therapies and alternative readings of the body and disease.

From the moment someone enters a village health clinic, approaches a *mor tham,* or waits in a queue at a district hospital, they enter into a complex web of discourses and practices. These include assumptions about the nature of the disease entities, acceptable explanations and modes of proper treatment and, as noted above, also encompass notions of 'modernity' and tradition'. The practices and technologies of traditional and biomedical systems mediate understandings of the body and self. By focusing on the meanings involved in utilising different forms of knowledge and practice we are led to an account which cannot be divorced from the tensions in the ways in which healing knowledge is distributed in society and the massive asymmetries of power which sustain Western biomedical practices in Thailand and throughout the world.

In Haiti, Brodwin has shown how the seemingly stable array of religious and medical traditions is deceiving and that there is a continual struggle over the effectiveness, political potential and moral meanings of healing power (1996:199). Similarly, the chapters which follow explore the contestation over the meanings of knowledge and practice in women's health-seeking. This contestation entails not only health behaviour but issues of identity within a society fragmented by tensions between 'modernity' and 'tradition'. Although a range of studies in medical anthropology centre around a 'core narrative' of the subordination of indigenous healing by capitalist biomedicine, they tend to minimise various forms of resistence and defiance in plural systems. The chapters which follow demonstrate a more complex and nuanced relationship. In their search for treatment and care women move pragmatically between conflicting sites and bodies of knowledge, at times accepting the discourses and practices entailed in their choice, at other times resisting, subverting or transforming it to create new meanings.

4 Intimate knowledge, wombs and flow

The previous chapter explored the notions of the body in Isan and the various healing systems utilised by villagers. Women's health concerns are dominated by notions of their fertility and the processes of pregnancy, birth and post-partum care. This is because all aspects of a woman's strength, vitality, her physical and mental well-being are understood to be intimately influenced by these processes. In this chapter I explore the local understandings of the inherent bodily difference between men and women's bodies. Women's bodies are simultaneously sites of pleasure and suffering, of positive values associated with their fertility and motherhood, and the danger of their contaminating body fluids. These values are reflected in understandings of the ways in which women's bodies work, knowledge about menstruation and in the range of health complaints specific to female bodies. Discussions of women's health thus also involves gender ideology as it is articulated at the site of the body.

In discussing the intimate knowledge of their bodies, women describe a complex interaction between social, physical, emotional and supernatural aspects of their lives. This chapter explores the 'explanatory models' used by women to describe such intimate matters as *men* (menstruation) *mat khaw* (vaginal discharge) and *mot luk* (the uterus) and the relations between them, what Kendall terms 'ethnogynecology' (1987:367-76). But health concerns and practices also carry socio-moral significance and metamedical meaning (Nichter & Nichter 1996:1). As discussed in Chapter 3, the bodies described here are not only physiological entities, but social bodies in relation to others and bodies influenced by broader social forces of the body politic (Scheper-Hughes & Lock 1987). The narratives of women throughout this chapter reveal their perceived linkages between their health and their socio-economic status and changing lifestyle. This chapter is a descriptive account of women's bodies, but an account which positions women's bodies within the broader context and material conditions of their lives.

Women's bodies: Dangerous substances, positive fertility

Nong Phai washes the household's clothes with raw red hands, scrubbing
them with soap powder in a big black plastic basin. She flicks her hair off
her face with a soapy elbow. After washing and rinsing them, she hangs
the clothes carefully on bamboo poles to dry in the sun. The men's clothes
are washed separately to the women's clothes. The women's clothes are
washed according to whether they are worn on the top or bottom. All
women's skirts and pants are hung away from men's clothes on lower
rungs. More intimate garments are washed separately and hung away from
public eyes (Fieldnotes, 1992).

Women's bodies are understood to embody both dangerous substances and
potent forces of fertility. In understanding the meanings of gynaecological
conditions for women in Isan it is important to understand the underlying
relationship of women's bodies to the moral and social order.

Nong Phai's fastidiousness with women's lower garments relates to
understandings of the inherent destructive powers of female bodies and
sexuality. This power is concentrated in female genitalia and bodily secretions
such as menstrual blood. In Isan menstrual blood is considered a dangerous
substance, highly defiling to men and capable of draining away their physical
and spiritual power.[40] Menstruating women are considered dirty and impure
and their blood as disgusting. Sexual relations are avoided through
menstruation. Women's underwear and skirts should not come into contact
with men, especially their heads. Women are careful to hang these items
discretely below waist level and in a discrete location to avoid men
accidentally walking underneath the washing line.

Ethnographic work on menstruation has tended to focus on the negative
meanings surrounding menstruation and the 'inherent pollution of the female
principle' (Buckley & Gottlieb 1988:3-53). But menstrual blood also carries
positive meanings (Skultans 1988). Menstrual blood is primarily a positive
sign of maturity, fertility and strength. The regular appearance of menses is
seen as a sign of a healthy fertile body. Paradoxically, then, the presence of
menstrual blood and lochia are signs both of female defilement and the powers
of female fertility.

Female fertility is an important source of female cultural power and
prestige. Through childbearing and maternity, a woman marks her status
within the moral order. Nurturing children is a source of much Buddhist merit
for women. To have sons who ordain as monks ensures her spiritual salvation.
Young women are expected to have children as soon as possible after they are
married, and it is through enduring the suffering of pregnancy, the pains of
childbirth and the post-partum that her status as a full adult is confirmed. With
the birth of the first child she becomes a *mae* (mother), a term of address that

encapsulates this transition from a young girl to that of a fully responsible adult.

However, the constant cycles of menstruation and childbirth are also understood as functions of essential differences between male and female bodies. Unlike Western biomedicine, which views sexual differentiation in anatomical terms, but still considers men and women's bodies as essentially the same, with livers and spleens having identical structures and functions, the Isan body is not only sexually differentiated, but essentially different in composition. Male bodies and female bodies have different requirements to maintain humoral balance and strength. Even medicines are gendered. As will be discussed later there exists a range of 'women's medicines' with properties specific to women's bodies.[41]

Women's physiological processes of menstruation and childbirth are understood to constantly disrupt the body's integrity or 'boundedness' leaving it open and thus allowing outside influences in and the strong heat/power and vital energy to be lost through the loss of blood. While men dislike menstruation because of its danger to them, women are less concerned with their polluting status and are more concerned with the debilitating effects of menstruation upon their energy and strength. Women have greater difficulty than men in maintaining the humoral balance of their bodies. As will be discussed later, with the loss of blood women have particular difficulty maintaining appropriate heat humor within their bodies. The precarious balance of the humors in women also has effects upon the *chit-jai* (mind-heart) and *khwan*. Severe disruptions in the flows of wind and bad blood through the body, such as occurs with the failure to observe post-partum proscriptions, can result in severe mental illness (see Irvine 1982). Because of the constant disruptions in humoral balance, women are considered to be inherently 'weaker-souled' than men. This ensures their greater vulnerability to natural and supernatural forces. Men are considered more rigidly bounded and less vulnerable, and so are able to manipulate supernatural power in its most potent forms (Irvine 1982:108). This discourse of boundedness and soul strength naturalises male dominance of positions of greater power/potency than women, as the most prestigious healers able to manipulate more dangerous powers, and as monks, soldiers and political leaders.

Gynaecological health thus carries a range of meanings beyond the physical experience of symptoms. As the following sections describe, the intimate workings of women's bodies express understandings of women's relationships with men, their social and moral status as well as commentary on broader social forces that affect women's lives.

The workings of women's bodies

Flows of blood are central to understandings about women's reproductive health and to ideas about gender. Apart from providing background ethnogynaecological information for the coming chapters, a discussion of blood provides an example of the ways in which the various dimensions of the body are linked in people's actions and understandings. It also provides an example of how gender is considered an essential embodied differentiation.

Blood is regarded as one of the essential liquid humors within the body, a 'hot' substance important to the overall humoral balance. An unobstructed flow of blood throughout the pathways of the body is essential for good health. A person with good blood will have rosy face and hands, these are considered signs of good health (Chirawatkul 1996). Blood that is too thin, either light red or too dark, or blood that is smelly is considered bad blood and may be poisonous.

Both men and women may have signs of bad blood or insufficient blood, for which a range of 'hot' tonics to strengthen the blood are available. Men and children remove bad blood through sweating and urination. However, women are especially susceptible to symptoms of bad blood as they have more blood than men due to their reproductive functions and because of the humoral fluctuations due to the constant loss of blood each month through menstruation and in childbirth.

Traditional medicinal texts describe women as having a special menstrual gland that matures at around age fifteen when it begins to produce menstrual blood (Irvine 1982; Mulholland 1989). Menstrual blood may affect a variety of organs in a woman's body. If it affects the heart it can make a woman agitated and easily provoked to anger. If it affects the gall bladder or liver it may make a woman listless, dull and dizzy. It may also affect the skin, making women flush with fever and feel itchy and may affect the tendons, making women have severe headaches and alternate hot and cold sensations. Its effects upon the bones result in severe waist and back pain. All such symptoms will be resolved when women menstruate normally, resulting in the cleansing away of the accumulated bad blood. Aunty Thiim below describes the sensations caused by the 'bad' blood rising in her body before it is expelled:

> Before I get my menstruation I am *ron nai* [hot inside her body] and *jai hai* [irritable] and I have *khwam dam sung* [literally high blood pressure, but describing a feeling of dizziness in the head and seeing stars in your eyes attributed to 'high blood pressure' in popular idiom].

Physical discomfort during menstruation is associated with bad blood moving through the body and the 'hot' state of the body. A number of women take locally purchased painkillers for their discomfort and some feel that this increases their flow of blood; others refrain from their use from fear that painkillers will stop the flow. Headaches, fevers and the symptoms of 'high blood pressure' are considered signs that the bad blood has moved upwards to the head rather than being expelled. This may cause long-term health problems for women if not corrected through the consumption of hot medicines to 'bring the blood down' and restore the humoral balance of the body.

Good menstruation is defined as a regular steady flow of red blood. This is a sign of good health and fertility. As will be described throughout this book, abnormal menstruation is a cause for concern for women. Menstruation that shows signs of thinness, that is smelly or dark is defined as evidence of too much bad blood. Sometimes, such bad blood becomes dry and forms a lump which may lodge in the abdomen or stick to the backbone. Such a condition is called *phit krabun lu'at* (womb blood toxin). Such blood may cause flatulence, diarrhoea, abdominal pain or chest pain. Another condition called *phit krabun lom* (womb wind toxin) occurs when wind rises up and causes the stomach to distend as though a woman is pregnant. For this reason, most women prefer not to use sanitary pads when menstruating as they say it blocks the flow of blood. 'If you wear pads the blood can't come out. I only use them when I wear trousers. After you take the pad off you bleed a lot' (Elder Sister Taa). Pads are not only expensive but restrict the flow of blood and cause itching where it is in contact with the skin.

When I menstruate and I use pants or underwear it's like my vagina is going to fall off. When I use pads it itches. I use them when I have to go out or travel. I get bumps all around the place that touches the pad. I can use some types like 'Lady', but not the small modern ones like 'Lori' or 'Modess' because they make me itchy. (Aunt Bun)

Women prefer to wear two *phasin* (skirts) and stay at home when menstruating, and will only wear pads if they must go out to the market. Some women use folded rags secured between the legs to absorb the blood if the flow is heavy. These are then washed in secrecy and reused.

Some restrictions of diet and activities are practiced throughout menstruation. Some of these remain as vague proscriptions that few women abide by, although if a women feels discomfort her failure to abide by them will be cited as causal. Such proscriptions include washing hair, using the teeth to peel banana leaves, touching needles, going under fences. Some of these proscriptions work metaphorically: touching a needle will make menstrual pains sharp, walking under a fence will block the flow of blood as a fence does the passage of people. Women are told not to pass by mint as the 'heat' emanating from menstruating women's bodies can wither 'cool' plants on contact. Likewise, during menstruation and in the post-partum period a number of foods that have 'cool' properties are avoided. For example, iced water and coconut milk are understood to restrict the expulsion of the blood and cause it to rise dangerously to the head (also see Chapter 6). This will affect the mind-heart and cause emotional instability and madness.[42]

Intercourse during menstruation is avoided. Not only is contact with menstrual blood considered defiling and potentially dangerous to the man, but intercourse during this time is also considered potentially damaging to the woman, as she is in an 'open' state and her womb is considered vulnerable.

As will be described in the next chapter, birth is an especially vulnerable time for women. Great importance is placed upon the need to fully cleanse the body of lochia after birth. The practice of staying by the fire is central to the cleaning and drying out of the womb of the dangerous lochia and the gradual reheating of the body after the loss of blood in birth. Lochia is considered a poison with long-term effects upon the humoral and mental stability of women if retained within the body.

Throughout a person's life-cycle there is a gradual change in the equilibrium between the elements of the body. As people age there is a gradual drying, cooling and shrinking of the body, understood through the reduction of the water elements and increase in the action of wind and fire elements. I was often instructed by Grandmother Bun, who was 64 years-old, about appropriate foods for the elderly, which she described as bland foods which do not disturb the bodily equilibrium too much. Although these processes apply to all aging people, maintaining a correct balance is more difficult for women. Most elderly women I spoke with described themselves as weak. They linked their weakness with their lack of fertility and the cessation of menstruation at menopause. Feelings of weakness or ill-health at this time are usually attributed to the retention of polluted blood in their bodies, whether through a failure to observe post-partum practice appropriately or inadequate menstruation when younger. Women's bodies are considered to be more permeable and less strongly bounded than men. Because they no longer menstruate, it is difficult for older women to rid themselves of this polluted menstrual blood and restore humoral equilibrium (Chirawatkul 1996).

Lumps of blood

While menstrual blood is considered contaminating, the womb also allows the positive process of conception to take place. Conception begins when the male and female fluids meet in the womb, blend and coalesce. Such a view is repeated in traditional medicinal texts such as the *Thai Book of Genesis* (*Khamphee prathom chinda*) which describes the early stage of pregnancy as little more than a lump of blood (see also the description in Hanks 1963):

> At the time of conception they say that [the embryo] is the finest particle, so fine. . . having been conceived in the mother's womb it can become liquefied more than seven times a day, it is so difficult to retain. After

seven days, first a cell is formed from the blood. . . When the pregnancy has lasted seven days without miscarriage the blood becomes thicker, like water which has been used to wash meat. After another seven days it becomes flesh. . . (Mulholland 1989:17).

Plate 4.1 Kaew and her mother admire her son.

At some point the lump of blood in the womb receives the soul of a reincarnated being. It is said to receive its *winyan* and *khwan* through the ancestral spirits, *pu thaen ya thaen* (paternal grandfather, paternal grandmother in heaven). These spirits are said to throw down the spirit of the one to be reincarnated from heaven and mould the form of the child in the womb. It is to these ancestral spirits that ritual appeals are made in *su khwan maeman* (tying the soul of the pregnant mother) ceremonies for the good health and good fortune of the child and a safe birth.[43] It is only at quickening when the mother feels the foetus move inside her body that she will refer to her pregnancy as a *luk* (child) or *dek noi* (a young child). Before that, women refer to their pregnancy as nothing more than a *gon lu'at* (a lump of blood). Thus pregnancies are only defined as sentient beings at this point. Only three days after the actual birth is the baby fully accepted as a human child, and not a spirit being (see Chapter 6). In this way a woman gradually becomes pregnant through a process which may for a variety of reasons stop or be expelled (see Chapter 7).

Infertility

Infertility carries considerable social stigma for men and women in a society that so values children and where having a child marks one's adult status. As noted in Chapter 2, the ability to bear and nurture children successfully remains important to the identity of women in Isan. Women are encouraged to have a child as soon as possible once they are married and some elder people discourage the use of contraceptives before having a first child due to a fear that they will cause the womb to become dry and hence cause infertility. It is assumed that people will not have difficulty conceiving, so when a woman fails to conceive, kin and neighbours begin to question why. Women in particular often suffer criticism from their kin for not bearing a child. They face accusations of being a sinful person with poor karma, of not trying or wanting a child hard enough and suffer fears of desertion by their husband (Boonmongkon 1997). Men suffer jokes and aspersions regarding their manliness and sexual ability.

Few women have access or even know about infertility clinics and counselling available at large public hospitals. The few that do face barriers of lack of money to pursue treatment. At one such clinic I observed, the attending specialist turned to me and said, 'Well, if they had money I might be able to help them conceive. If they were wealthy people in Bangkok I could help'.

Couples who have failed to conceive are often the subject of well-intentioned suggestions and enquiries. They are exonerated to try special foods and a range of herbal remedies. Men are encouraged to eat foods considered hot and strong, such as raw meat and whisky, to make them more potent. Women face questions about their general health and any signs of discharge or pain are cause for investigation. As with miscarriage the inability to bear children is also understood to reflect moral status. It is possible that one has offended supernatural powers, or not acquired sufficient merit, or that one is being punished in this life under the logic of karmic retribution for deeds committed in a previous life. Couples who wish to have children are encouraged to request children from the village spirits, or from a variety of particular Buddhist images that are famous for curing infertility. For example, Fai relates her experience:

I was married when I was fifteen and I didn't have a baby for two years, so I went with my husband to the statue of Lord Buddha at Jinarat to ask for a child and then that night my husband dreamed we should go and ask at another statue of the former King Narai of Ayutthaya and we did and I fell pregnant.

The onus for infertility generally falls on the woman. It is assumed that she has some abnormality or congestion in her womb or tubes that inhibits conception, or that her health in general is too poor or imbalanced to conceive. Toi, who is 34 years-old, and her husband Khem, who is 47 years-old, have been married for ten years and have not produced a child. At first people thought that Toi was infertile and she tried a variety of cures and herbal mixtures, but to no avail. Eventually, after consulting a doctor, she convinced Khem to go and be tested at the local hospital and was told that he was infertile. In the past it was also recommended that they go to seek help from a specialist who might have been able to help, but Toi was not able to convince her husband to go even though she really wanted a child. Although many friends have suggested they go to see particular monks or make offerings at particular temples, they no longer go as they think that if they were to fall pregnant now they would be too old to look after the child. Toi said that people in the village accept their childlessness but pity them. At this point, her brother-in-law walked by and joined us briefly. He joked that Toi should simply *long khaek,* invite the village men to all contribute their labour by sleeping with her until she did fall pregnant. I got the impression that the joke was one she has heard before.

Over time, villagers come to accept the childless status of some couples, which comes to be described in karmic terms. In some cases couples adopt children, usually from other kin. Several families in Ban Srisaket had adopted children from other families with large numbers of children. They were referred to as the *phor mae liang*, the 'nurturing parents' of the child.

Pregnancy loss

It is recognised that pregnancy can be a fragile process and women may suffer mishaps resulting in a natural miscarriage. Women attribute their miscarriages to a variety of physical causes, such as lifting heavy objects, being involved in accidents, working too hard cutting sugar cane or transplanting rice. Medical treatments, such as curettes, are also suspected of causing damage to the womb making it difficult to retain a pregnancy. Eating the wrong foods, especially 'hot' foods or consuming 'hot' women's medicines or other pharmacy drugs, are all understood to cause the expulsion of the products of conception.

But in cases of women who suffer the misfortune of repeated miscarriage supernatural causes become suspected. Aunt Amporn is forty-three years old. She is a rice farmer making a little extra money as a hired agricultural labourer at planting and harvest time. She has one 18-year-old son. After that first child, she fell pregnant again the next year and miscarried at five months. Two years later she fell pregnant again and miscarried again at four months. Another two years later she fell pregnant again and miscarried at three months, and a year later at two months. Each time she fell pregnant she had severe morning sickness. After her first two miscarriages she was very depressed, but after the third and fourth she simply felt angry that she should suffer with morning sickness so badly and yet never complete a pregnancy. After each miscarriage she went to the local hospital to have a curettage to clean out her uterus. She thinks her numerous curettes may be partly responsible for her repeated miscarriages. In addition she took *ya fon* (powdered herbal medicine), ate hot foods and had injections of *ya bamrung* (strengthening medicines) to enhance the health of her womb and her fertility. She also made votive offerings to village spirits and at the local temple, and underwent *su khwan* ceremonies during her pregnancies. She also called on the services of a *mor tham,* who identified a *phi phrai* as the cause of her suffering and undertook a ritual to chase the *phi phrai* to stop this from occurring again. *Phi phrai* is one type of demon that is said to appear as an owl and is associated with eating the bodily discharges of childbirth. She said that now people in the village believe that the first child she miscarried caused the second one to die, as it wanted company, and then they caused the third to die, and then those three caused the fourth to die. These children may have been siblings in their former incarnations and so do not wish to be separated. Such interference by the spirit of the former mother (*mae kaw mae lang*) or siblings of a child is also understood to be the cause of neonatal deaths (see Poulsen 1983:108-11). Presently, Aunt Amporn is using the contraceptive pill as she does not want another pregnancy or child at her age.

The most common supernatural cause of multiple miscarriage is the *suang.* A *suang* is a serpent in Isan folklore and women who have a mark on their skin are said to be cursed by a *suang* which causes her to become a *mae kin luk* (a mother who eats her children) before they are born (Phintong 1989:292).[44] Within Ban Srisaket a number of women had been successfully treated through this ritual by the local *mor tham* (spirit doctor) or by other traditional healers in nearby villages. Bai had a *kha suang* (kill the *suang*) ritual after her first pregnancy resulted in a miscarriage:

> On my first pregnancy I miscarried and people said I was a *mae kin luk.* I went and had Grandfather Bun who is a *mor tham* do a *kha suang* for me. He got seven needles from the house of a woman who was newly married and widowed, and then he used those and a knife to spike the skin where

there are marks on my body. This had to be done on three *wan sin dap* [holy days when the moon is waning]. It cost 12 baht. Now there is no one in our village who does this, you have to go to other villages.

Grandmother Nan described the ritual which cured her:

I had six miscarriages: one at four months, one at three months, one at five months, one at six months and one at seven months. Then, after birth, one of my children died at three months. I believe that there was a *suang*, there was something that ate the children. I went to see the *mor tham* who is a *mor kha suang* [doctor who kills *suang*], to have the ritual to get rid of the bad thing. Then I could successfully nurture a child.

The details of the ceremony may differ from healer to healer. Grandfather On told us how to *kha suang*:

You need to obtain a needle from each of seven houses of women newly widowed. Then on a Tuesday and then on two or three days in sequence I prick the place where the *suang* is. While I do that I repeat a *khatha* [a sacred Pali incantation]. A *mor tham* must do this rite. Many women still have it done for them if they have had miscarriages. You can do it for one day only when it is called a *takhai noi* or for three days when it is called a *takhai yai*.

Another ritual specialist in a village in Khon Kaen Province had a different technique. He said the ritual could only be done by a *mor tham* or by a *mahanigai*[45] monk. When he conducts the ritual he requires offerings of a *khan ha*, which is a standard votive offering consisting of five pairs of candles and five pairs of white flowers. In addition he requires one chicken's egg, one piece of white cloth, one piece of woman's *phasin* skirt material, one bottle of white whisky and finally the appropriate payment to the *mor tham*.

Firstly I would inspect the woman's body to find out the location of the *suang*. The mark of the *suang* is usually located in a secret place where it can't be seen by other people, such as the waist or breast. It is manifested as a red or black mark or a mole. I then ask the woman to lie down either on her back if the *suang* is located on her chest, or waist or on her stomach if it is located on her back. If it is anywhere else she doesn't have to lie down. Then I put half a coconut shell over the mark and I take a stick about as long as the length from my hand to my elbow and as thick as my thumb. I use that to tap around the coconut shell. At the same time I get a doctor's knife and pierce the hole in the top of the coconut shell, but the knife does not touch the skin. While doing this I chant *khatha*, sacred incantations. The *khatha* used are long and the whole ritual will

Plate 4.2 A collection of 'women's medicines' *ya satri,* **including a range of hormonal tablets and post-coital contraceptives used as menstrual regulators.**

last about thirty minutes. The ritual does not have to be done in secret but relatives and anyone can come along.

In restoring the supernatural order and removing the offending *suang,* the *mor tham* clears the way for the process of conception and the development of the foetus to occur without supernatural interference.

Women's medicines

The most common form of treatment for menstrual disorders involves the consumption of 'hot' medicines called *ya satri* (women's medicines) also known generically as *ya khap lu'at* (medicines to expel the blood). These medicines have a variety of drying and heating effects consistent with their hot humoral quality and are marketed throughout Asia (Ngin 1985). The use of menstrual regulators such as *ya satri* is very common cross-culturally (see Newman 1985). Different types of *ya satri* are found widely in village stores and district drug stores. The patent herbal medicines typically state that they are for women who have an irregular period, that they increase appetite, can be used to substitute staying by the fire after childbirth, help the draining away of lochia after childbirth, and help dry out the uterus and restore its position quickly and promote good breast milk. Some also are said to alleviate flatulence and heartburn, strengthen and nourish the body and blood.[46] As such they are presented as medicines which enhance a woman's fertility and well-being. Typically they come in the form of dark fragrant liquids or as blocks of herbs which are added to whisky (see Plate 4.2). In 1997 these *ya satri* cost around 30-40 baht per bottle or around 10 baht for the herbal blocks. According to medicine sellers *ya satri phen phak* (32 baht), and *ya satri ben lo* (24 baht) are the most popular brands.

Sixteen per cent of 164 women in the interview survey had used some form of 'hot medicine' at some time to bring on their periods or assist with their health. For example, Phen, who is 34-years-old, has used these medicines a number of times for different reasons. The first time was after her first baby who was diagnosed at one week old as having a condition known locally as *kamlert* which caused it to cry continuously and not drink milk. *Kamlert* is usually a fatal condition in neonates[47] and it is believed that only the actions of a *mor pow*, a traditional 'blowing' doctor, can cure the conditions by blowing magic incantations onto the baby's stomach and tying its wrists with sacred cotton thread to secure its *khwan*. Fortunately her child survived and she was encouraged to drink *ya satri* to ensure a plentiful breast milk supply for the child. Later, after giving birth to her third child, her periods did not come and she felt weak and tired, so she bought *ya satri singh*, as well as a *ya fon* (powdered herbal medicine) and another brand of women's medicine called *ya ang thong* in order to expel the blood. After taking these her periods did come, but she felt pain in her abdomen.

Although women differ in their evaluations of the effectiveness of these medicines, they are generally understood as very effective, working to restore menstruation within five to six days. As will be discussed in Chapter 7, these medicines are also widely used in attempts to test for pregnancy and to abort unwanted pregnancies.

Inflamed wombs and women's problems

In their discussions of their health, women focus upon the condition of their *mot luk* (uterus). A range of conditions are perceived to be associated with the health of the uterus. The term *mot luk* is used both in a general sense to describe the pelvic region, (also commonly called the *thong noi*, little abdomen) and also to refer to an actual organ. Women view the actual physiology in differing ways. Some differentiate between the center of the uterus as *mot luk* and the 'wings' of the uterus *pik mot luk* which roughly corresponds to the fallopian tubs and ovaries. How these are connected together is not always clearly understood. Other women describe the uterus as a sack with the urethra and vagina as a common channel (see discussion in Boonmongkon et al. 1998).

A range of terms describe gynaecological problems. Table 4.1 shows the terms used by women in a survey of 154 women conducted in 1997. Although some women complained of more than one condition, the term used first to describe their condition is listed below:

Table 4.1 Terms used by Isan women to describe gynaecological conditions.

Term	Translation of term
mot luk aksaep	infected/inflamed uterus
cep mot luk	pain in the uterus
cep pik mot luk	pain in the uterus 'wings'
pen mot luk	to have uterus [problem]
mot luk yorn	Prolapse
nuang mot luk	dull pain, heaviness in uterus
mot luk bhuam	Enlarged, swollen uterus
maleng mot luk	Uterine cancer
mot luk now	Rotten uterus
nu'ongok	Tumour, growth

In some cases women simply describe their condition in vague terms as *pen mot luk* (to have uterus condition). Often women describe their condition in terms of symptoms, such as pain. The most common complaint is *jep mot luk*, (sharp) pain in the *mot luk*, but some women use the other term for pain, *bhu'at mot luk*, which describes a more diffuse cramping pain. Other terms evoke imagery of the state of the uterus. For example, *mot luk bhuam* evokes an image of a swollen uterus and is described as characterised by throbbing pain. Other commonly used descriptions of *mot luk* conditions include having *mot luk bor di* (a bad womb), or the term *mot luk aksaep* (an inflamed/infected womb), which will be discussed further below.

Case studies of women's experiences show how these problems are manifested and the ways in which women seek care. Aunt Bua, 37-years-old, described her condition:

I have *mot luk aksaep*. I know because I get a lot of *mat khaw* when I work hard, like when I carry bags of rice. In the past I was never like this. Sometimes the *mat khaw* has a fishy smell when there is only a small amount, but I have had it for three weeks now. First I went to Rong Kham, to a private clinic and they had a test and gave me medicine to eat and an injection. I didn't get better, so I went again and I got more medicine and another injection. Each time cost 120 baht [approx. A$7] and 10 baht for my transport. Then I went to a clinic in Roi Et [the provincial capital] and I was told that I had *mot luk yorn* and then *mot luk aksaep*. I was told not to eat food which is hot or salty, and not to work hard, and they gave me a *ya chut* [a packet of unmarked pills to be eaten in combination as a complete treatment and often containing antibiotics]. When my *thorng noi* [lower stomach] started hurting I stopped taking my contraceptive pills.

As Aunt Bua states, a common complaint that women will describe is *mot luk aksaep*. There are discrepancies in the uses of the term *mot luk aksaep*. Trained medical staff use the term to mean a uterine infection and will usually prescribe antibiotics for women who complain of *mot luk aksaep*. It is also used in Thai medical literature in relation to acute pelvic inflammatory disease. When villagers and untrained healers use the term *mot luk aksaep,* they visualise a swollen and inflamed uterus and associate the condition with the presence of *mat khaw* discharge and a 'hot' state. Folk healers advise women to restrict their diet, especially 'hot' foods and fermented foods, such as *tam mak hung* (spicy raw papaya salad), and *pla daek* (fermented fish), as well as pickled foods, bamboo, and shrimps. Other foods less commonly cited were quail and *phak kha* (*Languas galanga*). 'Hot' foods are restricted so that the excess heat associated with the inflamed uterus will not be augmented.

A range of factors are associated with *mot luk* problems. As in Aunt Bua's description above, one of the most common causes women describe is that of lifting heavy objects and working too hard. These are consistently associated with *cep mot luk* and *mot luk aksaep* and are understood to also make the problems of prolapse more severe. Thum, who is 25-years-old, associates her *mot luk aksaep* with the heavy work she did as a labourer harvesting cassava. Aunt Siwi, who is 44-years-old, complains of pain and discharge when she does heavy work, for which she self-medicates with an antibiotic bought at the local store.

In addition, a complication of pregnancy or childbirth such as pushing too hard and tearing the uterus, poor hygiene, sexually transmitted diseases, and trauma such as falling down or being involved in an accident may all result in *mot luk* problems. For example, Saa, who is 34-years-old, complains of *mot luk aksaep,* which she attributes to an incident that occurred when she was fourteen. She was working in Bangkok in the construction industry and had to carry heavy sacks. She fell and a sack fell onto her abdomen. After this she had pain which she believes developed into chronic *mot luk aksaep.*

Other factors which are understood to make women more vulnerable to gynaecological problems include failure to practice post-partum restrictions after childbirth, which results in a wet uterus, and failure of the uterus to return to its proper position. A number of women who said they had no gynaecological problems explained that it was because they stayed by the fire after birth. As will be discussed in Chapter 6, younger women who give birth in hospitals and have a tubal resection, may forego post-partum restrictions as a consequence and are commonly said to suffer more gynaecological problems as a result.

In addition, the use of contraceptives such as intra-uterine devices (IUDs) are understood to be associated with pain and discharge, Depo-Provera is suspected of causing problems due to amenorrhoea, which allows the bad blood to accumulate inside the womb and be reabsorbed by the body, and sterilisation through tubal resection is associated with pain, weakness and the development of long term problems (see Chapter 5 for further discussion). Abortions may also result in immediate problems of massive infection and rotting *mot luk now,* but also long-term recurrent infections. This leads to vulnerability to gynaecological problems such as *mot luk bhuam,* and is believed to be associated with the eventual development of uterine cancer.

Unclean flows

The health of a woman's womb is reflected in the flows of blood and other discharges that are carefully monitored by women. I was first made aware of the significance of vaginal discharge to women when, upon asking a village women's group leader what was the most significant health problem women suffered in her village, I was informed, *'Mat khaw.* Nearly every woman here suffers from it.' *Mat khaw* refers to leucorrhoea (a normal white vaginal secretion), but in Isan the term is also used to describe a range of discharges and implies a state of ill-health. Any vaginal discharge other than menstrual blood is read as a sign that the womb is 'dirty', or unhealthy, not dry and clean (Chirawatkul 1993:203-205).

Discharge is a cause of great concern among women. In a survey of 153 women I conducted in four rural villages in 1997, 38.6 per cent of women said they had suffered from *mat khaw* in the last three months; 31 per cent of the women had sought care for the discharge.

Medical dictionaries and medical personnel translate *mat khaw* (*tok khaw* in Central Thai) into English as leucorrhoea, but this strict translation is too narrow. An Isan dictionary gives an explanation which reveals the broader significance of this term. It describes *mat khaw* as:

> One type of disease that occurs in women. When it occurs it makes the *radu* [menstruation] spoil. The red colour is white and is called *mat khaw* disease, *tok khaw*. It is said that if one boils the bark of the *lum phuk* tree and the bark from the *mui daeng* [red hardwood] tree and bark from the *mui khaw* [white hardwood] tree and drinks that one will be cured (Phintong 1989:856, my translation).

Women differentiate various types of discharge on the basis of colour, smell, consistency and the volume of discharge. For example, Aunt Thiaw stated:

> If the discharge has a smell, it is like *nam khaw pla* [water with the stench of fish) and you will be itchy everywhere that the discharge touches and you will get bumps and a rash. Usually *mat khaw* doesn't smell and it looks like *yang bakhung* [sap from the papaya], and I get it before and after I menstruate.

Many women noted that if *mat khaw* appeared just before or after menstruation it is normal and associated with the cleansing out of the womb. If *mat khaw* appeared at any other time however, women understand it as a sign of internal problems and will attempt to cure the problem.

Mat khaw is a sign of the presence of *chu'arok* (germs) in the womb associated with *sok ga prok* (dirtiness):

> I got *mat khaw* two or three times, and was itchy in the vagina four times, so I went and had an internal examination, not for the itch but for cramps, and the doctor found that I had an infection. So I use a drug from the doctor, sometimes I use 'Tonaf' [an analgesic] also. I work with hemp and so stay in the dirty water too long and so I get really itchy. I use a drug in the village called *phong phiset* [literally 'special powder', containing sulphur] or else I sit over hot water. (Aunt Pui)

Women also speak of having *thit chu'ra,* having caught a 'fungus'. *Chu'ra* translates as a fungus, but is used by villagers in a much broader sense. It denotes a type of organism or germ which enters the body from outside, through dirt entering the body during work outside in the fields, through sexual intercourse or as something which grows inside a damp, dirty womb which has not been adequately dried out and cleaned through the post-partum practice of staying by the fire. The action of this organism may be to cause ulceration and eventually cancer (see description in Boonmongkon et al.

1998:15). The linkage between the presence of discharge and cancer was mentioned not only by village women, but also by many health centre nurses in my discussions with them about cervical cancer.

Mot luk yorn (prolapse) is a common complaint among women in village communities and is also associated with discharge.

> I get something like *mat khaw* except that it's not the same. It's yellow and white and I have had it for two months with *mak lu'at* [blood colour] in it. Two months ago my uterus collapsed. (Grandmother Thii)

> I get *puat thorng noi* [pain in the lower pelvis] and a pulling-down sensation and it pulls to my waist like I have a baby and like my vagina will fall off. I have to carry my pelvis when I walk. When it is very bad, I have to stop working hard. (Grandmother Bau)

In my 1997 survey, 27.3 per cent of 154 women complained of a pulling-down sensation and pain which was exacerbated when lifting a heavy object, and 27.1 per cent had sought care for this problem. It is a common complaint especially among older women who had large numbers of pregnancies and births combined with a life of heavy work. The heavy lifting and bending when working in the fields exacerbates the problem and incapacitates women, as Grandmother Bau described above.

Local healers are often called upon to correct prolapses by massaging the womb and then gently pushing it into place again. Grandmother Yid explained her technique:

> A woman nearby was pulling sacks of rice when her uterus came out. She called for me and I got her to lie down with her legs and knees raised. I massaged and compressed her and then gently pushed it back up.

Grandmother Seen told the story of a travelling doctor who said he provided services to women with prolapse. For a fee of 500 baht, 'he put his hand in and pushed it up into you! . . . Right up into my box! [laughter]'. When confronted by her husband the 'doctor' ran off. 'He didn't even get his money! . . . He was scared we'd catch him. He never came back again.'

Other common complaints of women are incontinence and urinary tract infections. In the 1997 survey, out of 153 women, 11.8 per cent complained of incontinence problems, defined as problems withholding urine when sneezing or laughing; 7.9 per cent of these women had sought care for this problem. Incontinence is an issue which is rarely brought to the notice of public health authorities despite the effect it may have on a woman's quality of life.

Many women associate urinary tract infections with reproductive tract problems and do not differentiate the two. Many women described stinging after micturition and 'red' urine and attributed it to a variety of causes. For example, Aunt Dorn attributes her infection to a variety of causes:

I get red urine and it stings when I work hard and so I buy 'Kano' [tetracycline] or drink boiled *nuat maew* ['cat's whiskers', a herb noted for its diuretic properties]. It stings after I pee. One time I thought it was because I was infected with some STD, or because of walking too often, or working too hard, or because of drinking dirty water. I thought that I had a kidney stone, but the doctor told me it was because I had *phae lom* [an air allergy]. So I stopped drinking rain water.

As Aunt Dom states, urinary tract infections are attributed to working too hard, sexually transmitted disease, or due to drinking dirty water. In her case, she was told by a healer that it was due to *phae lom*, an ambiguous term which may mean allergy but may also imply a wind illness. Aunt Dom self-medicates with single tetracycline tablets when she experiences symptoms, a treatment which is ineffective.

The consequence of chronic problems: cervical cancer

Cervical cancer is greatly feared among rural women over the age of thirty who suffer from chronic gynaecological problems (Boonmongkon et al. 1998). Cervical cancer is a leading form of cancer amongst women in Thailand. The national incidence of cervical cancer was 9.81 per 100 000 population in 1981, with the highest incidence in women 50-59 years of age (Kanchanaraksa 1987:66). Records at Srinagarind Hospital in Khon Kaen Province reported an incidence of 11.1 cases per 100 000 women in 1987 (Pengsaa et al. 1989). In Ban Srisaket, five women died from cervical cancer between 1988 and 1992, according to official death certificates. One of my neighbours, Aunt Liang, was fortunate in that her cancer was diagnosed early. She sought the advice of several doctors over irregular bleeding. It was finally investigated at the major teaching hospital in Khon Kaen and found to be caused by an early-stage tumour. Prior to that diagnosis she had been told by doctors at other clinics that her irregular bleeding was simply a sign of menopause. She was glad that she had continued to seek help when her symptoms continued and was full of praise for her treatment at the teaching hospital.

A recent study in the North-east found that cancer is considered the common endpoint for a series for twelve gynaecological conditions if they are left untreated. Cancer is visualised as an ulcer, tumour, pus, infection or fungus/germ inside the uterus, images encouraged by graphic close-up posters displayed at health stations and hospitals. The pathways were found to differ from woman to woman but with common themes. The initial problem could be *jep mot luk, mot luk aksaep, mot luk bor di, or mat khaw,* which gradually transforms to more severe symptoms such as excessive discharge or fungus, an ulcer or tumour, which eventually culminates in cancer

Plate 4.3 An image of cervical cancer from a health education poster by the Ministry of Public Health.

(Boonmongkon et al. 1998). For example during our survey work we met Aunt Bom aged forty-three. She has three children all now in their twenties: one son and two daughters. Twelve years ago her stomach bloated up as though she was pregnant and she felt pain. She went to see a doctor who diagnosed a tumour in her uterus and immediately put her into surgery where she had a complete hysterectomy. She thinks her cancer may have had something to do with one unwanted pregnancy that she aborted at one month gestation, which she thinks left a wound that never properly healed. Now she says her health is no good as she suffers from poor *sen prasart* (nerves) and 'thinks too much', symptoms exacerbated by her lack of a uterus and the build-up of menstrual blood which is poisoning her system.

Women also understand that cervical cancer can be caused by sexually transmitted pathogens from their husbands after they had visited prostitutes.

While certain sexually transmitted pathogens are involved in the aetiology of cervical cancer, women in the North-east understood them as capable of doing so in a much shorter time period (Boonmongkon et al. 1998).

Since my initial fieldwork in 1991–93, there has been a major campaign to promote cervical cancer screening. But it has been suggested that one unfortunate by-product of this campaign has been an increase in fear among women about cancer (Boonmongkon et al. 1998:26). In part this may be due to a common perception that such public health campaigns follow a model of past campaigns against problems, such as dengue fever, which occur whenever there is an epidemic. For example, I have heard one person explain that now that the AIDS campaign is not as heavily promoted means that it was not going around as in the past. Following such reasoning, a campaign for cancer screening may be understood as due to a current epidemic of cancer.

In 1991–93 few women from Ban Srisaket had had a pap smear. Few older women in Ban Srisaket admitted to having had an internal examination, and those who did had gone for treatment for a specific problem. They usually went accompanied by friends for support. By 1997, when I conducted a survey in four rural villages, 69.7 per cent of 152 women stated that they had ever had a pap smear. In villages where a special mobile pap smear clinic had been organised nearly every women had had a test done.

Pap smears are widely understood to be diagnostic procedures in which the nurse or doctor can actually physically see and evaluate problems or can immediately test for cancer, rather than seeing a pap smear as a screening procedure separate to an evaluation of reproductive tract problems. Many women equate pap smears with internal examinations for other problems. For example, when I asked Aunty Dii what her pap smear was like, she answered, 'The doctor uses an instrument to open you up and gets some discharge and then goes and looks at it to see if you have cancer or anything'. There seems to be little explanation given to women about what pap smears indicate and the difference between a smear test and internal examination for other gynaecological problems.

Sexually transmitted diseases

Discharges and *mot luk* problems may also be interpreted as signs of infection with a sexually transmitted disease. Some village women recognise that their partners' behaviours place them at risk of contracting a sexually transmitted disease. Aunt Dii whispered her experience:

> It is normal for men to go and see prostitutes, but my husband used to go and get syphilis and infect me too. I had a green discharge and so I went to see a doctor at the STD centre in Khon Kaen who gave me a suppository. I got better but my husband, who lives in Bangkok, took care of himself. He didn't tell me he had an infection.

Aunt Dii's story reveals many aspects of women's risk of STD infection. She used a term *sifilit* (syphilis) in a generic sense here for STDs rather than as an accurate diagnosis of her condition which is more suggestive of gonorrhoea or trichomonas infection rather than syphilis. She described her husband's extramarital sexual behaviour as the cause of her infection. But she excused his visiting prostitutes as 'normal' behaviour for men, especially in the case of a man who is living and working far from home. His failure to tell his wife about his infection also shows how shame and silence surrounds discussions of infection with STDs. It remains uncertain whether Aunt Dii's husband would have been treated appropriately for his condition. Men with suspected STDs tend to self-medicate with antibiotics until the symptoms subside.

Men use the term *rok phuying* (women's diseases) to refer to STDs as diseases that are transmitted to them from women, especially prostitutes. The term *rok kari* (prostitutes' disease) makes this association specific. Women sometimes refer to STDs as *rok phuchai* (men's diseases). STDs are typically described in terms of coloured smelly discharges and rashes, although men and women are understood to display different symptoms. As mentioned earlier, for women, infection with STDs is understood as a serious infection that is likely to lead to the development of cervical cancer.

Infection with an STD also carries the shame of association with promiscuity and prostitution. For women is it understood as evidence of a husband's infidelity. Women speak with anger but also resignation about their partner's behaviour. Visiting prostitutes is an institutionalised form of male recreation, even in village society.

HIV/AIDS

Presently it is estimated that between 557 000 and 696 000 people are infected with HIV (Brown & Sittitrai 1993). As of September 1996, official public health records stated there were 57 504 AIDS patients (47 701 male and 9 803 female AIDS cases) and 15 449 deaths across the kingdom. Roi Et province reported 642 cases and 109 deaths from AIDS (Alpha Research 1997). However, these figures are likely to be underestimates due to the stigma involved in declaring AIDS to be a cause of death. AIDS is likely to have a broad impact upon Thailand's social and economic structure with direct and indirect costs associated with projected AIDS cases and AIDS deaths from 1991 to 2000 estimated to total between US$7.3 billion and $8.7 billion (Viravaidya, Obremskey, & Myers 1992).

HIV/AIDS has become one of the dominant tropes in recent writings about Thailand.[48] There has been a plethora of research on sexual practice, prostitution, sexual networking, social impact on communities and care for AIDS patients. Most studies of AIDS in Thailand have focused on Northern Thailand as it accounts for over a third of the national total infections. Although remote, even the district in which Ban Srisaket lies is experiencing the epidemic. Although the prevalence of HIV is lower than nearly all other districts of Roi Et Province, in 1992, the district in which Ban Srisaket is located reported 2 HIV positive people and a neighbouring district reported 14 HIV positive people (Thailand, Roi Et Provincial Health Office 1992).

During my stay in Ban Srisaket in 1991–93, HIV/AIDS was a new disease and not yet regarded as a threat. The Thai government had started an advertising campaign and a billboard was erected in front of the local district hospital reading, 'Warning! Promiscuous sex, injecting drugs will cause death because of AIDS'. But the threat seemed distant to this rural community. People then were more concerned with liver cancer and motorcycle accidents. Everybody knew friends and relatives who died from accidents, but no one in Ban Srisaket was publicly known to be infected with HIV, except for the occasional rumours. More pressing issues for villagers involved the struggle to support their families. As Aunt Thong stated, 'Some people are poor, they're not afraid of AIDS, but they are afraid of having nothing to eat'. This attitude is gradually changing as more communities experience the deaths of people infected with HIV and face the social burden of caring for affected families. By 1997, when I visited several rural district hospitals to study abortion, most reported that they had programs for local HIV infected people to help them maintain their health for as long as possible. As there are no publicly known cases of people infected with HIV in Ban Srisaket, my observations are restricted to an exploration of factors placing women at risk.

Perceptions of risk

An early construction of the disease in Ban Srisaket was that it is a disease of people with money and bureaucrats. From the perspectives of villagers, risk was constructed in terms of urban lifestyles, a disease of prostitutes and foreigners and those with money. As Aunt Liam joked, 'We don't have any of those diseases because our husbands are too poor to *pai thiaw* [go out to have fun and see prostitutes]'.Wealthy urban men were said to be at risk because they frequented brothels. Nurses were considered at risk because of their contact with the sick. Police are also considered likely to be infected as they are commonly recognised as being protectors and clients of brothels. Although AIDS was greatly feared, few village women considered themselves at serious risk of infection.

Yet discussions with villagers revealed a range of factors which put them at risk. As already mentioned, migration is seen ambivalently by many villagers. In terms of HIV, migration came to be seen as risky not only due to the opportunities for extra-marital sexual relations, but also due to the possibilities for women to become involved in the sex industry. Migration often entails long periods of separation between partners and is perceived to provide the motive and opportunity for extramarital liaisons for both men and women. One woman joked that to avoid infection 'the thing to do is never be away from your husband for more than two days'. Yet for most people in Ban Srisaket this is not possible. As described in Chapter 2, the majority of couples in Ban

Srisaket undergo long periods of separation as one or both partners migrates for work. Men from Ban Srisaket working at sugar cane plantations in Central Thailand spoke of the local prostitutes in nearby towns whom they could visit when life in the fields and dormitories became too dull.

But men do not have to be away from home to visit prostitutes. Discourses of male pleasure in rural and urban settings emphasise enjoying oneself by spending money on drink, gambling and women, referred to as *pai thiaw* (literally, to make a trip, to wander). Seeking pleasure at local brothels forms another dimension of this and usually takes place when a group of male friends spend the evening together eating and drinking (Fordham 1995, VanLandingham et al 1998). Although Lyttleton (1994a) suggests that many village men are morally averse to patronising brothels, it is still true that there is little public condemnation of those who do. Local brothels in the district towns near Ban Srisaket offer sex for 40 baht (A$2). Sex with discretionary workers, such as waitresses and hostesses at restaurants, varies in price from 150 baht (A$9) to 500 baht (A$31) with singers at nightclubs, beyond the economic means of most village men. Roi Et Province is conservatively reported to have a total of 82 sex establishments with 497 prostitutes, a figure that would not include many covert sex workers at establishments such as restaurants where services other than sex are offered. In 1993 at the small local district town there was one brothel operating with ten women working as prostitutes. The larger neighbouring district town about 24 kilometres away was reported to have two brothels and two other establishments where sex was offered with other services, with 65 women working as prostitutes (Thailand 1992b).

The issue of extra-marital sex brings to the fore tensions between men and women and the double standards that apply to men's sexual behaviour. Women view their husbands' patronage of prostitutes as undesirable but normal behaviour (see also Maticka Tyndale et al. 1994a). Husbands are expected to be faithful to their wives, but women say 'it is men's nature' to visit prostitutes occasionally to satisfy their need for sexual variety. Aunt Kaen stated, 'For men to go to prostitutes is common because that makes them happy'. In focus group discussions women spoke with scepticism about their husbands' fidelity. Aunt Nuk bluntly calculated: 'Out of a hundred I can believe him fifty–fifty. He told me that after he got married he never goes to see prostitutes and I believe about fifty per cent'. Aunt Mali does not believe her husband's protestations: 'If I don't believe him, he keeps telling me to believe him, but I don't believe him at all!'

Women dislike and fear their husbands having second wives more than them visiting commercial sex workers. Many express the view that casual commercial liaisons are preferable to their husbands having *mia noi* (minor wives) whose household and children would be a permanent financial and emotional drain.

Another risk behaviour recognised by villagers is intravenous drug use. Although intravenous drug use is not common in rural villages of the North-east,[49] Ban Srisaket village death records register a 32-year-old man who died in 1991 in the village from an injected drug overdose. Conversations with health workers and returned migrant workers suggest that many people are exposed to many forms of drug use when working outside the village, when they may either use drugs recreationally or in their employment, for example taking stimulants so as to work the long shifts in factories. In villages closer to Khon Kaen I heard reports of young men injecting amphetamines.

Whilst intravenous drug use may be rare, shared intravenous needle use by *mor chit ya* (injection doctors) also provides a possible means of transmission of HIV. There are many active injection doctors in Ban Srisaket giving injections with poor hygienic practice and usually re-using a glass syringe and steel needle. Similarly, women seeking illegal abortions reported that injections per vagina often involved a re-used syringe. Such practices are not yet addressed in current AIDS campaigns.

Condom use and prevention of STDs/HIV

With regard to STDs and HIV transmission, the important question is whether sexual contacts involve the use of condoms and 'safe sex' practices or not. Studies suggest that condoms are more likely to be used in commercial sexual transactions and rarely in longer-term non-commercial relationships (Havanon et al. 1992). Few women in Ban Srisaket or in other villages surveyed in 1997 reported using condoms with their husbands. In my survey in 1997, although women knew about condoms, only 7.5 per cent of women reported having ever used condoms with their partners. Condoms still carry an association with illicit sex and it is difficult for a woman to negotiate the use of condoms with her husband as it implies she does not trust him. As will be discussed in Chapter 5, condoms are not promoted as a means of family planning. In this way, women as wives and mothers are vulnerable to infection.

Even within commercial sex, men are reported as not using condoms because of reduction of sensitivity and characterise condoms as tight and uncomfortable. Sex workers also complain of losing tips by using condoms, more painful intercourse with condoms, particularly when used without a lubricant, poor quality of condoms leading to breakages, and financial incentives not to wear one. Studies suggest that even if commercial sex workers use condoms with clients they are unlikely to do so with their non-commercial sexual partners (Havanon et al. 1992). Condoms are also less likely to be used by men when having sex with discretionary sex workers who may be perceived as less risky and with whom a more personal relationship may have developed (Havanon et al. 1992:21). Men rationalise not wearing condoms through beliefs that it is possible to select safe commercial sex workers. A hot body, signs of ill-health, thinness, smell and the presence of obvious signs, such as ulcers or discharge, are considered signs of infection. If a woman seems clean and cool, she is regarded as 'clean'. HIV/AIDS is associated with external signs such as skin eruptions and thinness. Some men believe that germs can only enter their bodies when they are 'open' during climax. Withdrawing before climax is thus understood by some as a measure to avoid infection. Other men are reported to take diuretics or antibiotics before sex and some reported cleaning their penises after sex using eye lotion, toothpaste or soda water as means of protection against disease (Havanon et al. 1992).

Management and medication of women's problems

When gynaecological conditions persist women will resort to a wide variety of treatments and consult a range of healers at considerable expense. For example, Grandmother Phai is fifty years old. She has had five pregnancies and has three surviving children, having miscarried her third pregnancy and fifth pregnancy. Last year she fell over whilst working: 'It was like my *mot luk* broke or snapped. It stung and stung and now it *ok hon* [gives out heat].' She usually experiences a little *mat khaw*, 'If I had a lot of *mat khaw* it is no good, that would mean I had cancer. Last year it was so bad I couldn't work either to plant rice or to harvest.' When she experiences pain she buys the analgesic 'Win' from a local grocery store in the village. But sometimes her problem becomes severe. Last year she sought care at a government hospital in Roi Et, the provincial capital, where she was given an internal examination and a *ya kae aksaep* (medicine to correct infection, usually an antibiotic) and was told not to do heavy work. She was also given a *ya nam* (liquid medicine). This visit cost approximately 200 baht (A$10).

When her problem persisted she went to a private clinic in Roi Et. At this clinic the 'doctor' did not need to give an internal examination, but just put a stethoscope onto her belly to diagnose her problem as *mot luk aksaep.* That visit and medicines cost her 95 baht. This year, she has gone seven times for the treatment of her *mot luk aksaep* and *mot luk yorn* at a clinic in the local district town of Rong Kham. She has been told her *mot luk* is *phadong* (referring to a category of diseases causing itchiness). Each time she goes to this clinic it costs 150 baht for the medicine and 70 baht for extra medicine for her *mot luk yorn*. Despite the repeated injections of 'Kano', she still complains, 'I am still hot inside and my vagina is hot.' She has also tried a herbal medicine of barks and herbs called *sak mot luk* (clean the uterus) which she bought at a district market for 20 baht per bundle. She boiled the herbs and then drank the water but it was also ineffective: 'I'm not going to take it any more, as I am not better.' At rice planting time she received a series of four injections from the *mor tahan* (a former army medic) at a nearby district town for 30 baht, so that she could work as a hired labourer. But her condition remains and she will continue seeking treatments when the symptoms become unbearable.

Grandmother Phai narrates typical patterns of health-seeking behaviour involving a number of different treatments taken in combination or in sequence for chronic gynaecological problems. She has tried self-medication, private clinics, government hospitals along with a variety of drugs, antibiotic injections and herbal medication. Like most women with gynaecological problems she has taken 'Kano', a brand name for tetracycline along with analgesics. She has also seen a *mor tahan,* which refers to an army medic who now practises as an unregistered injection doctor.

In a village where the wage for a full day's work harvesting rice is 50 baht (A$2.50), Grandmother Phai has incurred considerable costs for the treatment of her condition. She explains her condition in terms of the initial trauma of falling over and by the consequent heavy work she must undertake. Although she is advised by the doctor 'not to work too hard', this is advice which is hard to follow.

In treating these conditions, like Grandmother Phai, women often pragmatically choose to self-medicate, in the hope that that will cure the problem quickly and inexpensively. Only when self-medication has failed will they seek more expensive cures. As Aunt Khiaw stated:

> The trouble with going to see the doctor is money. I just try to carry on
> even though feeling pain. Women have responsibility for the other people
> in the family, my husband and children, and so I will be the last one in the
> family to go to see the doctor.

Delays in seeking care may also be a product of the cycles of work and productive activities. Aunt Khiaw delayed seeking care for her itchy discharge until after harvest time: 'I don't go to see the doctor if it's not serious. Everyone waits until they can't stand or waits until they have finished harvesting.' Aunt Lua was in a similar situation:

> My husband said to me not to go [to see the doctor] because my problem
> would never be fine, and if I go we wouldn't have the money to buy
> something else. Women are the ones who have to save and spend money,
> but not for ourselves.

Antibiotics are widely used in self-medication by women suffering from *mat khaw* and *mot luk* problems. A recent study in the North-east found that over 80 per cent of women self-medicated when they had *mot luk* problems, with 82 per cent of them obtaining the medicines from village grocery stores. In Ban

Srisaket, seven different forms of tetracycline as well as penicillin, sulphamethoxazole/trimethoprim and sulphdiazine were available.

The most common treatment supplied for gynaecological problems is tetracycline (see Appendix 2). Brand names such as 'Kano' (500 mg tetracycline) and 'Hero' (250 mg tetracycline) were commonly cited as medicines purchased for *mat khaw* and *mot luk aksaep*. The 'Kano' packet specifically states that it is for *mot luk aksaep*, wounds, pox or abscesses, pus and any infections. On the front of the packet there is a male and female symbol seemingly suggestive that it is useful for STDs as well. As described in Chapter 3, these medicines are widely available, sold by the single tablet in village grocery stores and drug stores. Women tend to take the medicine for only as long as symptoms exist, very few would take a complete course of antibiotics. Despite their illegality, *ya chut* (combinations of pills) specific for *mot luk* problems are also still available at some local stores (see Chapter 3). These combinations of drugs usually include powerful antibiotics.

The widespread use of self-administered antibiotics for *mat khaw* and *mot luk aksaep* may mask a range of serious reproductive tract infections, including STDs, exacerbate conditions such as candida, and may promote the development of resistant strains. For example, Sompong is thirty-seven years old and described symptoms consistent with a serious reproductive tract infection that has been treated inappropriately. Three to four months ago she suffered with a smelly discharge which caused itchiness and was associated with pain and fever. She always gets severe pain with menstruation and suspects she has a prolapse as well. Although she would like to consult a doctor, she has not seen a doctor about her prolapse or about the discharge as she cannot afford to. She tried to self-medicate with 'Kano' purchased at the local store and visited the local health station where she was given pain-killers and antibiotics. Although these helped reduce the symptoms, the discharge, itchiness, fever and pain have returned.

Men also widely use self-medication to treat suspected STD infection or after sex as a prophylaxis against infection. Drugs sold to men for these purposes as *ya khap lum khlong (*medicine to clean the pipes) include rifampicin and norfloxacin and tetracycline (Nichter 1996). A 1997 surrogate patient study found that the overwhelming majority of men presenting with either symptoms consistent with gonorrhoea (*nong nai*) non-gonococcal urethritis or requesting prophylaxis were sold inappropriate medicines (Boonmongkon et al. 1998). In addition, 84 per cent of drug stores were found to offer inappropriate biomedical irrational medicine advice to patients presenting with reproductive health problems. Few drug store attendants asked appropriate questions necessary to make appropriate recommendations as to treatment and only 5 per cent of drug store attendants asked about the sexual partner's health. In only 6 per cent of cases was the patient not sold medicine and recommended to see a doctor.

Even when women do seek care in medical clinics, they are sold medicines in unmarked plastic bags which may contain information on how to take the medicine, but not the name of the drug. This leaves people ignorant of what they have already taken for a given condition. As women often seek care at a number of practitioners, they sometimes are consuming several different medications from different practitioners simultaneously.

Likewise, health centre staff use the antibiotics available to them inappropriately to treat *mot luk* problems. Suntaree, who is 40 years-old, went to the health centre complaining of *nuang mot luk*, and was given four different medicines to take. Daeng, who is forty-six years old, told of receiving three different medicines for her symptoms of *mot luk bhuam*. These most likely consisted of paracetamol for pain, along with an antibiotic and vitamins. Research with health centre staff found that they wanted further training on appropriate protocols for gynaecological problems and requested access to a supply of antifungal vaginal tablets and metronidazole for treatment (Boonmongkon et al. 1998).

Along with a variety of medications, avoidance of particular foods is also commonly practiced by women with gynaecological problems. Women and healers are often unable to articulate the reasons why they need to avoid certain foods. As in the post-partum food avoidance, reasons include both humoral properties of certain foods as well as metaphorical properties. Pickled and fermented foods appear to be 'hot' foods as in the case of 'pickled medicine' mentioned earlier. Metaphorical linkages may also be operating in the banning of strong-smelling, fishy foods, so that the discharge will not have such an odour. I have also heard that seafood and shrimps are banned for women with cervical cancer. Seafood, shellfish and shrimps are generally recognised as foods that may be *phae* (allergic) for people, causing rashes and itching. It may be for this reason that they are restricted, given that many women complain of vaginal itching when suffering from *mat khaw*.

Encounters with the formal health sector

What happens when a woman seeks care for gynaecological problems? The experiences of women using public health services and the private registered medical practitioners which constitute the formal health sector in Thailand reveal dissatisfaction with the service they receive. Whilst some doctors, clinics and hospitals are said to give a good service, women are generally critical of impolite treatment, a lack of privacy and poor communication from doctors and nurses. Village women recognise that health staff 'don't treat you friendly at all' and are uncommunicative. Aunt Twii expressed her frustration:

The doctor gives you medicine just because you annoyed him, but always takes lots of money. Taking medicine never cured my problem. The doctor never asked any questions and it's the same everywhere. The doctor just asks us the symptoms and gives us the medicine. I would like to see a very good doctor who you could talk to.

Poor communication promotes fear and anxiety. Aunt Jai came up to us as we sat by the village headman's house in Kung village during our survey. She is forty-nine years old and raises pigs for a living. She started telling us how one month ago she had an internal examination and was diagnosed with a tumour in her *mot luk*. She has an appointment next month to see a doctor to be told her diagnosis after a test. She is presently taking medicine he prescribed for her. She said he did not explain things to her. She was unsure of what sort of test she had had and was unsure of what was to happen next and sought reassurance from us. I tried to explain the many stages involved in making a firm diagnosis of cancer and reassure her that there are many treatment options available for women which her doctor will know about. I encouraged her to ask questions of the gynaecologist to explain anything she is not sure about, advice that sounded hollow to me at the time. Her desire for knowledge and her fear were palpable.

Observations in clinics reveal the ways in which the interactions between doctors and women, patient flow and spatial organisation affect the quality of care women receive. In the consultations I observed at a major gynaecological outpatient's clinic the patient flow was organised so that the small room always had three patients present. One patient sat waiting for her consultation while another woman sat giving her history to the doctor. This occurred while another women undressed behind a screen to await the internal examination. The doctor then moved to do the internal and when finished told the woman to dress and return to the desk. Then the other woman was instructed to undress for her internal while the doctor gave a diagnosis and medicines to the other woman. In the intervening time he would start taking the history of the third woman. Despite long waiting times of up to one hour, the actual consultations including the internal examination rarely took more than six minutes.

Under such conditions, going to see a doctor about intimate matters is an encounter filled with potential embarrassment. While undertaking observations at a public health clinic in Khon Kaen, I came across a group of five women from the same district as that of my village fieldsite. Although there is a local district hospital in their town, they had hired a pick-up truck and travelled 120 kilometres to a clinic, 'where no one will know that we have come for internal examinations'. Both rural village women and urban middle-class women I interviewed spoke of being *yak ai* (ashamed and embarrassed) at speaking about their symptoms, internal examinations and exposure of the genitals to another person, especially to a male doctor. In the gynaecology outpatients section at a major hospital in Khon Kaen, I observed elderly village women crying and struggling at attempts by staff to take pap smears, weeping with indignation and fear. But the discourse about the shame of internal examinations has other consequences. It is standard practice in some clinics for nurses to place a cloth over patients' eyes before the examination, despite some patients' objections to the contrary. In one such case I watched a woman repeatedly remove the blindfold only to have it replaced by the nurse who consequently scolded her. The nurses explained that covering the eyes was a standard procedure as otherwise the woman would be 'too embarrassed' if she could see the doctor doing the internal examination.

Privacy is clearly an important concern of village women, yet there is a common notion among government health staff that privacy is not a concept prioritised by villagers, who live in situations where everything is known by others. Consultations at the village health centre are very public affairs, easily overheard by anyone waiting or visiting. Similarly, in gynaecology and antenatal outpatients departments and family planning departments at hospitals and public health centres, a number of people may hear intimate details of consultations with doctors and may inadvertently see examinations between hastily drawn curtains. Village women rarely fully undress; even bathing is performed whilst covered with a cloth *phasin* tied above the breasts, and birthing at home is monitored by the midwife with only the minimal necessary glances under the *phasin* of the woman in labour. The notion that village women do not need privacy is a patronising excuse for the indifference of the health staff to the feelings of their patients and permits 'cultural relativity' to be used as an excuse for a poor quality of care (see also Boonmongkon et al. 1998 for a detailed discussion of service delivery issues).

The micropolitics of care: dirt and ignorance

The lack of sensitivity to issues of communication, privacy and space discussed above are indicative of a more generalised disdain for villagers within the health system. In hospitals, the middle-class staff tend to look down upon Lao-speaking village women who come clearly marking their class and ethnicity by wearing cotton *phasin* skirts. Attitudes of professional health providers are informed by discourses which represent Isan villagers as dirty, ignorant and naive. For example, within a large provincial hospital jokes circulate among nurses of the 'real stories' of Isan women clients seeing gynaecologists:

> An Isan village woman was told that she should wash herself before coming to see a gynaecologist, so the next time she did. . . she washed her hands.

An Isan village woman was told by a nurse to go to the bathroom and clean up before seeing the doctor. One hour later they realised that she hadn't returned. So they went to the toilets and there she was, cleaning the toilets.

When discussing gynaecological problems of village women at the same provincial hospital I was told by a group of interns that 'the reason they [village women] get problems is because they are not clean and their hygiene is poor. This is because they have low education'. Such stories of the dirtiness and ignorance of villagers are frequently repeated by the urban middle class and in official discourses about village health. Discourses of development and good health and hygiene frequently disparage the traditional beliefs, practices and knowledge that villagers have about their bodies and health (Cohen 1989:165). Descriptions of Isan villagers as dirty are articulations of their marginal status in the eyes of the elite. It forms a part of the common discursive contrasts, described in Chapter 1, between Lao villagers as ignorant, uneducated, poor, traditional, dark-skinned and dirty and the Central Thai elite as educated, wealthy, modern, light-skinned and clean. Attributions of dirtiness also carry with them assertions of worthlessness, pollution and immorality. In health institutions, such descriptions of impurity are mapped onto the medical parlance of hygiene, germs and disease. Thus ill-health is linked in the statement by the interns at the hospital to villagers' poor hygiene and lack of cleanliness, with the implication that ignorance is to blame and that villagers are thereby responsible for their ill-health. Health and disease thus become coupled with class and ethnic-specific discourses. Isan village women's bodies mediate these discourses in their interactions with health staff and institutions.

The meanings of gynaecological health

Women's intimate understandings of the workings of their bodies demonstrate the complex indigenous system of gynaecological knowledge and treatment practices. Women's bodies are understood as fundamentally different to men's bodies, requiring different sorts of medicines, food regimes and care. Women's experiences of their health are invested with complex meanings referring to a woman's potency as a fertile woman, mother and sexual being. Flows of blood and fertility are intimately associated with a woman's strength and well-being. Any disruptions to bodily rhythms are associated with a vulnerable and weak body. Signs of disorder in the workings of the womb, through discharges, infertility, or irregular menstruation reflect a disordered body and are linked to feelings of weakness, loss of vitality and strength and, in severe cases, to incidents of mental illness.

The chronic results of these conditions, such as pain, malodorous discharge, discomfort during intercourse, itching and painful urination affect the social, economic and psychological quality of women's lives (Cook 1993). As described throughout this chapter, the experience of a gynaecological problem is accompanied by social shame and embarrassment. Discharge and pain is associated with dirt and 'germs', and so imputes ideas of a woman's lack of hygiene. Odorous discharge is considered contagious and may lead to women becoming socially isolated. Pain inhibits a woman's daily productive activities and affects her sexual relationship with her partner.

Gynaecological health also carries a range of meanings beyond the merely physical experience of symptoms. It serves as an idiom for commentary upon the social and moral order. As a range of writers have asserted, physical disorders are inextricably related to emotional and moral worlds and notions of disease and healing emerge out of an organising realm of moral concerns (Brodwin 1996; Douglas 1966; Farmer 1992). Statements that a woman has *mot luk bor di,* a 'bad' uterus carries moral implications beyond the physical, but becomes a statement of identity as well. The issue of STDs and HIV highlights inter-gender tension over the extra-marital sexual activities of men, repeated miscarriage is a sign of supernatural interference, cancer may be associated with past abortions. Apart from commentary on an individual woman's behaviour or that of her husband, the experience of illness for women is also embedded in their socio-economic context. Women relate their health to their roles as workers, involved in heavy labour. They are women who can no longer afford the time to fully observe post-partum practices. They are women who must limit their fertility through contraceptives, sterilisation and sometimes abortion, thus disrupting the fertility and strength of their bodies.

Women's accounts of their illness and health-seeking behaviour reveal the linkages between gender, class and health in Isan communities. For example, Grandmother Noi stated: 'I went to see the doctor and got some medicine and the doctor said to me, "Don't work too hard!" But I have too! I don't have the money to get medicine often so that's why the problem's never gone.' Grandmother Noi's statement clearly links the need to work hard with the continuation of her chronic ill-health. Village women must work because they are poor, yet the forms of work they must undertake because of their poverty are understood as fundamentally detrimental to their health. In their encounters with the formal health care services, these links between their social position and their health are reinforced as women are faced with embarrassment, shame and attributions of dirtiness and ignorance.

5 Many children, little land

I've got very little rice land, very many children. I am poor. What am I to do? Many children, little land. (Grandmother Mun)

Thailand is considered a success story in the narrative of population regulation and demographic transitions. It has been hailed by demographers as accomplishing a 'reproductive revolution' as it has achieved a rapid fertility decline during a period in which the majority of the population has remained rurally based (Knodel, Chamratrithirong, & Debavalya 1987; Knodel, Havanon, & Pramualratana 1983; Krannich & Krannich 1983). In the Northeast region of Thailand, the family planning program has been associated with a decline in total fertility rates from 7.63 births per woman in 1969, to 3.82 births per woman in 1984 (a decline of 49.9 per cent) (Knodel et al. 1987).

This chapter describes the ramifications of this 'revolution' for women in the small rural community of Ban Srisaket. At one level, the objectives of state policy coincide with those of village women since they relate to women's desire to have control over their own fertility and their views of themselves as having primary responsibility over reproduction. However, the side-effects of contraceptives and their negative experiences with government staff counter women's enthusiasm for the family planning program.

As Ginsburg and Rapp have argued, such tensions in the implementation and lived experience of family planning programs draws the researcher into the fundamental anthropological question of the problem and process of people's agency in daily life (Carter 1995; Ginsburg & Rapp 1995b). As this chapter demonstrates, people act as agents in their acceptance, incorporation or resistance to flows of family planning technology and knowledge. The failure or success of family planning programs across the world hinges upon the ways in which people in local communities actively incorporate, revise or resist the various political and economic forces seeking to influence their choices.

In the past, family planning programs tended to efface the importance of clients' views and experience. More recently, the development literature increasingly displays recognition of the importance of local agency in the success or failure of family planning programs. This concern emerges in the new discourses of the need to incorporate 'user perspectives' into program design, greater emphasis upon the 'quality of care' and safety of programs, and a recognition of the broader implications of family planning policies for gender equity and human rights issues (AbouZahr, Vlassoff, & Kumar 1996; Bruce 1990; Donabedian 1988; Pittman & Hartigan 1996; Whittaker, Rezina Mita, Hossain, & Koenig 1996). Much of this critique and revision is derived from feminist and Third World analyses of population policies and programs (Correa 1994; Dixon-Mueller 1993; Kabeer 1992; Koblinsky, Timyan, & Gay 1993). Although a number of studies demonstrate that improvements in 'quality of care' produce practical gains in the efficiency, sustainability and impact of programs, such changes in the discourses of population policy design are yet to be fully incorporated within the implementation of programs on the ground (Bruce 1990; Hull 1996; Simmons, Koenig, & Huque 1990; Vera 1993).

Despite an enormous literature on family planning programs, little is written about the real-life interactions of women in the services (Simmons & Elias 1994; 1990). This chapter documents the ambiguities of the relationship between women and family planning services, not only their enthusiastic participation in family planning, but at the same time the burden of health effects they experience and the social and political context in which the health services operate.

State population policies and Thai national development

Since the 1960s, family planning has been a key component in international development discourses (Johnson 1995; Kabeer 1992). The contemporary nation-state is understood to have a legitimate right to monitor and shape the reproductive lives of its citizens (Jolly 1998b). A number of recent works have explored the powerful economic, social, religious and political forces at national and international levels affecting the private intimacies of reproductive decision-making (Ginsburg & Rapp 1995b; Greenhalgh 1995b; Handwerker 1990; Jeffery, Jeffery, & Lyon 1989; Stein 1995).

Population control through family planning has been an important strategy of Thai national development since 1970. A National Family Planning Program was incorporated into the Third National Economic and Social Development Plan (1972–76). In 1976, the contraceptive pill, the IUD and sterilisation were offered free of charge at all government health stations and there was a rapid increase in contraceptive acceptors. In addition to government programs, non-government organisations also have been involved in the promotion of family planning, notably the Population and Community Development Association, which has been conducting community-based family planning projects since 1974.[50] The family planning program has been accompanied by an extensive maternal and child health program.

The Seventh National Economic and Social Development Plan (1992-1996) directly links the control of population growth to the 'international competitiveness of the economy' and identifies specific populations as 'remaining problems' in need of intervention. The targets set are to:

> reduce population growth rates to 1.2 per cent by the end of the Seventh
> Plan period . . . with special focus on the target groups in the north-east,
> and the south, and the special target groups such as hilltribe peoples, Thai
> nationals of distinctive cultures in the south, slum dwellers and industrial
> workers (Thailand, NESBD 1992).

Within the historical context noted earlier, the targeting of the North-east for family planning can be seen as not only a reflection of the poverty and high birth rates of the region, but an extension of state concern over a population that has emerged in the national imagination as a potential threat to state solidarity. In the case of the North-east, the adjustment of the population by the Thai state is motivated not purely by concerns for the quality of life of the citizens, but by economic and political objectives.

Traditional practices to limit fertility

Before the availability of modern contraceptives, women of Ban Srisaket practised a number of techniques to control their fertility. Fertility control was personally managed with resources within the community. Although a number of authors claim there were no traditional contraceptives other than abortion, in Ban Srisaket women stated that herbal and magical means were also used for the control of fertility (Hanks 1963:16-17, Mougne 1978:82, Riley and Sermsri 1974:13, cf. Poulsen 1983). Grandmother Sow, a traditional midwife, demonstrated the grinding of two types of bark into a powder which she said 'makes the uterus *hiaw* (dry), so your menstruation will come but you will not get pregnant'. The powder is mixed with water and drunk every day. Grandmother Sow also said that eating white clay was a contraceptive, 'but now we have *ya khum* [contraceptive medicine] and women don't have to eat clay'. Drying out the womb through the post-partum practice of staying by the fire is still practised and is also said to delay the next pregnancy, 'If you stay by the fire you will have children slowly, in one to five years, you don't have to take any contraceptives' (Grandmother Sim). The herbal tonics drunk through the post-partum are also said to help in this drying out process.

Periods of abstinence were not mentioned as a means of delaying or avoiding pregnancies, nor is withdrawal a widely used technique (Knodel, Chamratrithirong and Debavalya 1987:108).

Avoiding food with metaphorical associations was also used in the past to help prevent pregnancy. One grandmother recalled being told not to eat *pla kheng* (cramming perch) which is said to increase desire for sex which will lead to more children. Prolonged breastfeeding and subsequent post-partum amenorrhoea also helped space births but grandmothers in the village state that they had 'two children in three years' which suggests that this may only have had limited effect. As will be discussed in Chapter 6, abortion appears to have been the main technique for spacing births. Although these various techniques continue to be used in the present to a limited extent, women recognise the greater efficacy of modern contraceptives.

Contraception as women's responsibility

In Isan, contraception is considered a woman's responsibility and is seen as an extension of her domestic and procreative duties. Such a pattern of unequal responsibility for contraception is common throughout the world and is due to a lack of promotion of male methods within programs, a lack of contraceptive method choices for men and cultural issues affecting the acceptability of methods (Ringheim 1993). From the outset, the state family planning program in Thailand has been gender-specific, targeted at women. Stated objectives of the Third National Plan were 'to inform and motivate eligible *women*, particularly those living in rural and remote areas . . .' and placed family planning in the context of maternal and child health services (Sittitrai 1988). The emphasis placed on female use of contraception continues to the present and is reflected in the low number of condoms being distributed by village health stations and the low numbers of men having vasectomies (Prasartkul & Sethaput 1982).[51] Records of the local district hospital nearest Ban Srisaket show only two men were admitted for vasectomies in 1992, whereas according to hospital records 83 tubal ligations were performed. Female sterilisation remains the most used method of contraception in Thailand (Chintana 1986). Despite the HIV/AIDS epidemic, condoms remain associated with illicit sexual encounters and very few women in Ban Srisaket described ever having used condoms for contraception, even for short periods (Ford & Saiprasert 1993; Havanon et al. 1992:25).

Apart from the lack of promotion of male methods within the Thai family planning program, the low number of men having vasectomies also reflects cultural attitudes concerning masculinity and fertility. Vasectomies are unpopular with men and women as it is feared that they deplete a man's physical and spiritual strength and virility, weakening him and making him incapable of the heavy work necessary in the fields.[52] Some men described vasectomies as having similar effects to that of castration of male cattle and express fear that it will 'feminise' them and cause impotence. People also consider it important for men to retain their fertility in case of remarriage:

> Men have to work the fields and do heavy work. If they have a vasectomy they can't do heavy work. I know a man who had a vasectomy and then his first wife died and he married another woman and now she wants to have children but he can't. (Aunt Wii)

For both men and women, physical and spiritual strength is considered intimately linked to one's fertility and sexual potency (Irvine 1982; Sparkes 1995: 68-70; Whittaker 1996b). Because they are understood to possess greater physical and spiritual potency, men are ideally characterised as the religious and ritual specialists, the economic mainstays of families, and as the ones most responsible for productive labour in the fields and elsewhere. Vasectomies are believed to jeopardise male potency.

Likewise, female strength is linked to their fertility. Female sterilisation is also understood to make the woman weak, but villagers say 'women only have to sit at home and look after children, but men have to do heavy work' despite the fact that, in practice, women share much of the heavy labour in the fields with men. Already weakened by their physiological processes of menstruation and childbirth which is understood to cause a constant loss of heat/power and blood, the further weakening caused by sterilisation is equivalent to the weakening associated with menopause and considered part of the inevitable burden of being a woman.

Women's views of modern contraceptives

> In the past we got married and we were so young. After we got married we had children right away. But now we have got family planning. (Aunt Som)

Official village records in Ban Srisaket report that 87 per cent of couples between the ages of fifteen and forty-four use some form of contraception (Thailand, Dept. of Rural Development 1989a).[53] Local health station data states that 152 people in a total of 667 visits used the family planning services in 1992. Sixty-seven per cent of clients used the contraceptive pill, 30 per cent used injectable contraceptives and 3 per cent used condoms.[54] Data from my survey of 146 women in four rural villages in 1997 shows the high familiarity women have with a wide variety of contraceptives.

Table 5.1 Number of surveyed women who have ever used various forms of contraception in rural villages, 1997 N=164.

Method	Ever used	Per cent
Pill	99	77.3
IUD	74	50.3
DMPA	66	44.9
Norplant	17	9.6
Female sterilisation	49	33.6
Male Sterilisation	2	1.4
Condom	11	7.5

SOURCE: Interview survey, 1997

Family planning in Ban Srisaket is being used to space children after the birth of the first child and to prevent further pregnancy rather than to delay childbearing. This is a pattern common throughout Thailand (Knodel & Chayovan 1989). The average number of children of family planning clients in Ban Srisaket was only 1.8, though very few (only 0.3 per cent) had no children. Use of contraception before the fertility of a couple has been confirmed by the birth of a first child is believed by some to make the body weak and possibly jeopardise fertility. Uncle Wan warned me, 'If you take the pill, contraceptives for a long time before you have a baby, the womb is no good and the baby won't have good health, won't be strong."

Women of Ban Srisaket have embraced family planning as the high number of couples using contraceptives suggests. A consistent theme from older women was the lack of control over their fertility in the past. New contraceptive technologies have freed women from 'balancing the water buckets on a pole over one shoulder, having a baby in a sling at your breast and another child on the hip'. Grandmother Sian compared the past with the present, 'In the past we didn't have contraceptive medicines. If you had children you had them, ten, twelve children. We only had the local doctors and the midwives. Some died in childbirth.'

Before the availability of modern contraceptives, women of Ban Srisaket had few means to control their fertility. Grandmother Seen, who is now 55, says she was the first woman in Ban Srisaket to take the pill. She had 'two children in the first three years' of her marriage. After six children and one miscarriage she simply 'didn't want to have any more children'. She heard that medicine which stopped you having more children was available from the health station and took the pill for ten years.

Two children are enough!

Village women and men speak positively of the changes in reproductive attitudes and behaviour. This desire of women and men to control their

Plate 5.1 A family planning poster recommending that women should have their first child when they are 25 years-old. It also demonstrates a variety of contraceptive techniques. The caption reads, 'After having two children, sterilisation is best'.

Plate 5.2 The caption on this family planning poster from the Ministry of Public Health reads, 'Our mother loves us two children. So she has been sterilised.'

fertility coincides with state population policy. Now the norm is that of two children per family. This trend towards smaller family sizes is supported by young and old. Younger women consistently stated that 'two children are enough' as an ideal family size. The majority have a tubal ligation after the birth of their second child.

The global trend towards two children per family norms remains an under-analysed phenomenon in anthropological studies of reproduction (Greenhalgh 1995a: 260). Within the village the financial burdens of feeding and raising many children and sending them to school are the factors most frequently stated for smaller family sizes and this accords with demographic accounts (Knodel et al. 1987; Knodel, Havanon, & Sittitrai 1990; Sittitrai, Wolff, Knodel, Havanon, & Podhista 1991). Several women also indicated that having only two children allows them to continue working and remain economically productive, which would not be possible if they had more children. Apart from economic realities, small families are also understood to be more modern and women make distinctions between their mothers' times and 'modern times' (*samai mai*) in their discussion of family sizes (Muecke 1984; Sittitrai et al. 1991). This linkage between participation in the modern Thai state and small families is reinforced by family planning promotions which stress in posters and slogans the better quality of life for parents and children of two child families and display images of various contraceptive methods surrounding a happy, prosperous couple dressed in Western clothing sitting in the garden of a western style suburban house (see Plate 5.2). The 'two children and a ligation' ideal is promoted in every antenatal clinic I visited. In one such clinic a poster in the antenatal clinic shows a picture of two children declaring, 'Our mother loves us. She has been sterilised!'

The appeal to *kanphatana* (development/progress/advancement) and *samai mai* implicit in family planning promotions, aligns the desire for large families with ignorance, poverty and backwardness. As other writers have described for Indonesia (Hunter 1996) and India (Ram 1998) the bodies of women are regulated in accordance with state development agendas. The family planning discourses in Thailand position Isan villagers, especially women, as the subjects of a broader 'project of enlightenment' (Ram 1998) revolving around the acquisition of appropriate knowledge and behaviours consistent with the development priorities of the state.

Disjunctures between women and state policies

The objectives of the state and of women coincide at various points, but vary at others. It is difficult, then, to characterise the adoption and administration of family planning as purely the product of patriarchy: women clearly desire to control their fertility. However, while modern contraceptives are viewed positively by village women as a means of controlling their fertility, this advantage comes at a cost. Contraceptives are understood as the source of a range of unwanted side-effects that affect women's well-being. The administration of family planning also involves a series of encounters with government representatives in which women are subject to monitoring and subtle reinforcements of their subordinate status.

Unwanted side-effects

Many of the contraceptive side-effects described by women are culturally specific and refer to humoral concepts of wetness and dryness, heat and cold, and the perceived linkage between fertility, regular menstruation and vitality. Women commonly discuss contraceptive side-effects and their attempts to find a contraceptive method suitable to their body and lifestyle. The side-effects described for modern contraceptives usually highlight the effect of the contraceptive on the humoral balance of the body.

As described in Chapter 2, the body is understood to consist of four humoral elements: *din* (earth), *fai* (fire), *nam* (water) and *lom* (wind). Disequilibrium in one of these due to eating wrong foods, fluctuations in climate, or behaviours which jeopardise the balance of these elements increases one's vulnerability to ill health. Modern methods of contraception are understood to disrupt the bodily humoral balance leading to a range of complaints, the most common of which is a loss of vitality and an inability to work hard. Aunt Uay described her contraceptive history:

> In the past we didn't have the pill and so I had seven children and then after that I went and used an IUD. It was painful and I got a lot of *mat khaw* (discharge) and I smelled so strongly that I couldn't get close to other people. I got the doctor to take it out and I had another child right after it was taken out. After that child I took the pill and I got a dry throat and I didn't feel well so I stopped and then I had another child and after that child I made the decision to have a tubal ligation. That was three years ago. After the tubal ligation I get really tired and can't sleep and have vision problems.

The side-effects Aunt Uay describes are suggestive of an iatrogenic reproductive tract infection, caused by the IUD. The pill causes a drying out of the body and so results in the sensation of a dry throat. Finally, her tubal ligation is understood to leave her weak and tired as her strength and vitality is lost.

Despite the controversy surrounding the use of Depo Provera in some countries (Archer 1985)[55] women in Ban Srisaket appreciate the convenience of injectable contraceptives as there 'is no need to remember to take a pill every day'. In addition, injections are valued highly in the local culture (Reeler 1990). Yet injectable contraceptives are frequently associated with side-effects, such as tired arms, amenorrhoea, thinness, weakness and chills, as the 'bad' blood which is normally expelled through menstruation accumulates in the body causing a cold state. Aunt Naam described the effect of Depo Provera in humoral terms as causing a cooling of her body, similar to that believed to take place at menopause. 'After I had the injections (Depo Provera) I never menstruated, I was thin and cold and I had to take warm water baths, whereas in the past I could always use only cold water.'

The contraceptive pill is associated with dizziness, blotchy skin, weight gain and tiredness. IUDs are known to cause discharges and pain and are notorious in some villages for coming out and allowing women to fall pregnant.

As noted in the previous chapter, women's reproductive health is invested with complex meanings which refer to women's potency, fertility, maternity and sexuality, but also to women's fundamental vulnerability and weakness due to the unavoidable consequence of the cycles of menstruation, pregnancy and parturition (Irvine 1982; Whittaker 1996c). A regular heavy menstrual flow of red blood is indicative of a healthy body. This ensures that the 'bad' blood that builds up in a woman's body has been expelled. Irregular menstruation, or blood that is 'thin' or 'black, bruised and congealed,' or any discharges, are signs of ill-health and bodily imbalance. The retention of bad blood within a woman's body may cause varied bodily and emotional states: weakness, bad moods, irritability, insanity, skin rashes, headache, dizziness, ulcers and paleness (Chirawatkul & Manderson 1994; Whittaker 1996c). The presence of leucorrhoea and other discharges signifies a 'dirty' womb and is associated with an inflamed or infected uterus requiring cleansing and drying out through the restriction of 'hot foods'. Any contraceptives that disrupt menstruation or increase discharges are thus understood to jeopardise a woman's physical and mental well-being. Table 5.2 lists the most common side-effects mentioned by village women in interviews and focus groups.

Table 5.2 Common side-effects attributed to contraceptives in Ban Srisaket.

Pill	dry throat, tiredness, lack of appetite, skin problems, thinness, dizziness, obesity, abdominal pain, lower back pain, *mot luk haeng*
IUD	Abdominal pain, heavy discharge, inability to work hard, can fall out
Injectable	Headaches, thinness, weakness, amenorrhoea, dizziness and confusion, numbness, coldness, obesity, eye problems, blotchy skin, dries breast milk
Tubal ligation	lower abdominal pain, weakness, discharge, forgetfulness, waist and back pain, leg pain, change in consistency of menstruation, amenorrhoea
Vasectomy	Weakness, inability to work hard
Condom	reduces sensitivity
Norplant	weak, tired arm, inability to work hard, implant moves through body, skin problems, tiredness

SOURCE: Fieldwork 1993

The stories of women relate their varying needs and experiences. For example, Thim is twenty-eight. Before the birth of her first child she used the pill. She stopped using it when she wanted to start a family and gave birth to her daughter, now 8 years-old. She decided to use an IUD but had heard that many women in her district had fallen pregnant on IUDs inserted at the local district hospital so she decided to travel to the Maternal and Child Health Centre in Khon Kaen to have it inserted instead. That was eight years ago. She wants to have another child but says she will have to wait until the economy improves.

Pui is 31-years-old. She first started using Depo Provera but found it didn't suit her body as she found it made her very tired and so switched to the pill. She stayed on the pill until she started her family. Six years ago, after the birth of her first daughter, she wanted an effective contraceptive but said that the pill makes your breast milk *jang* (thin, weak) and so she had an IUD inserted. She had the IUD until she decided to have another child, a son who is now one year-old.

As each woman has different bodies and different circumstances, there is a need for a variety of types of contraceptives. What is noticeable in these stories is the lack of use of male methods such as condoms or vasectomies for long-term contraception. In my 1997 sample of 164 rural women, only 12 couples (7.2 per cent) had ever used condoms and only 3 (1.8 per cent) had male partners who had had vasectomies.

The effects attributed to contraceptives are understood to be consequences of the interference with the normal reproductive processes balancing the female body. Most women have very good knowledge of the different forms of contraception available. Women speak of contraceptives as either *thuk* (correct) for their bodies or not. Each woman's body is considered to have its own idiosyncratic characteristics so women accept that a contraceptive that suits one woman may not suit another.

A new contraceptive: Norplant

A newly introduced contraceptive method, Norplant, demonstrates the ways in which contraceptives are incorporated into women's understandings of their bodies. Norplant consists of five small tubes containing laevonorgestrel which are inserted beneath the skin of the upper arm and offer contraceptive protection for five years (Sivin, Robertson, & Stern 1980). Norplant was first tested in clinical trials in five hospitals in 1980 and more widely introduced from 1986. Studies of the acceptability of Norplant in Thailand have consistently shown high acceptability and long continuation rates compared to other methods. Side-effects documented included menstrual irregularities such as spotting, weight gain or loss, and amenorrhoea, as well as headaches, dizziness, nausea, vomiting and skin problems (Bhiromrut no date; Koetsawang, Varakamin, Satayapan, & Dusitsin 1984; Thailand, Ministry of Public Health & World Health Organisation 1994; Thailand, Ministry of Public Health 1988, no date). Although two-thirds of women in a 1988 study reported side-effects, they generally considered them to be less severe than the side-effects of other methods (Thailand, Ministry of Public Health 1988). However, in other countries there have been concerns raised about the unethical use of the method. Like all provider-dependent methods there exists the possibility of abuse. In Bangladesh and Indonesia there have been concerns raised about the lack of follow-up of acceptors and possible severe side-effects. In these countries when women had problems they associated with Norplant, they had difficulty locating a person trained or willing to remove the implant (World Health Organization, 1994:24-5; Correa, 1994; Hull, 1996; Widyantoro, 1993).

In the survey I conducted in 1997, 14 women (8.5 per cent) of my sample of 163 women had ever tried Norplant. Of those, eleven women were current users. Most were pleased with the convenience of Norplant, they did not have to remember to take the pill every day nor go for quarterly visits to the health station for a DMPA injection. None were using Norplant as an initial form of contraception, but were using it to space their pregnancies, or as a permanent method if they were scared to have a tubal ligation. For example, Prapan started on Norplant after her sister introduced it to her. She wanted a more permanent method but was scared of the thought of an IUD inside her and said that DMPA dries the womb and so causes infertility. She wants another child but will wait until the economy improves. Khaek, 21 years-old, had an unwanted pregnancy on an IUD and experienced leg pain on DMPA so she is now trying Norplant and said it suited her body well.

Siwii is 26 years-old. She is very poor and owns no land. She and her husband earn money by cutting cane in the Central provinces for three to four months of the year. She started using contraception after the birth of her first son when she was seventeen. He is now nine. She started on the pill but said it made her *mot luk haeng* (uterus dry) and so switched to injections of Depo Provera. She stopped her contraception to have a second son, who is now six. Her husband used condoms while she was still breastfeeding. She fell pregnant again but had a miscarriage while she was cutting sugar cane. After this she went onto Norplant but found that she had a weak, tired arm where the implants were inserted which made it difficult for her to do the heavy work of cutting cane. She could feel the rods move inside her arm and it bruised whenever she worked hard. She also felt that it was dangerous as she felt it might dislodge from her arm and move in her body. She had Norplant removed whereupon she fell pregnant with her third child, a daughter now 2 years-old. Now she has returned to using Depo Provera as she feels it suits her and she doesn't want any more children but is scared of having a tubal resection.

The idea that Norplant might move through one's body seems to be common. It is understood that the rods can move along the *sen* connecting the body. This understanding is also based on the fact that the rods do in fact move a little under the skin and women experience a sensation of movement when working with their arms. The heavy work which women must do exacerbates the problems. Women say the rods make their arms weak and tired, and cause pain and bruising when they work hard. For example, Sompong who is 41 years-old, liked Norplant as a contraceptive and had no side-effects except for the pain in her arm when she worked hard.

I won't use it again as I have to work hard with mushrooms. I need to stretch the muscles in my arm as I work and it used to hurt. If I didn't need to work like that it wouldn't be a problem. If I could just sit, then it'd be comfortable!

I first became interested in Norplant when I visited a local district hospital near the village. As part of the local campaign to introduce Norplant, 488 women had Norplant inserted *en masse* in April 1992. When I visited the district hospital, many of the women were having the rods removed, complaining of sore tired arms, tiredness, weakness and dizziness, amenorrhoea, irregular bleeding and a fear that the rods could move through the body. Staff of the district hospital said the women were from the same set of villages and were acting on rumours. They did not acknowledge the cultural understandings of the clients, nor try to address their fears.

Interviews with women raise some concerns about the way in which the early promotion of Norplant was conducted. Although most women were happy with the convenience of Norplant, some women told of inadequate explanations of possible side-effects and inadequate screening (few had their blood pressure tested). Although it was free to have Norplant inserted, most women had to pay from 200-250 baht to have it removed (a disincentive against early removal). When the contraceptive was first introduced, there were special efforts made by hospitals to recruit women to use it, even though many were already using contraceptives that suited them and were cheaper. For example, Pu who is thirty, was encouraged to have Norplant inserted even though she had been happy using an IUD for over a year. During a special promotion of Norplant, she was picked up by health staff in a car along with five other women to go to the hospital and try the new contraceptive. She said she was told by the health staff there were no problems with it, that it was convenient and that she could be a leader using the new 'modern' contraceptive. She was happy with Norplant for four years but then felt her body was colder than before:

I was so cold and I felt so hungry that my hands shook . . . In the first, second and third years I never felt dizzy, but in the fourth year I was planting mushrooms and I got dizzy and I went to the doctor who gave me a saline injection but I didn't get any better. I rested for two months but I didn't get better and then I thought that it must be because the Norplant was near it's end so I had it removed.

Similarly, Phen who is twenty-six went onto Norplant after she was diagnosed with *mot luk aksaep* associated with an IUD she had had for one year. She received no physical examination or counselling before having the rods inserted: 'I just signed a card and they sent me to have it put in'. She only used Norplant for nine months after developing a skin rash.

It made my whole body tired. I was itchy and scratching all over and so I had it out . . . I developed blood blisters on my body and I went to see a doctor at a clinic who gave me an injection for my blood, but it didn't get any better and so I had it out.

Whether such symptoms are due to Norplant or not, stories such as Sompong's make other women suspicious; some women told me frankly that it was 'dangerous'. Despite the early enthusiasm for Norplant for long-term spacing of children, with the current economic crisis it is unlikely to be as heavily promoted by family planning authorities as in the past due to its expense. Family planning workers told me that they are receiving instructions to promote IUDs as the most cost-efficient form of contraception.

The ubiquitous tubal resection

'Do tubal ligations hurt?' Dii asks. Her body is all covered in green surgical cloth except for a square around her abdomen. Before they started the nurse put a surgical cloth over her eyes. She protested, 'I don't want that!' But it was placed over her anyway. The staff shared jokes and light chatter while the nurse swabbed her belly and three hypodermic needles of local anaesthetic were injected on either side of her navel. Her stomach looked jelly-like, etched with stretch marks, as she had given birth less than an hour before. A student doctor was undertaking her ligation with an experienced surgeon in attendance. It took a long time for the student to locate the fallopian tube on the right side and by the time he was pushing around on her left side the anaesthetic was beginning to wear off. Dii had made no sound during her birth, but now she was saying, 'Oh doctor, it hurts, *cep, cep.*' Finally, more anaesthetic was injected and she was sewn up and wheeled off to the post-partum ward. (Fieldnotes, Provincial Teaching Hospital, 1992)

Tubal resections are the most common form of permanent sterilisation and have become the norm for women of Ban Srisaket. Women encourage each other to have resections and although women complain of chronic tiredness and weakness, an inability to sleep, vision disturbances and abdominal pain after a tubal ligation, they say that the benefits and relief of knowing that they will not fall pregnant again outweighs the ill-effects. Having two children and then a tubal ligation has become conventional behaviour for women within Ban Srisaket. Tubal ligations are free and usually performed directly after birth. [56] Lek is typical in that she has had a 'wet' tubal resection immediately after the birth of her daughter. Lek is twenty-eight and has two children, one boy aged six and one girl who is now five-months-old. She used Depo Provera after her first child to space the births as she was too scared to take the pill in case she forgot to take it every day. She had the tubal resection because she has 'enough children already and *bor wai* (couldn't cope) with another'.

Women's discourses relating to modern contraceptives reveal a perceived disruption of the traditional ordering and balancing of the female body caused by the new technologies. Whilst women acknowledge the benefits of the control over their fertility, this is perceived to be achieved at the price of their vitality and strength, to the extent of interfering with their productive capabilities. Many women say that women who have tubal ligations have more problems with their health and are not capable of as much hard work because *bor dai yu fai lang het man* (they did not stay by the fire after they had a tubal ligation). In this statement the disruption of traditional symbolic sources of social and physical strength and status is blamed upon modern contraception. Women's productive capabilities are linked to the health of their reproductive bodies.

Delivery of services: embodying ethnic and class status

Government hospitals and clinics remain the most important source of supply of contraceptives and clinic procedures (Chayovan, Kamnuansilpa, & Knodel 1988). Whereas women of Ban Srisaket regard contraception as a means of control over their bodies, their experiences of family planning services within government clinics are encounters that are far from empowering. In particular, I explore what Simmons and Elias have termed the latent dimensions of client–provider interactions:

the relatively hidden, but nevertheless powerful components of the interactions. Client–provider exchanges reflect, and are shaped by, fundamental difference in the status, power and culture of participants in the encounter (1994:3).

Health service encounters are micropolitical situations that parallel relations in society at large (Waitzkin 1991). Observations of government clinics reveal a range of micro-relations of power enacted in clinic procedures and counselling. Staff in these clinics are often of elite Central Thai or Chinese Thai backgrounds with middle-class aspirations who look down upon Lao-speaking village women (Cohen 1989). The institutionalised subordination of villagers in health settings is replicated throughout bureaucratic culture in Thailand.

The spatial organisation and mode of service provision at the district hospital near Ban Srisaket provides an example of the ways in which government services subordinate the needs of clients to the priorities of staff members. The family planning unit is in a room positioned between a secretarial administration room and the outer hall, and staff are constantly passing through the room down the passageway between the benches of the patients and the desks of the staff. Clients to the clinic are forced to stand in order to speak to nurses sitting behind their desks, as no chairs are provided. No private space exists for consultation or counselling except for the brief period while a woman is placed vulnerably on the examination bed to be injected in the buttocks or examined for an IUD. While clients are consulting, any number of non-medical staff pass through the room and overhear conversations. As may be expected, the behaviour of most clients I observed was passive, with little conversation or questions asked of the nurses:

> One young woman came at 9.30 a.m. into the family planning room filled with clerks and other staff reading magazines. She handed her card to the first staff member whose greeting was 'chit ya' (injection). She was pointed in the direction of the examination table and had to negotiate her way between the staff standing talking between the desks. There was much interest in the 20-baht raffle tickets the police were selling to the nurses. Eventually the curtain was pulled around the bed and she was given her injection and told the date to come back. (Fieldnotes, District Hospital, 1992)

The organisation of clinic space not only defines the arena for action but also has effects in the structuring of the interactions and identities of patients and the staff who work within it. The fact that women must travel to a specific place for their family planning services, rather than obtain them from community workers, defines boundaries between the village and the clinic as the space for health practices. The demarcations created between nurses and clients by desks, the social differences embodied within staff uniforms, the restricted and awkward spaces the patient must negotiate, even the picture of the King of Thailand on the wall of the clinic, all reflect and provide a material basis for state-sanctioned action and contribute to the moulding and reinforcement of the staff's superior social position and power. As Mallett has described for clinics in New Guinea, these spaces are mimetic in their evocation of globalised Western medical practice and authority (Mallett 1997:112-13).

Once within the clinic space, women become 'contraceptive acceptors' with the doctor or nurse as the superior knowing agent, and the woman as ignorant passive recipient of this knowledge. Little detailed counselling is given to clients and there is little opportunity for questions. Within the village health station, the experience of women seeking contraceptives is a similar perfunctory consultation with few questions asked about difficulties women may be experiencing with their contraceptives. Women in Ban Srisaket are aware of the subtle discrimination operating with many officials and they criticise staff for neglecting their needs, 'speaking rudely' and failing to provide information. However, there are few options for women to subvert the relations of power enacted in these consultations. Women endure their inattentive treatment for the sake of obtaining their contraceptive needs.

Conclusions

Thailand has an extensive and successful family planning program which has institutionalised the motto 'two children are enough' in the minds of its citizens and has been responsible for a large reduction in the average birth rate in the last two decades. Family planning programs have enabled women to control their fertility and release them from the pattern of high parity and high maternal mortality which their mothers describe. In this respect the objectives of the state programs coincide with the desires of women to control their fertility.

As Giddens has noted (1990) modernity involves a 'disembedding' in space and time of social relations, from local face to face interactions to interactions with large, impersonal institutions. In health care, along with the growth of government health services has come changes in the nature of medical consultations from those with local healers within the community to encounters with representatives of government institutions. Throughout this book there exist ongoing tensions in the transitions between women's health as a process that used to be locally managed within the community to a process actively monitored and managed by the state. Traditionally, fertility regulation, pregnancy, and childbirth were conditions to be managed within the community, often with the services of the village midwife. Modern contraceptive techniques, whilst appreciated for their effectiveness, have shifted control of fertility from the intimate realm of the personal into the public realm of the state. Thus the wombs of women are being managed and disciplined as the locus of interventions and new technologies in family planning, birthing, breastfeeding, and child-care. These technologies have effects that become explained and experienced through local understandings of the body and health. New contraceptive technologies are understood to dry out the womb and tubal ligations lead to long-term weakness and ill-health. Women are strongly encouraged by health workers to be sterilised immediately after the birth of their second child, an act that both frees them from further strains of pregnancy and birth, but which they believe will weaken them and leave them unable to work as hard as they did in the past.

In their interactions with service providers women also carry markers of their subordinate ethnicity. They are addressed as targets of reform, whose high fertility—and by extension their poverty and lack of education—may be reversed by a pill, IUD or tubal ligation so as to become part of the modern, developed Thai state. Isan women are sensitive to and critical of the relations of power inherent in the implementation of the family planning program. They often express dissatisfaction with their treatment, but with their choices constrained by poverty and geographic isolation they have few options but to tolerate the service they receive.

6 Bearing tradition and modernity

Grandmother Dam holds her lower stomach as she demonstrates how women give birth in the village:

It hurts a lot, hurts a lot, and when it hurts you want to push and then the *mor tam yae* [birth attendant] says 'Push!' You want to push and you push it out. Then the head comes out, it's really difficult to get out the first time, when you are a new mother. The old people, they say 'The body's coming now! . . . Dropping now!' Like that. 'The body's coming down now. The head's come out now, the head's come out now'. The head comes now and you push and it all comes out. When the baby is out then they let the placenta come out, the *hae* we call it. My husband, he was the one who cut it. Andy, you mightn't believe, the old people took a shellfish shell to slice the cord, the shells used as dippers, spoons. My husband cut the cord of Nong. He got a well washed stalk of lemon grass, washed in boiling water to make it clean first, and then got the white part of the stalk and cut it on it. First you tie it. Imagine my finger is the cord like this, here you tie once, tie here also, then you take this part and cut like this, the cord isn't soft, it's like this, you push the blood and fat out. We tie it first to stop the blood and fat from coming out. We get the placenta when it comes and save it. The old people told us to wash it and put salt on it, then you wrap it up and bury it in the earth. Bury it under the eaves of the house . . . Then you take the new child and wash it . . . When the baby is clean, you take it and put it in the *kradong* [flat basket]. And then the mother washes herself in warm water. She is cold and shivering. Then you build the fire and take her to it, to the *sanen* [the bed for the mother to lie on by the fire].

Feldnotes, District Hospital, October 1992:

A 20 year-old woman was in labour, already dilated six centimetres. An
older woman was rubbing and massaging her back as she changed
positions on the bed, sometimes lying on her side, sometimes sitting.
When she had dilated eight centimetres the nurses brought a wheelchair
and took her into the 'birth room'.
'Are relatives allowed into the birth room?' I asked.
'No,' the nurse replied.
'Why?' I asked.
'Villagers . . . ' she smiled.
So I followed the two midwives into the birthing room. The woman was
told to get up onto the steel bed, into a lithotomy position with her legs in
stirrups. Her pubis had been shaved before I arrived. The nurses prepared
their instruments as the woman's contractions became stronger. They
occasionally told her to push as they continued to prepare their cloths and
instruments. The whole birthing room was shiny aluminium and steel.
Chairs scrapped along the floor and trolley wheels reverberated loudly.
The woman in labour asked for water, receiving no response to her
request. Eventually I got the nurses' aide's attention and a glass of water
was brought to her. There was no physical contact. I decided to
'intervene' and went over and held her hand, she squeezed strongly. With
my other arm I supported her neck when she raised her shoulders off the
bed with the painful contractions and whispered in her ear. 'Good . . . a
little longer . . . the head is coming.' She screwed her face and clenched
my hand but did not yell or cry. The midwives droned 'Errrrrrrrrrrrrrrrrr',
in unison through the contractions. Finally the head could be seen and an
episiotomy was performed. The body of the baby slid out and he started to
cry. The new mother craned her neck to try and see the baby, but couldn't,
as the cord was clamped and cut and the baby taken away to be cleaned
and weighed by one of the midwives. The young mother smiled and
smiled at the sound of her child's cries. And so did I. The midwife now
went to sit on the bed but it collapsed down a rung when she did. The
midwife cried out in surprise; the mother cried out with the pain. The
midwife cranked the bed up again to a slight decline (through the birth it
had been horizontal). Then she sat on it and vigorously massaged the
woman's belly to deliver the placenta. The mother moaned with the pain.
With the placenta out and checked and weighed, the mother was given a
single local anaesthetic injection and her episiotomy was sewn together.
The anaesthetic must have begun to wear off, as the mother started
showing pain and distress at each stitch. When finished, the midwife
pushed strongly down on the woman's abdomen, forcing out urine,
causing more pain to the woman. Then the woman was accompanied as
she slowly walked to her bed, about 30 metres away. *Jep, jep,* ' she

complained of the pain. She lay down and her baby was brought to her. About ten minutes later her waiting relatives were admitted and they gathered around the bed.

The extension of government health services in Thailand has fundamentally changed women's experiences of giving birth. This chapter explores some of these changes. The majority of women in Ban Srisaket now give birth in a local hospital rather than at home. Hospital births are perceived as the safest alternative for women both by government health staff and by village women themselves. This change is accompanied by shifts in the meanings and significance of local health practices. As the practice of birthing within the village declines, 'modern' medical expertise regulated by the state is increasingly undermining the authority of traditional knowledge and practices.

In hospital, women become participants in a process wherein their bodies are constituted as sites of reform and 'modernisation,' just as village society has become the site of similar reform and development. The technologies of birthing operationalise a field of discourses about health and hygiene that are linked to ideas of development and modernisation within Thailand. These discourses seek to rid village women of what biomedicine defines as 'superstitious beliefs' and 'traditions', and in doing so challenge and alter the subjective meanings of female bodies and the authority of traditional knowledge. Within state hospital and clinic institutions, medical practices and structures monitor, categorise and act upon the flesh of women and in doing so communicate and enact discourses that construct the modern Thai citizen.

Related to this view of modernisation and development is the assumption that medical systems will also come under the influence of Western modernity and that people will desire, aspire to and accept Western biomedicine as the 'rational' choice of health resources. In this view local medical cultures eventually will be subordinated to the globalising influence of Western medicine.

However, while the majority of village women give birth in hospital, they continue traditional post-partum practice within the village. The post-partum practice of staying by the fire relates to a different system of knowledge which stresses the importance of restoring heat to women's bodies after birth. While the post-partum period is relatively neglected by the Thai state biomedical system which concentrates on the birthing process, within local tradition the post-partum is a crucial time. Not only is post-partum practice considered an important prophylactic for the continued strength, fertility and well-being of women, but constitutes a rite of passage which affirms women's ethnic and feminine identity. The village is a social space in which the globalising definitions and practices of birthing imposed by the dominant biomedical discourse are contested. In birthing and the post-partum period, women move between the spatially separated domains of the hospital and the home, and in doing so move between discursive frameworks: the first where the knowledge and practices of biomedicine and state development prevail, and the second where community knowledge and practices dominate.

Such contests over definitions and control of knowledge within childbirth has been documented in Jordan's ethnographic description of cross-cultural birthing which offers an account of the worldwide processes through which biomedical authority has come to dominate the childbirth experience (Jordan 1993 [1978]; see also Steinberg 1996). Implicated in this process is what Jordan terms 'authoritative knowledge'. She suggests that when more than one knowledge system exists in a given domain, one form of knowledge is afforded ascendancy and social legitimacy, and serves as grounds for action. People actively engage in the production and reproduction of authoritative knowledge, constantly reinforcing its validity until it comes to appear natural, reasonable and shared. As Sargent and Bascope note, the basis for authoritative knowledge lies not only in the control of technologies of birthing as suggested by Jordan, but may also 'reflect the distribution of power within a social group' (1996:213). In their study of three communities Sargent and Bascope found that even in the absence of high technology, the social status and cultural authority of biomedicine created through discourse and embedded in the status of physicians and midwives maintained its ideological dominance (1996:232). Authoritative knowledge thus involves differential power relations between differing knowledge systems and different groups in society. In other terms, authoritative knowledge is a form of what Bourdieu termed 'cultural capital', which is distributed unevenly within a society and allows the holders to address a certain audience in a relationship of subordination (Bourdieu 1977; Bourdieu & Passeron 1977). In this chapter I expand the concept of authoritative knowledge, by addressing the fundamental issues of power inherent in it. In particular, I concentrate upon the ways in which biomedicine has been introduced and supported by the state as 'authoritative knowledge' and as such carries implicit state imperatives, linking health behaviour to wider social agendas of modernisation and social education.

Fundamental to my discussion of these themes is the recognition of the power relations underlying the organisation of health care in Thailand which shapes the choices women make and the meanings of their actions. It makes explicit the linkages between power and knowledge within pluralist medical systems. Riley and Sermsri (1974) describe the Thai medical system as one in which patients 'choose freely' among many alternatives similar to a supermarket, where consumers of medical services choose freely between different medical ideologies and practices. While the women described in this book make active choices about where and how they give birth, these choices take place within unequal relations of power between the institutionalised biomedical state health system and local practices and knowledge. The 'quest for therapy' is not a simple exercise of choice, but involves movement between discursive frameworks which co-exist in unequal relations of power (Ram 1998).

Changing patterns of birthing over time

The birthing experience has changed dramatically in the space of a single generation within Ban Srisaket. Before the extension of government health services, all women in Ban Srisaket gave birth at home either alone or in the company of their husband, kin or traditional birthing attendant. Although some women continue to give birth at home, the majority now give birth in hospitals, in accordance with the aims of the Seventh National Development Plan, which seeks to have 75 per cent of women give birth in hospital (Thailand, NESDB 1992a). Within most families it is possible to trace the changes:

> I go to visit Faa, a 22 year-old woman who has just given birth to her first child, a boy. During my visit I talk with the members of the household about giving birth, and women compare their experiences. Faa's grandmother tells me that she had nine pregnancies, and gave birth to four sons and four daughters, six of whom survived. Faa's grandmother gave birth at home, on some occasions by herself, sometimes in the company of an elderly *mor tam yae* (TBA). Faa's mother gave birth to five children at home, with her own mother and a traditional birth attendant present. When contraceptive services became available Faa's mother had a tubal ligation and so limited her family. Faa gave birth to her son at a local District Hospital. Before the birth she attended antenatal care at the local *sathani anamai* (health station). Faa and her husband plan on having only two children (Fieldnotes, 1992).

Table 6.1 summarises the results from a birthing survey conducted of women of various ages. It gives a sense of the generational changes. In Ban Srisaket 97 per cent of women surveyed over the age of thirty-five gave birth to their children at home. The age of thirty-five is used as the age of contrast, as most women over thirty-five were giving birth approximately fifteen years ago, before government health services were accessible. This pattern continued for their second child with 97 per cent giving birth at home.

Women younger than thirty-five have had more choices as to the place of birth since the development of government health services in the 1970s in Ban Srisaket with the establishment of a primary health station with a trained nurse-midwife in attendance and the extension of District Hospital services. Fifty-eight per cent of women of this age range gave birth to their first child at home, usually attended by a trained nurse-midwife or trained TBA. However, only 33 per cent of that age group did so for their second child. Most gave birth in hospital, explaining that by doing so they were able to have a free tubal ligation immediately afterwards. Within Ban Srisaket the current desired norm for women is to have only two children (preferably one of each sex) and a tubal ligation immediately after the second birth.[57]

Table 6.1 Percentage of women who gave birth at home for their first child and for their second child, by age group, Ban Srisaket.

Age (years)	First birth at home	Per cent	Total number	Second birth at home	Per cent	Total number
>35	35	97	36	32	97	33
<35	18	58	31	7	33	21

SOURCE: Birthing survey 1992

In 1992, only six (10 per cent) of the fifty-eight women who gave birth that year did so at home. Of these six, five gave birth at home to their first child, but indicated that they would attend hospital for their next birth for a tubal ligation. Seventeen women (29 per cent) gave birth at the local District Hospital, while twelve women (21 per cent) gave birth at two other District Hospitals further away from the village. Thirteen women (22 per cent) gave birth in the provincial hospital, over sixty kilometres away. Three (5 per cent) chose to give birth at private hospitals, also over sixty kilometres away. Two other women gave birth while living temporarily in other provinces.

Antenatal care

From the beginning of her pregnancy to after the birth, women in Ban Srisaket negotiate the different understandings of pregnancy and birth offered by local knowledge and government health services. They are admonished to be responsible in traditional and modern terms, by observing local customs and practices as well as attending government antenatal clinics and following the nurses' advice. The tension between the two is evident in the ways in which women answer questions about their actions throughout pregnancy. Some were reluctant to speak about 'old' customs they followed and certainly do not admit them to nurses at the health station.

Discussions with women about their pregnancies revealed that they followed a range of practices said to ensure a safe and easy birth and healthy baby. Women declared that they 'ate everything' during their pregnancy, although a few mentioned avoiding particular foods that are said to make the baby fat, thus resulting in a difficult birth, or which have metaphorical associations. One woman said that throughout her pregnancy she avoided 'hot' foods for fear of a miscarriage and another said she avoided *mak bok* (wild almond, *Irvingia malayana*) and *makham* (tamarind) for fear that the child would be fat, like the creamy flesh of these foods, and therefore difficult to deliver. Tubers and roots such as taro and sweet potatoes are said to make the baby feverish. Eating foods such as white clay was common in the past, and although in the opinion of Grandmother Sow it is no longer necessary because of the vitamins women now take instead, it is still possible to find clay biscuits for sale in district markets.

Cravings for particular foods are believed to be caused by the child inside the womb and must be obliged. But women are exhorted not to over-eat for fear of a large baby and difficult birth. Grandmother Wau described pregnant women as either *man mu* (pregnant like a pig) that is, fat all over, or *man ma* (pregnant like a dog) which is 'skinny all over except for the belly!' She suggested that being *man ma* indicated an easier birth. Pregnancy does not provide an excuse for a diminishment of household duties nor farm work. Indeed some women spoke of the need to work harder through pregnancy to avoid a fat baby and difficult birth. Women continue to undertake heavy work throughout their pregnancies.

Morning sickness, vomiting, nausea and dizziness are recognised as signs of pregnancy: a woman is said to be *phae thorng* (allergic to her pregnancy).[58] 'Women are *phae* for about one month. It's difficult to say who will be *phae* and who won't. Some say that if you are *phae* like this it will be a boy, like this and that and it will be a girl . . . that's what they say' (Grandmother Sai). Women who are *phae thorng* may take herbal tonics recommended by other women and avoid those foods which make them nauseous.

A *su khwan mae man* (soul-tying ritual for pregnant women)[59] may be conducted, especially if they are apprehensive about the coming birth or have been unwell. Tying the *khwan* (soul) back to her and tying her into her community helps both her and the baby with the trauma and pain of birthing: 'If a woman is strong and not *phae* [allergic] to her pregnancy we don't *su khwan*. If she is *phae* then we do' (Grandmother Yim). As mentioned in Chapter 3, *su khwan* ceremonies are performed at all important life transitions and especially with regard to health. The transformation of a woman into a mother is one such important transition.

A range of actions are considered possibly harmful to the mother or child. Within the womb, the developing foetus can be influenced by outside forces and the balance of elements in the mother's body. The mother's temperament and emotional experiences likewise may influence personal characteristics of the forthcoming child, or the physical characteristics of the child, such as skin colour or blemishes. Thus women are instructed not to become upset or angry, which may affect the baby's character or darken the skin. A pregnant woman should not see ugly sights, or the child may be ugly also. Metaphorical associations are also made between certain actions and their effect upon birth. Pregnant women are instructed not to sit on house steps or the house threshold as this may result in an obstructed labour. Grandmother Huu, a traditional birth attendant, said pregnant women should not wash in the late afternoon or the baby will be big; nor should they eat anything while walking, as it will cause prolonged labour pains. Some of these rules also concern the behaviour of the woman's family, particularly of the father-to-be. He should not kill anything during the term of his wife's pregnancy, as it will risk the death of the mother or child in childbirth.

These rules are flexible and few seem to be observed today with great consistency. Rather, they tend to be used in retrospect to help explain an unfortunate birth or miscarriage. In a case of one maternal death in the past, the family had killed a calf for a wedding the night before the birth and this action was seen as linked to the daughter's death.

In addition to the extra care women take with their behaviour and food intake throughout pregnancy, some women also visit the local birth attendants regularly for checks. In contrast to the regimentation of the health station, consultations to traditional birth attendants are marked by their informal personal nature and convenience. The TBAs offer services and advice not available from the health station. They massage women's stomachs each month to ensure an easy birth. If women are fearful or are feeling unwell, it is often to the TBA that they turn for advice. In the last few months, women go to a TBA for her assessment of the size of the baby and whether they will have difficulty in labour. Grandmother Sen declared:

> When women come I massage their bellies for them. I get five or ten baht for it. Grandmother The's daughter gave birth fast and easily because she had many *uay thorng* [abdominal massages] before the birth.

Grandmother Yim described her role as one of assessment and referral:

> Pregnant women come to me to find out how they are. They come to have me push their stomachs and massage them and tell them the truth. 'Young daughter, you aren't well. Go to see the *mor* at the health station and have them give you some medicine and an injection. Nourish yourself well.' I say, 'You are not strong my child'. If they are weak, not strong, I tell them, 'Go to the doctor!'

Whereas traditional midwives refer women to the government health services, nurses at the health station never refer women to the traditional midwives. For health staff, antenatal care consists of attendance at antenatal clinics. All women who gave birth in 1992 reported that they had attended at least one antenatal clinic, either at the local health station or clinics at the various hospitals. On antenatal screening day at the village health station several pregnant women can be seen waiting in a queue. There are two antenatal care clinics each week. Although health station records show an average of four women attending each antenatal clinic, in practice, the nurses instruct all women to attend on the same day each month. Consequently, one day a month, a large number of clients attend the antenatal clinic with long delays, while on other antenatal care days and through general clinic times there are few patients and no waiting time. While this practice is convenient for the staff, for the client it ensures maximum inconvenience, long delays and rushed consultations.

Only one nurse does the checks while the other staff members do other tasks; so woman have to wait for approximately forty-five minutes depending on when they arrive. Women come from all the surrounding villages to this health station and they say that in the wet season the dirt tracks turn to mud, which can make transportation difficult. Some of the women are accompanied by their children and some female kin who help look after the children. Other women have come in a group with friends who are also pregnant. There is not enough room for everyone to sit on the wooden bench in front of the health station; so women sit in the small rest shelter further away in the health station grounds. For all the waiting, the antenatal checks received by women seem very quick:

'Next!' A young woman, six months pregnant, goes into the office as the previous woman leaves. She passes her card to the nurse sitting behind the desk, stands on the scales and calls out her weight without needing to be asked: '53 [kilograms].'
'Any problems?'
'No. I'm tired only.'
The nurse scribbles on her card and writes down the woman's name and details in the antenatal care book.
'Come back on this day next month, please! Next!'

Antenatal consultations tend to be perfunctory, monitoring the pregnancy through ritualised testing, manual examinations and recording. In contrast to local views of pregnancy as a natural state the outcome of which is largely outside of human control, the biomedical profession views pregnancy as controllable, manageable and knowable through the disciplined monitoring of the internal and external spaces of the pregnant uterus/body (Foucault 1973; Muecke 1976). Women are admonished to give birth in the local District Hospital when they come for antenatal visits. Although this health station has a trained nurse/midwife, she no longer offers to attend births at the health station, as she declares herself tired of the responsibility of caring for birthing women and scared of the consequences should anything go wrong. Thus women in Ban Srisaket have a limited choice as to where and how they give birth.

The antenatal consultations at the health station involve a series of ritualised procedures. Tetanus toxoid injections are routinely administered. The name, age, address, number of months gestation, and number of previous pregnancies and live births of the pregnant woman are recorded and an identification number assigned. In addition, the nurse is supposed to record weight, height, blood pressure and test for syphilis. However, in practice, height is not measured or recorded. Although the sphygmomanometer to measure blood pressures was inoperable, blood pressures were entered as 110/70 for nearly every woman. There was clearly greater concern that the antenatal book appear complete for evaluation by superiors than the need to accurately monitor blood pressures. The antenatal care records therefore function less as a means of identifying high-risk mothers than as a display for the eyes of other bureaucrats. The emphasis placed upon institutional record-keeping, what I term a 'culture of display' for bureaucratic eyes, seems to be the *raison d'être* for much of the interaction.

Women said they attend antenatal care to *chit ya* (receive tetanus injections) which they perceived as making the baby and mother healthy and strong. Village records indicate that 90 per cent of pregnant women received at least one tetanus immunisation (Thailand, Dept. of Rural Development 1989b). According to the antenatal care records of the health station, most women attending antenatal care at the health station in Ban Srisaket are pregnant for the first or second time. The sharp drop at three pregnancies indicates the growing norm of permanent sterilisation after the birth of the second child. On average women presented to their first antenatal care visit when they were four months pregnant. Some presented late in the third trimester for their first check. Women pregnant for the second time presented earlier on average than those pregnant for their first time.

A cohort of twenty women who attended their first antenatal check in the first three months of 1992 averaged only 1.8 antenatal care visits throughout their pregnancies. Ten of these women (50 per cent) attended only once, with five (25 per cent) attending three times and the other five (25 per cent) attending four times. This is below the targets set in the Seventh National Plan (1992–96) for all women to have at least four antenatal care checks (once for the first two trimesters and twice in the final trimester) (Thailand, NESDB 1992). The low figure may be because women attend antenatal clinics elsewhere at hospitals, or private clinics, or that women attend only to receive injections and see little benefit in continuing to participate in the ritual.[60]

Birthing the old and new ways

In giving birth the 'old' or 'new' way, women embody divergent world views. At home, the success of the birth process is governed by karmic status, tradition and the goodwill of the spirits in contrast to hospital births, where technical interventions are relied upon for ensuring a safe and successful delivery (Muecke 1976). All the women who gave birth at home in 1992 were attended by trained TBAs. In Ban Srisaket there are six women who are recognised by the community as *mor tam yae*, all aged in their sixties. Five of these women received a five-day training course in 1977 and one has not received government training, but is a massage therapist and has assisted with births in the past. Of these six women, only two trained women continue to actually attend births, but attend so few births now that they fear losing their skills. Grandmother Yim complained that in the past she attended five or six births a month, but now that people only have two children she only helps deliver one or two every few months. Mother Uan is one of the six women who gave birth at home in 1992 the 'old way', attended by Grandmother Yim, a trained TBA:

> I went to visit Mother Uan who gave birth to a girl yesterday (in 1992). She was lying close to a post-partum fire. Her husband was making a wooden stand for the baby's cradle. She described the birth to me: 'I didn't hurt much, only for four or five hours. We called Grandmother Yim and she came and she helped me to hang onto a rope and helped me push. She washed the baby and my husband buried the placenta underneath the window. My husband got the water and wood for the fire and he helped by washing the clothes and boiling water. I decided to give birth at home because I saw that Grandmother Yim [a TBA] did lots of births and was a good woman who speaks well. She is very skilled at births, so I thought I would give birth at home' (Fieldnotes, 1992).

The traditional position for giving birth at home is kneeling or sitting. The woman in labour holds the shoulders of her husband, or in his absence, pulls on a *khaen pha* (cloth) tied over a roof rafter or post. The traditional midwife makes discrete inspections to check progress under the woman's *phasin* skirt, retaining the woman's modesty at all times. The midwife employs massage, moral support and a variety of prayers and spells to assist the labouring woman. She presses a cloth against the woman's perineum as the baby's head crowns to minimise tearing. No episiotomies are performed. Grandmother Yim informed me that in the past the umbilical cord was cut with a sliver of fresh bamboo or an oyster shell against a root of tumeric (*Curcuma domestica*), a stalk of lemon grass, or piece of charcoal. Now, Grandmother Yim uses pre-boiled scissors, or a blade as she was taught during her midwife training. Ordinary cotton thread is used to tie and sew the cord. The navel of the baby is commonly treated with alcohol and *phong piset* (special powder), a sulphur-based powder bought at the local village store. In the past the powdered nest of a mud-wasp, or the fine dust from underneath a woven floor mat was used to aid in the drying out of the navel.

Plate 6.1 Grandmother Yim, a traditional birth attendant, plays with two of the children whose births she attended in 1992.

The treatment of the placenta affects the personality and health of the new child. When a woman has given birth at home, the placenta is carefully cleaned in warm water and then salt is applied to it. Salt is added, 'because the old people told us to put it in, to make it healthy or happy or something' (Grandmother Yim). The placenta is then wrapped and placed into a bamboo container and buried by the husband or the midwife in a place determined by the sex of the baby.[61]

In hospital, childbirth is a medical event controlled by doctors and nurses (Muecke 1976:381). The simple material culture of birth at home—knife, string, and herbal remedies—is replaced in hospital by impressive specialised technology, procedures, and surgical interventions. English technical language used by staff in hospitals keeps the birthing woman ignorant of medical procedures or the assessment of her condition. In the hospital, birth occurs under the care of anonymous trained nurses, without any family member present. The woman is dressed in a hospital gown, marking her status as a patient. Her abdomen, pelvis and perineum become the site of interventions. The lithotomy position was used in all the hospital births I observed. Women cannot see the baby when it emerges, nor see what the midwives are doing. They get to see their babies for the first time after they have been cleaned and accompanied back to the ward, at which point relatives are permitted to see the mother and child. After a short rest, the mother may have a 'wet' tubal ligation, or be examined and allowed to return to the village.

Western obstetrics organises birthing in terms of metaphors of efficient production and speed (Martin 1987). Such production metaphors fundamentally contradict the traditional Isan view of birthing as a process that occurs in an undefined length of time, under the auspices of the spirits. Birthing in hospital involved a high likelihood of interventions such as augmentation and episiotomy. Of 199 births at the District Hospital in 1992, 120 episiotomies were performed, representing 60.3 per cent of all births. Thirty-three women (16.6 per cent) were reported to have first or second degree tears (District Hospital records, 1992).

Few hospitals provide families with the placenta so that it can be buried according to tradition. In Ban Srisaket, women believed that staff at the nearby District Hospital throw away the placentas, with one woman suspicious that they were used by the nurses to feed fish in a nearby pond. Their comments recognise that hospital staff are dismissive of local practices and knowledge deemed 'traditional' and treat with disdain the desires of villagers to follow 'old' customs.

The role of men

In hospital births, husbands are not allowed to be present at the birth as it is considered inappropriate. In denying men active involvement in birth, health staff give explanations of the customary modesty of women. Nurses also say that men do not wish to be present. However, many women speaking of village births in the past spoke positively of the involvement of men in assisting a woman through labour. For example, Grandmother Jom held her husband's arms through her labour: 'I sat and held his arms. I held his arms and pushed my baby out.' Grandmother Sadau chuckled as she told of her daughter Thip's birth: 'She held onto her husband's shoulders. If she gave birth elsewhere she wouldn't be able to [give birth] if she didn't have her husband's shoulders. Who else could she grab but her husband? How did she hold around his neck without him dying?' As well as active involvement by husbands, women described calling upon male massage practitioners and spiritual specialists at times of crisis to assist with obstructed labour or when a woman was feared to be in danger from the actions of *phi* spirits. As they are capable of manipulating more powerful spiritual forces than women, male *mor tham* (spirit specialists) could assist when the traditional birth attendant had exhausted her knowledge. Men still assist in Ban Srisaket during the post-partum period: building the post-partum fire and bed, burying the placenta and helping with laundry and food preparation. The effect of hospital bans on kin being present at birth has been to deny male involvement in birth.

Relations of power enacted in hospital encounters

In their movement between the village and the hospital, women also move between different interpretive models of health and illness, and different relations of power. As Fiedler (1996:195) observes in her paper on Japan, 'the physical location of birth reflects and creates social territories' which affect the physical process of labour and women's experiences of it. The movements between the hospital and the village community likewise involves a movement between different 'social territories', and different systems of knowledge, practice and power relations. The issues of the social distance between women patients and health staff has been noted for numerous cultures, including Western settings.[62]

Within Ban Srisaket numerous stories circulate of the hospital staff's rudeness and lack of concern for patients. These criticisms of the care and service received in hospitals centre around the staff's failure to provide the nurturing relationship that is culturally expected of healers. During labour, hospital staff provide only minimal necessary care to patients and do not perform the many significant acts of nurturing expected of traditional midwives. In hospital, births are routine medical events, and attention through labour is reduced to occasional checks on the progress of labour and monitoring dilation, with greater attention concentrated upon the final stage of labour and the newborn. Unlike traditional midwives, hospital staff do not assist through massages or moral support, nor is food supplied for patients during their stay in hospital.

The demise of home birthing

Why then do women give birth in hospitals despite being critical of the uncaring attitude of the staff? An important motivation for giving birth in hospital is the understanding that childbirth is a dangerous and vulnerable time for both mother and child, and the perception promoted by the government that hospitals offer safer, 'modern' births. The danger of childbirth is well described in Isan lore. The woman giving birth is understood as especially vulnerable to a number of *phi* (malevolent spirits).[63] *Phi phai* spirits are attracted by blood, especially the blood of parturition. If a woman loses consciousness or has uncontrollable bleeding, these are signs that a *phi phai* has possessed her and is sucking her body dry. *Phi porp* are malevolent spirits that will invade the bodies of the weak and are also attracted to blood.[64] Women relate stories of friends and kin who died in childbirth. As Grandmother Sow said: '*samai korn* [in the past], many women died in childbirth. There were no doctors'. Grandmother Thee told me of her niece who died in childbirth:

> The child of Ii Joi was eaten by a *phi porp* which came and ate her blood. [If eaten by a *phi porp*] a woman doesn't have any strength, [she will be] tired. No blood or anything comes out. They just die.

Grandmother Yai still cries when she thinks of her daughter who died with an obstructed labour:

> There never used to be any hospital doctors in the old days. My daughter died when she gave birth to her first child. We couldn't get the child out. It was a very long time and we couldn't get the child out. Grandmother Dii was called. She was a *mor tam yae*. Then we went to Ban Don Ling and called the *mor nuat* [the massage doctor] to come and help. My daughter was twenty-nine. Both she and the baby died.

The demise of *mor tam yae* and birthing in the village reflects the extension of state health services and the hegemony of biomedical control over women's bodies and reproduction, but also the real risks of child-bearing as perceived by women. There is often an element of nostalgia in anthropologists' descriptions of non-Western maternity and home births (Ginsburg & Rapp 1991; Jolly 1998; Mallett forthcoming; Ram 1998). Romanticised visions of woman-centred maternity are evoked in implicit contrast to an image of demeaning, unauthentic, medicalised birthing in Western hospitals. Yet such romantic visions of non-Western maternity are countered by discussions with Isan women themselves who describe childbirth as a process posing life-threatening dangers, vulnerability and pollution. Romanticised accounts of traditional childbirth often overlook the difficulties women faced in the past and the high maternal and perinatal death rates they suffered (Jeffery & Jeffery 1993; Rozario 1998). Women from Ban Srisaket choose to give birth at hospitals to ensure a safe birth for themselves and their children. They are willing to endure the loneliness of birthing with strangers for the perceived safety that modern medical technology provides.

Other changes have also influenced the demise of home birthing and traditional midwifery. As mentioned earlier, the availability of free tubal ligations conducted within hours after one's second birth is an important motivation for giving birth in hospitals and is heavily encouraged by all levels of the government health system. The enormous success of state-sponsored family planning has provided a means of limiting family size but has also made pregnancy and birthing events that are experienced only once or twice by most women. With fewer births taking place in villages, there are also fewer opportunities for traditional birth attendants to practise their skills. Moreover, there is little government support for the continuance of the local traditions (see also Newman 1981).

Representation of TBAs and traditional knowledge

In 1978, WHO suggested the promotion of the training of traditional practitioners such as traditional birth attendants (TBAs), along with other traditional healers and medicines for incorporation into the primary health care system (Grand & Sri-ngernyuang 1989). This was in recognition that the health needs of women and children in many countries were not being met. An implicit assumption of the superiority of Western obstetrics was embedded in the early calls for the training and 'incorporation' or 'articulation' of TBAs into biomedical health systems by the WHO. In Thailand, attempts were made to train and incorporate TBAs into the primary health care system with the goal of reducing maternal and infant mortality by ensuring that ensuring that a trained attendant was present for all births. At the time, the public health care system was developing and unable to provide access to trained midwives. Traditional birthing practices were selectively incorporated into the Thai government health system through a system of training and exclusion which legitimated only some practices and subordinated traditional knowledge to biomedical knowledge. An aim of the training was to modify 'harmful' practices, replacing them with approved techniques, while retaining 'beneficial' and 'harmless' TBA practices (Verderese & Turnball 1975).

In Ban Srisaket, the six women who were chosen by health workers for training were not necessarily those who were practising as *mor tam yae* at the time of selection. Many of the women who were practising as traditional birth attendants were considered too old to be trained and were no longer encouraged to practise and younger women were selected. Women who gave birth ten to twenty years ago provided the names of eighteen women considered to be *mor tam yae*, apart from the grandmothers and aunts who helped women birth but were not considered *mor tam yae*. After training, only the six trained women were allowed to continue their practice.

Of these six women, only two continue to attend births, Grandmother Yim, now 64 years-old, and Grandmother Say, also in her sixties. All the other women have retired. Grandmother Huwat, a mother of six, had never practised as a midwife but was selected to be trained for five days in 1977 by a public health doctor from Roi Et. In 1991 she attended five births, but in 1992 she did not attend any as her eyesight had deteriorated. Now she simply refers women onto the nurse/midwife at the health station. However, women still come to her when they are seven or eight months pregnant for her to massage their womb and ascertain if the child will be male or female according to the shape and position of the foetus. She also continues to be called to lead women to sit by the fire after birth and visits each day for the first few days to check that the mother and child are well. Grandmother Wandii also trained in 1977 when she was 53 years-old. She only attended births for three years and now has retired. Like Grandmother Huwat, women continue to seek her advice on their pregnancies, for assistance with prolapses and to oversee the rituals of staying by the fire during the post-partum. She gave birth to nine surviving children from fifteen pregnancies with two miscarriages. Grandmother Saa, now in her late sixties, also had been trained at the district public health office to be a midwife, but has long since retired. Grandmother Bay is 60 years-old. She had six pregnancies and five surviving children. She learned from the old women how to be a *mor tam yae* and had helped deliver many children in the past, but now no longer practices.

In addition to these women, there is one woman who has practiced as a TBA in the past but has not been trained. Grandmother Sen, 60 years-old, is a *mor sen* (massage doctor). She is called upon by many people every day to manipulate and massage sore muscles. She has practiced for over twenty years and her skills are largely self-taught. She attended a massage doctor in Mahasarakham in her younger days and learned through observing and experiencing his massage and then by manipulating her own body and by observing the results. In addition to her massage services, she is called upon to assist with prolapses and sometimes asked to assist with abortions (although she denies involvement in this). She has attended births since 1972. She has not been trained but learned through watching her mother and elder sister who were *mor tam yae*. Although she did not attend a birth in 1992, she states she is available to do so if called upon.

The power relations involved in the representations of traditional practices revolve around issues of the legitimacy and control of authoritative knowledge. Giddens (1990) suggests that modern-society derives from a set of dominant institutional practices and structures through which power relations are established and sustained. One of these involves the transformation in the distribution of social and cultural knowledge. Under modernity, most everyday institutions and practices operate under 'expert' knowledge. Within health care, this can clearly be seen in the institutionalisation of expert knowledge in the form of Western biomedicine over other forms of local knowledge and subjective ways of knowing about the body. In discussions with medical staff about birthing they frequently recounted 'horror stories' of the dirty knives of the traditional midwives and their lack of education and ignorance of basic sanitation. The following narrative from Grandmother Yim relates an incident which highlighted the contested legitimacy of different sources of knowledge:

> Last year Ii Bai was giving birth [at home] and asked me to come to her. She was in labour a long time and I said to get the nurse from the *anamai* [the village health station] to come and see. [The nurse came] and said, 'Why has she been in labour for so long?' She was rude and criticised everything . . . I swore at her and said, 'You studied, you paid to study, I haven't paid to study, I'm stupid.' She refused to look after Ii Bai and left, saying to her, 'Look to Grandmother Yim, she's the one with the white-haired head.' She didn't want to help save her life. It took until the afternoon for her to push the baby out . . . [The nurse] persecuted me. She said, 'Don't dispute the old one!' . . . She said, 'Don't argue with the old one! The old one knows more than me!' She had a manner different to villagers. She came and called out, 'The old one has studied high already! The old one hasn't studied at all, but still she is higher than me!' She came and scolded, yelled at me. She said, 'If the pain comes, why don't you go and get a doctor, the doctor at the *anamai*!' She came and swore whilst the woman was in pain. She came saying this, saying that, she criticised the woman who was in labour. She came speaking like that and so I was angry with her.

This narrative is extraordinary for the public articulation of conflict in a society where open criticism is rare. The body of the woman in labour became the center of a contest between the different systems of knowledge and practice, and of conflicts over traditional values of respect for elders. Traditional authoritative knowledge, embodied in the elderly, white-haired midwife, conflicts with the 'modern' scientific knowledge of the nurse. The nurse's criticism violates Grandmother Yim's view of herself as a skilled elder woman worthy of respect from the community, with authority derived from her age, experience, knowledge of ritual practices and remedies. Instead, the sarcastic criticisms by the nurse challenge Grandmother Yim's knowledge and authority, and suggest that Grandmother Yim is ignorant and harmful. Both Grandmother Yim and the nurse 'lose face' in this encounter. At stake is the legitimacy of opposing systems of authoritative knowledge and cultural capital.

Plate 6.2 Twi stays by the fire in 1992. Above the fire hangs a pot of hot *ya tom* tonic for drinking and bathing. The bamboo pole prevents Twi from accidentally rolling into the fire while sleeping.

The persistence of post-partum practice

Twi lies by a fire in the large area downstairs where food is normally prepared (Plate 6.2). She gave birth two days ago to a girl. She is dressed in an old dark *phasin* with another piece of black cloth over her breasts, a stark contrast to her pale skin. She massages her breasts as she sits on a small narrow plank that serves as her bed, less than a metre from the low fire made from some thick logs. She looks tired and pale, sweat rolling down her forehead. It is very hot, as outside temperatures are close to forty degrees centigrade, the height of the hot season. In front of the fire are bamboo poles that form a barrier against Twi accidentally rolling into it. Nearby, over a charcoal fire sits a large pot with *ya tom* (boiled medicine) bubbling inside. A thermos of hot water is also nearby as are the packets of pills, paracetamol, antibiotics and iron supplements given by the hospital. I ask how long she will stay by the fire. She replies that she does not know yet.

'Oei! Pen ta sang! [How disgusting!]', we say when we see her newborn girl, so the spirits won't want to take the child away. She lies on a pillow outside on a bamboo platform, underneath a mosquito net, little sack-like gloves on her hands to stop her from scratching herself. We tie her wrists, 'May you have health, happiness, wealth and be as beautiful as your mother!'(Fieldnotes 1992).

The authority of biomedical and traditional knowledge is contextually and spatially bound. Despite the dominance of biomedical models of birth, women assert traditional knowledge and practice during the post-partum period. In doing so they affirm the importance of this period for Isan women as a period with important consequences for their strength and health and as incorporating rites marking their ethnic and feminine identity. As it is a time relatively ignored by biomedical models of birth, it remains a space in which traditional knowledge remains ascendant. In contrast to the strong encouragement given to women to attend antenatal clinics, there is little emphasis placed upon women having a postnatal check-up and, according to the records of the village health station and hospital interviews, only a few village women ever have post-partum examinations. For most women the next contact they are likely to have with medical staff is when they bring their child to the local primary health clinic for its first immunisation. The relative lack of biomedical supervision and surveillance of women during this time creates a space for the assertion of local practices and knowledge. The persistence of local modes of care during the post-partum period not only underline the continued influence and authority of older female kin, but constitutes a form of defence of local practice against the hegemony of Western medical discourse. As Ginsburg and Rapp have noted (1995b) reproduction may be a site of defence of cultural identity (see also Sesia 1996). Post-partum practice is an important site of the continuance of local identity, asserted despite biomedical warnings about its possible ill-effects.

Various modes of post-partum care remain important for women in a range of different cultures as opposed to its relatively unelaborated position in Western biomedical practice. Post-partum warming designed to redress the 'cold' condition caused by childbirth has enduring importance in a number of cultures in South and Southeast Asia with humoral medical traditions.[65]

For Isan women the post-partum period is elaborately marked by beliefs and practices which represent the post-partum state as one of vulnerability for both mother and child. It is a time characterised by a reduction of household and work responsibilities, minimal social interactions, and support from female kin. Despite being told by nurses and doctors that it is not necessary and may be detrimental, most women take the advice of their mothers and female kin and assert the importance of staying by the fire and observing post-partum food restrictions and rituals. At the village health station some women avoid answering when the local nurse/midwife asks if they stayed by the fire after birth or are restricting their diet; in doing so they resist the biomedical profession's disapproval of such practices, and assert local authoritative knowledge, traditions and values.

The practice of *yu kam* or *yu fai*[66] involves a period of lying close to a constantly burning fire for a period that varies from five to eleven days (see descriptions in Irvine 1982; Mougne 1978; Poulsen 1983). This practice has been termed 'mother roasting' which implies a roaring fire. In reality, the fire is kept quite small and at times reduced to warm coals. A more appropriate description would be that of 'staying by the fire', rather than 'roasting'. Throughout her confinement the mother is encouraged to drink warm water and herbal medicine as well as to wash in the mixture.[67] Antibiotics, pain killers, patent herbal medicines called *ya satri* (women's medicine) bought at the local village store, or Chinese herbs bought from Roi Et, are often used in conjunction with local remedies. The longer one can stay by the fire the more efficacious it is said to be. As Grandmother Say explains, women are encouraged to maintain the practice despite the discomfort to ensure their strength and to make the mother 'ripe' or matured:

> You should stay for the full time! If you don't stay like this your body won't be strong after you leave the fire, it makes you strong quickly. When you stay by the fire you should stay like we did in the past and drink hot water all the time . . . On the first day you shouldn't allow the fire to be hot. If five or six days have passed, then it can be very hot and you must persevere and endure the roasting and the toasting; that's when you want to leave. On the first day . . . you shouldn't let the fire be too strong or else you'll be toasted like a roasted toad . . . if you let it be strong, you'll be scorched, almost burnt, you'll be burnt before you are made *suk* [ripe] by the fire.

The warming effects of the fire, combined with drinking herbal tonics, is understood to cleanse the womb of the accumulated 'bad blood', lochia and waste fluids that have built up in the body throughout the pregnancy. If these poisonous fluids are not expelled, they will stay within the body for the rest of a woman's life and cause weakness and chills (see also Chirawatkul 1996; Jirojwong 1996). It is also said to flatten and tighten the belly of the newly parturient mother and ensure the correct position of the uterus, help remove stretch marks, heal perineal tears, and make her beautiful with clean, clear skin. Combined with massage, staying by the fire is said to help women to produce an ample supply of breast milk, as it makes the woman's body *suk* (ripe). Women believe that if they do not *yu fai,* they may suffer from long term problems with their *mot luk* (womb) as a result. Most women who suffer from abdominal pain, weakness, dizziness or reproductive tract symptoms, such as discharge or prolapse, attribute their symptoms in part as a result of inadequate time spent staying by the fire. If a woman does not dry out her uterus after childbirth, it remains wet and cold, causing cold to rise to the head causing wind symptoms of headache, dizziness and in some cases madness (Irvine 1982; Muecke 1979). Without the action of the fire to cause the uterus to return to its original position, it may move down and prolapse. A 'wet' uterus also may become 'bad' leading to a range of symptoms and eventual development of cancer. Over a quarter of women in a recent study felt their current reproductive health problems were the result of inadequate *yu fai* (Boonmongkon et al. 1998). Some women said that drying out the womb also helped delay another pregnancy too soon after the present birth. Thus *yu fai* is an important health practice with consequences for women's continued health, strength and fertility. Although women may substitute the consumption of 'hot' herbal medicines such as *ya satri* (see discussion in Chapter 3 and 7), or are told by doctors that the injections and antibiotics given after birth replace *yu fai*, women agree that they are a poor substitute.

Post-partum practices also involve dietary restrictions. Consumption of particular foods and avoidance of others is a prophylactic measure observed throughout the post-partum period. Some foods are considered to be *phit* (harmful, poisonous) for a woman after childbirth and so are *khalum*, a term which refers to the range of restricted behaviours for post-partum women. However, the foods considered dangerous to women during their confinement differ from village to village and from individual to individual, as seen in Table 6.2 which lists the foods identified as potentially dangerous by a variety of informants in Ban Srisaket and other villages. For example, some women consider chicken dangerous, while others do not. Villagers believe that some women have particular constitutions which allow them to partake of some foods which cause ill effects for other women. The most consistently and frequently mentioned foods that are avoided across Isan is *phak kha* (galangal) and the strong smelling herb *cha orm* (*Acacia pennata*). Eating, touching or even smelling such foods might cause nausea, headaches, vomiting, diarrhoea, and long-term weakness and ill-health. In Ban Srisaket, such a condition is termed *lom phit* (afflicting wind) due to the disruption and movement of the wind element in women's bodies, which may rise up to the head causing madness or even death (see descriptions in Irvine 1982; Mougne 1978; Muecke 1979). In other areas of Isan, this condition is called *phit krabun* (womb toxin).

The effects of these foods may continue for the rest of a woman's life. For example, Grandmother Im described the effects of eating grilled quail as *gin phit* (eating a food that is wrong/poisonous) for her. When her daughter was seven years-old she ate some grilled quail and suffered dizziness, severe headache and stomach ache. She boiled water with a type of fern called *wan phit mae luk on* (poison of mothers of young children fern). She drank the mixture which caused her to vomit twice and then she was cured. There are a number of different reasons for categorising foods as *khalam*. As a woman is considered to be in a cold state after birth, some of the foods avoided are 'cold' foods, and some of the fishes are considered to be 'itchy' foods that would make the skin and vagina of the woman itch. The prohibitions also operate through metaphorical associations. *Mengda* beetles *(Lethocerus indicus)* and fermented fish have strong smells and are said to possibly cause strong-smelling discharge and affect the quality of the breastmilk. One informant also spoke of avoiding foods that are *yang* (sappy), that included fruits such as jackfruit *(Artocarpus integra)*. They may cause the 'bad' lochia to remain stuck in the womb.[68]

Foods which may be eaten include sticky rice with salt, toasted sticky rice cake, rice soup with salt and fish sauce, sour fish soup with banana flowers, small amounts of grilled fish, rat and mice, and garlic, ginger, lime, tamarind, as well as medicinal tonics. Some people also permit the consumption of grilled chicken or pork. As Laderman found in her study of Malay post-partum diets, many foods in the unmarked, 'safe' categories are those essential for life, whereas foods in the 'dangerous' categories are supplementary foods that are easily removed or reduced in the diet (Laderman 1983:70).

Even discussions about *khalum* reveal perceptions about the differences between women's bodies in the past and the present. Older women said that when they stayed by the fire, they were only allowed to eat *khaw ji* (grilled sticky rice cakes) and salt supplemented with a little dried fish and banana flower and fish soup. According to Grandmother Say, in the past women were more vulnerable to the ill effects of foods after giving birth. Now with modern medicine, birthing in hospital and a more comfortable lifestyle, she rationalises that young women are stronger after birth than her generation.

> In the past we didn't let them eat roast chicken or things with rice, we were scared it would be wrong for their bodies. Now these young ones eat only roasted chicken, anything roasted! We ate only rice and salt, vegetables, never roasted crab or chicken...My generation, we didn't get fat, we never got bigger bodies. We never had medicine to eat; so we could only eat rice and salt. We were very tired all over when we stayed by the fire because we always used to do all our work ourselves . . . Nowadays, we let them eat roast crab, roast fish, anything, we let our daughters eat it all and it doesn't matter at all. I tell them they are strong and they don't have anything wrong. I tell them to eat everything and drink lots of water, each day eight glasses at least. I just don't let them eat fatty foods, pickled foods or strong salty or 'hot' foods.

Paradoxically, at the same time as some biomedical interventions are said to strengthen young women's bodies, making them capable of eating a range of

Table 6.2 List of foods restricted by various informants during post-partum period.

Foods to be avoided post-partum		
Thai/Isan name		English/Scientific Name
Plants	phak kha	galangal, *Languas Galanga SW.*
	phrik	chillies
	thua yau	long beans
	phak kachet	water mimosa, *Neptunia Oberacea*
	makheua	eggplants, *Solanum melongena* L.
	horm	shallot, *Allium ascalonium* L.
	katiam	garlic
	phak	any vegetables/grasses
	nomai	bamboo, *Bambusa arundinacea Willd.* And other *Bambusa spp.*
Animal	nua khwai phai	white buffalo meat
	nua khwai	buffalo meat
	nong khwai	buffalo placenta
	khai ping	roasted eggs/ any eggs
	pet	duck
	nua nok	any bird meat excluding chicken
	kai	chicken
	nok khum	type of quail
	nu	rats/ mice
	mengda	giant water bug, *Lethocerus indicus*
Fish	pla bu	sand goby, *Oxyeleotris marmoratus*
	pla duk	walking catfish, *Clarias batrachus* or *Clarias macrocephalus*
	pla ikam	morulius
	pla khor	striped snake-head fish, *Channa striatus*
	pla lat	*Notopterus notopterus*
	pla suay	*Pangsius sutchi*
	pla thu	mackeral, *Rastrelliger chryozonus*
Other	phak dorng	pickled vegetables
	khong dorng	pickled/hot/salty foods
	phet/khem	
	luk jin	Chinese meat-balls
	pla det	fermented fish, strong smelling
	tam mak hung /som tam	papaya salad contains *pla det* and is very hot and considered 'itchy'

foods after birth, other biomedical interventions such as tubal ligations are said to weaken them. In such ways, the customs regarding birth and the post-partum are being re-interpreted and negotiated with reference to both local discourses of women's health and 'modern' medical discourse and practice.

The continued importance of post-partum practices for women has been disputed by some writers who suggest that it is dying out in Thailand.[69] Assertions that the practice is in decline appear to be influenced by an assumption of the inevitability of a loss of traditions within the context of modernisation. Rather, the picture is more complex with variation in practice across different regions and between rural and urban areas. Field data confirm the persistence of the practice of post-partum *yu kam* in Ban Srisaket. In a survey I conducted in 1992, 83 per cent of women 15–24 years-old reported staying by the fire for their first birth. As a comparison, 88 per cent of women over 45 years reported staying by the fire for their first birth (see Table 6.3). Fewer women stay by the fire for second births than in the past because of the popularity of tubal ligations after the second birth, but the importance of staying by the fire after the first birth remains.

Table 6.3 Percentage of women who stayed by the fire for their first birth and the number of days spent, by age groups, Ban Srisaket.

Age groups (years)	Per cent of women who stayed by the fire, (1st birth)	Average number of days spent by the fire
> 45	86.7%	7.67
36-45	88.9%	8.86
26-35	77.8%	8.38
15-25	82.4%	7.45

SOURCE: Birthing survey 1992, 1993 (n=87).

Ten of the twelve women who did not practise *yu kam* in 1992 had stayed by the fire after their first birth, but did not for the current child as they had tubal ligations immediately after the birth. The reasons are not clear as to why women do not practise staying by the fire after tubal ligations. Muecke reports that in Northern Thailand the perception that hospital birthing affords greater protection to mother and child reduces the imperative to observe the custom as conscientiously as their mothers may have done in the past (Muecke 1976:381). However, this observation does not explain the persistence of the practice in Ban Srisaket for first births, the majority of which also take place in hospitals. Ban Srisaket women offered a different explanation. They stated that doctors warn women against staying by the fire because it will make the surgery scar *aksaep* (infected) through the heat of the fire. Such a notion is consistent with humoral notions of the action of the fire, in the local Lao language the term *aksaep* implies a notion of inflammation and overheating. Staying by the fire is also said to be unnecessary after a tubal ligation, as there is no further need to dry out the womb and delay the next birth. Health workers confirm that they discourage women from staying by the fire after sterilisation for fear that some sutures may dissolve prematurely due to the heat of the fire (Boonmongkon et al. 1998). Women do take tonics *(ya satri)*, and use other practices as substitutes for the fire after tubal ligations, but observe that these are a poor substitute for the effects of the fire. Although the injections and antibiotics from the hospital are said to strengthen women, most women in Ban Srisaket suggest that they suffer long-term weakness these days because *bor dai yu fai lang het man* (they were not able to stay by the fire after a tubal ligation). Inadequate time spent by the fire makes them unable to properly correct the cold imbalance in their bodies nor fully cleanse their wombs of dangerous lochia.

Although women consider *yu kam* as inconvenient and unpleasant and some do suffer burns and heat rashes, the persistence of the practice after first births draws attention to the meanings of the practice for the continued fertility of women and is an important aspect of their identity. Apart from the health benefits it is understood to impart, the practice persists owing to its social significance as a rite of passage marking the achievement of mature adult status. Hanks (1963:71) suggests that staying by the fire in Central Thailand is regarded as 'care and treatment', but also regarded as 'one of the series of rites of the life cycle which marked the course of an individual from birth to death,' through which a woman attains full maturity. She writes that to stay by the fire:

> perfected her [the mother] as a human being; restored and strengthened her body; improved her capacities as a nourisher; and strengthened her own *khwan* (soul) . . . As one man explained, 'the very nature of water is changed by boiling over a fire. It becomes *suk* (ripe)'. Similarly a woman's body, her very nature, was permanently changed to *suk* by the fire's heating. The fire, in fact, made *suk* all the food she ate beside it. Since this food was turned into milk, her breast milk became *suk* and so more nourishing, and did not disturb elements (Hanks 1963:73-4; see also Keyes 1984:229).

The term *yu kam* used for staying by the fire in the North-east may be translated as 'being/living in karma.' Keyes notes that the same term is used in Northern Thailand to describe both a period of seclusion observed by newly ordained monks for three days and a traditional rite which involves monks withdrawing to a cremation ground to meditate on the dissolution of the physical body (Keyes 1986:81,94). For both men and women, the use of the term implies a threshold marking a significant change in one's karma or destiny and the fulfilment of that destiny. Just as the suffering of labour and staying by the fire prepares women for their new status as mothers and makes them *suk*, so the denial and discipline of ordination is said to make men *suk* and prepare them for the responsibilities of marriage and fatherhood (Hanks 1963:71; Keyes 1986). Post-partum practice persists not only because of its benefits for women's health but also because of the symbolic significance of the period of seclusion and regulation as a marker of female maturity.

Social recognition of the newborn child

Tell the *phi phai* and the *phi pau*
The white bird sings '*Ku ku ku kuu*',
If this is truly a spirit child
Then come take it this day,
For after today it is mine!
(local saying at birth, my translation 1993).

Another post-partum practice is that which marks the social recognition of the newborn child. This ritual continues within the village despite the large proportion of women giving birth in hospital settings (see also Poulsen 1983:194). Only three women did not have the ceremony in 1992, all of whom delivered in hospitals. One woman said, 'you don't do that when you are delivered by a doctor'.

The newborn child is placed onto a small kapok mattress in a flat woven basket normally used for breeding silkworms, a *kradong morn*. This basket is rotated three times as an elder woman or midwife recites the chant above three times and then hits the basket three times with a knife. This rite informs the spirits that the child is claimed as a human child. The knife is used to scare the spirits away.

The newborn remains on the *kradong* on a small kapok mattress for three days. Some women swaddle the child, placing the child on its back and straightening out the legs. A book and a pencil are usually placed on the *kradong* with the baby, so that the child will be adept at school (see Plate 6.3). Sometimes a knife is placed beside the child to protect it from the spirits and to ensure the child will work hard in later life. Women said that in the past a sickle and knife for boys, and a sickle and sewing needle for girls, would be placed beside the child.

After birth the midwife or a respected elder will be called to come and chase away the *phi* that may come and harm mother and child. Grandfather On, a *mor tham* (spirit doctor), was asked to come to *lai phi* (chase the spirits) and to tie protective cotton threads around Thoei who had just given birth to a newborn son. She had given birth at the district hospital the day before and her son lay asleep on a silkworm basket. On top of the baby's blankets was a

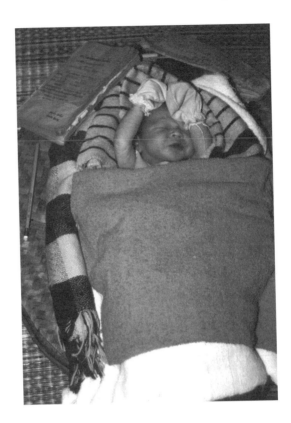

Plate 6.3 Twi's newborn baby lies on the *kradong* with schoolbooks and a pencil at her head to make her successful at her future education. Her hands are covered to prevent her from scratching herself.

bowl containing *khaw san* (raw dehusked rice), five flowers and cotton thread. Grandfather On chanted in Pali and in Lao as he tied the baby's wrists. He then chanted some more as he proceeded to scatter rice in the room where the baby would sleep, upstairs and around the outside of the house, to chase the spirits away. Then Grandfather tied both wrists of the mother. Other elders came and tied the baby's wrists and also Grandfather's wrists. Then the elder men sat to eat rice and sip rice whisky together. The women sat together admiring the sleeping infant.

Through rituals such as these traditional standards of correct behaviour regarding birthing are reasserted within the social context of village society. They mark the social recognition of the newborn as a human member of the community.

Bearing tradition and modernity

The continuation of post-partum practices draws attention to the contestation of power involved in the relationships between 'traditional' and 'modern' knowledge and practices. The persistence of post-partum rituals in the village draws attention to the need to analyse reproductive health behaviour through an approach that includes the agency of people and incorporates an appreciation of the political and historical processes at individual, social and national levels that shape the social construction of reproduction. Women assert their agency in making choices about where and how they choose to give birth and which practices are meaningful for them. However, this process is not a simple exercise of choice within a pluralistic health system but rather takes place within unequal relations of power between the institutionalised biomedical state health system and local practices and knowledge. The concept of pluralism needs to be expanded to account for differential power relations implicit in the choices people make between different therapies, knowledge and practice.

Further, an examination of birthing and post-partum practice suggests the importance of context and place in discussions of medical systems of knowledge. As this chapter has shown, while women appreciate the safer motherhood provided through the extension of biomedical services, they also assert the importance of post-partum traditions in defiance of biomedical advice, and in doing so resist the total subordination of their identity within the modern Thai state. Women are able to resist disparaging constructions of Isan people in certain contexts and spaces. For example, the persistence of the practice of staying by the fire within the village draws attention to the importance of place as socially constructed and politicised (Rodman 1992). As Scott has argued, acts of resistance to 'symbolic incorporation' are often spatially discrete, usually occurring within the village realm where the 'mask of obsequiousness, deference, and symbolic compliance *may* be lifted . . . a social space in which the definitions and performances imposed by domination do not prevail' (1985:328).

Within the spatial confines of the village, healing rituals and practices are not only practical health behaviours, but an assertion of cultural identity and meanings not accessible through biomedical practices. In this regard the fact that practices such as staying by the fire are maintained in the village setting is a significant statement of the importance of context and place in the construction of health meanings and practice.

7 More painful than birth: Abortion

(Summary from District Hospital medical records, 1997)

19/04/97

Patient aged 28 years presented to hospital at 3.00 a.m. with fever, abdominal pain and acute bleeding per vagina. Age of pregnancy, 12 weeks plus 5 days, patient said she had an abortion one day before by an illegal practitioner in his clinic at Chaiyaphum who gave her a single injection per vagina. She presented to hospital after experiencing fever and heavy bleeding

12:00 noon: Patient appears weak, complains of vertigo, shivering. Vital signs: Temperature 38°C, Blood Pressure 100/70, Pulse 96/min., Respiratory rate 39/min. Medication: Paracetamol, 1 amp stat, IV fluids. Medical Officer prescribed Valium, 5 mg, also Floxacillan[70] 500 mg, Metronidazole 250 mg, Bactrim 2 amp. Continue to observe condition.

8.00 p.m.: Vital signs: Temperature, patient has fever 40.4°C, given Paracetamol, 1000 mg stat and other medications as prescribed plus give lots of fluids. Patient has pain, tenderness, given sanitary pads to observe bleeding. Changing pads frequently as they are soaked through…

10.00 p.m. Temperature dropped to 39°C. Patient complains of abdominal pain. Pad is changed twice. Bleeding is black in colour with a fishy smell. Pad changed to continue to observe bleeding . . .

20/04/97

6.00 a.m. Temperature 39.8°C. Given Paracetamo! 1000 mg, and given further IV fluid. Has normal bleeding. Changed pad, allowed to rest, given medicine, Blood Pressure 110/70. Condition much improved . . .

21/04/97

6.00 a.m. Vital signs: normal, no fever, no bleeding, no pain in abdomen, Blood Pressure 90/60. Condition appears good, pain in abdomen, slight yellow discharge, able to walk and conduct own hygiene by herself. Rest in semi-position.

23/04/97

6.00 a.m. No fever, resting, able to care for herself, no vertigo and no bleeding per vagina, no abdominal pain. Given 5% normal saline fluid, another 1000cc. Vital signs: normal. Doctor assessed condition and gave permission for patient to be discharged. Patient supplied with medicines to continue at home . . .

These hospital records tell a story repeated daily across Thailand: women resorting to illegal abortions conducted by untrained practitioners, leading to complications and the need for hospitalisation. The question of abortion in Thailand lies at the core of the state control of women's bodies and reproduction, and the cultural and social meanings of gender and reproduction. Abortion is illegal in Thailand unless under restricted circumstances. Despite the illegalities, field and hospital-based studies in Thailand suggest that induced abortions are common, with over 200 000 to 300 000 performed each year by a variety of methods, with a high number performed inadequately resulting in complications including injury, infection, infertility and maternal death (Chaturachinda et al. 1981; Population Council 1981; Koetsawang, Saha, & Pachauri 1978; Ladipo 1989; Narkavonnakit 1979a; Narkavonnakit & Benett 1981). As Germain writes, the question of access to safe abortion services is important to women's health status throughout the world:

an estimated 200 000 or more Third World women die needlessly every year due to botched abortions. Additional uncounted thousands suffer severe morbidity, including infertility and chronic health problems due to unsafe clandestine abortions. . . (1989:1).

The title of this chapter follows from interviews with women who have had abortions. Many described their experiences as 'more painful than birth', a statement reflecting not only the physical pain they suffered, but the emotional pain their decision to abort involved. This chapter explores this vexed issue. I begin by describing the legal and ideological context in which abortions occur. Then I describe the various abortion techniques utilised by women in Northeast Thailand, exploring their connection to reproductive and general health practices. I describe the slippage between abortion as such, and efforts at menstrual regulation and the social and ethical implications of these cultural categorisations. Finally I place the stories of women who have had abortions within a broader analysis of gender and the power relations that structure sexuality and women's reproductive health decisions. I explore the conflict within Thailand between the state goal of population stabilisation and female reproductive health rights within the context of Buddhist values which oppose abortion and affirm traditional gender and family structures. As was apparent at the International Conference on Population and Development in Cairo, such issues remain concerns for many developed and developing countries (Johnson 1995).

In every society the meanings of sexuality, contraception, pregnancy, maternity and abortion change through history and cannot be separated from relations of power (Ginsburg 1989; Luker 1975; Luker 1984; Petchesky 1990). Recent works by Sobo (1996), Cecil, (1996) and the collection of papers edited by Rylko-Bauer (1996), demonstrate how the meanings surrounding reproduction and abortion and pregnancy loss are shaped by the sociocultural and historical context and issues of class and gender. Similarly, social conflicts over abortion in Thailand are affected by and serve to symbolise broader economic, social and ideological concerns over women's status and roles—including competing constructions of gender, sexuality and motherhood. State policies, institutional religion, traditional and modern constructions of gender and the material conditions of women and men's lives all influence reproductive health decisions.

The issue of abortion thus also poses an important question about the nature of the agency of individuals within relations of power. The study of the politics of reproduction has focused upon the intersections between the interests of states and powerful institutions such as international corporations, development agencies, Western medicine, and religious groups, as they construct the local contexts in which reproductive decision-making takes place (Ginsburg & Rapp 1995a). Such institutions are centrally involved in the production and dissemination of discourses concerning the management and disciplining of women's bodies. This analysis emerges in Foucault's notion of 'bio-power' and from feminist theorists of women's bodies as the sites of, and expression of, power relations (Bailey 1993:102). But the exercise of power is not absolute. The possibility of resistance draws attention to the agency of individuals and the ways in which they fashion their lives and identities. As Bordo writes, 'even the most subordinated subjects are therefore continually confronted with opportunities for resistance, for making meanings that oppose or evade the dominant ideology' (Bordo 1993:193).

But recently a number of writers have critically examined the notion of resistance. Lewin suggests that the term resistance is being too loosely used by anthropologists, who have been over-eager to accept 'the discovery of evidence of indirect or unconscious resistance' (Lewin 1998:164). Similarly, Abu-Lughod has criticised anthropologists' romantic notions of resistance as desire to show that subordinated people are not unreflective passive objects of power but find ways to respond critically to their situation (1990). As Kielmann suggests, a central theoretical question is 'how does one investigate the ways in which women's bodily knowledge and practices are limited through asymmetrical power structures and at the same time treat women as knowledgeable actors in the constitution of social life?' (Kielmann 1998:135). She suggests that resistance needs to be defined in terms of intention, that the meanings of resistance can only be attributed when women themselves envisage the possibility of options diverting from orthodox frameworks of meaning surrounding the body (Kielmann 1998:136). But Lock and Kaufert problematise this notion of intention, arguing that resistance rarely takes the form of public demands for reform but is shaped through practice and within the existing moral order while simultaneously involving a re-imagining and challenge to that order (Lock & Kaufert 1998). Further, Lock questions whether the responses of individuals are always reactive, that they may not be actions of compliance or resistance, but pragmatic actions as individuals strategically negotiate networks of power (Lock 1998:208). Issues of resistance and agency inform the discussion throughout this chapter.

In Thailand, studies of abortion remain within the realm of demographic surveys and descriptive case studies. Primarily shaped by a public health perspective, these studies are concerned with rates of the incidence of abortion, the health consequences and measures of risk, morbidity and mortality characteristics of women who abort, correlations with contraceptive use and family planning, and the practices and characteristics of abortion practitioners.[71] The majority of research on the issue in Thailand has coincided with debate about the laws and policies concerning abortion that occurred in the 1980s when there was a significant push to amend Thailand's restrictive abortion laws. A number of these studies surveyed the social acceptability of abortion under various circumstances, and have provided important public health information to support the amendments and documented the incidence of women resorting to illegal abortions.[72]

Table 7.1 Summary of abortion legislation in Thailand.

Section 301- an offence for a woman who causes an abortion to herself or allows another to procure an abortion for her. The penalty is 6000 baht or 3 years jail, or both

Section 302 – punishment for the administrator of an abortion or procurer. Maximum fine of 20 000 baht or 10 years jail if it results in the death of the woman

Section 303 – procuring or administering an abortion without consent. Maximum fine of 40 000 baht or 20 years if causes woman's death

Section 304 - exempts from prosecution unsuccessful or unfinished abortion attempts

Section 305 - allows abortion to be performed if performed by medical practitioner and necessary for a woman's health, or because the pregnancy is due to offences such as rape, seduction of girl under fifteen, fraud, deceit, violence, etc. in the procuration or seduction.

SOURCE: (Population Council 1981)

Recent history of abortion debate in Thailand

Abortion is illegal in Thailand unless performed by a medical practitioner for the sake of a woman's health or if the pregnancy is the result of rape, or unlawful sexual contact as defined in other clauses of the Criminal Code (Population Council 1981:101-102). Prosecutions of women procuring abortions and the practitioners and owners of clinics remain common. As in the rest of the world, in Thailand the issue of abortion remains controversial. Several attempts have been made to amend the abortion laws and each has sparked emotive debate. The current law on abortion in Thailand has existed since 1957 under the Penal Code, without amendment. In September 1981, the House of Representatives passed the Abortion Bill sponsored by the Member for Parliament for Nakhon Si Thammarat Supatra Masdit, by 79 votes to 3. This allowed the amendment of Section 305 of the Penal Code to broaden circumstances permitting legal abortion (Anonymous 1981c; Anonymous 2524 (1981)b). Senator Chamlong Srimuang attacked the passing of the bill.

At that time he was Secretary-General to the Prime-Minister, prominent member of the Buddhist Santi Asoke movement and Vice-president of the Buddhist Association of Thailand. He led a powerful anti-abortion lobby which launched an intensive and emotive campaign against the passing of the Bill by the Senate (Anonymous 1981a; Anonymous 1981b).

In December 1981, the amended Bill was rejected by the Senate by a vote of 147 to 1 (Anonymous 1981d; Anonymous 2524 (1981)a; Anonymous 2524 (1981)c). Attempts by the Prachakorn Thai and Prachachart parties to reintroduce the bill in February 1983 failed again under pressure from Senator Chamlong. It was again resubmitted in April 1988, but Chamlong's opposition to the bill was firmly supported by a coalition of religious groups and the issue faded again. In April 1990 Chamlong's Palang Tham party again provided heated opposition to consideration of the bill once again. But while it was awaiting scheduling on the House agenda, the Chatichai government was ousted in a no-confidence vote (McDonnell & Sukpanich 1996). In February 1996, the Thai Medical Council again lobbied parliament to make amendments to the Bill to allow abortions in the cases of pregnancies where the child might be born mentally retarded or in the case of HIV-positive mothers, but such changes are yet to be debated and ratified (Anonymous 1996; Tansubhapol 1997).

Abortion rhetoric in Thailand

Representations of abortion in Thailand are dominated by sensational police raids, public humiliation of women seeking abortions and strong public rhetoric. A typical example of anti-abortion rhetoric is that produced by The Buddhist Association of Thailand as part of the lobbying campaign headed by Chamlong in 1981 against the passing of the abortion law amendments. A booklet produced during the campaign was titled *Tham thaeng . . . khong sut-thai haeng haiyanatham* (Abortion: The last curve on the road to moral catastrophe). This booklet was published three times during the period from 1 November to 3 December with a total print run of 20 000 copies. It consists of a series of essays by prominent Buddhists such as Chamlong, who wrote the introduction, and several eminent monks. Throughout the booklet, graphic images of aborted foetuses are juxtaposed with that of a smiling baby and of wanton Western women enjoying bars, gambling and materialism. The argument throughout the text declares that abortion is the antithesis of Buddhist beliefs in the sanctity of life and is therefore un-Thai. As Chamlong states in his introduction:

'This [abortion business] should not arise in a religious country like Thailand, the world centre of Buddhism.' It constructs abortion as a product of corrupt Western materialism and its ascendancy over

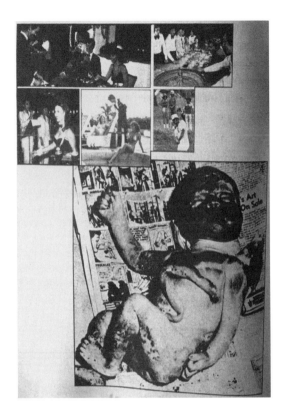

Plate 7.1 An image from the booklet *Tham thaeng . . . khong su-thai haeng haianatham* (Abortion: the last curve on the road to moral catastrophe) showing a dead foetus juxtaposed with images of a decadent western lifestyle. Such images appear throughout the book.

spirituality in the present age (*Kong-thap tham mulanithi* 1981:11).

Lurid images construct abortion as a symptom of a morally corrupt society. The themes within this literature occur repeatedly not only in anti-abortion material, but in other media accounts of abortion.

Another theme appealed to in anti-abortion rhetoric is that of the sanctity of motherhood as opposed to imagery of women as whores. In this same booklet photos of beautiful, smiling, pregnant mothers are juxtaposed with pictures of mangled foetuses. Sithsatcha writes:

Alas, nowadays we have the spectacle of women referred to as mothers, being given the legal right to kill their innocent unborn children. If this nightmare becomes a reality the word 'mother' will no longer mean anything at all. Henceforth, how much will the glory [*sak*] and rights inherent in motherhood diminish and become tarnished? We have become so ruthless with our own flesh and blood, what remains precious to us and how can we live together in peace? (In *Kong-thap tham mulanithi* 1981:35, translated by Scot Barme).

The issue of abortion within this rhetoric becomes a potent symbol of the failures of Thai democracy, and of social and moral corruption.

Although several women's groups and the Thai Medical Council argue for amendments to the present laws, their voices struggle to compete with the sophisticated campaigns waged by the anti-abortion lobby. Women's groups seek to disassociate the debate from the emotive religious rhetoric by recasting abortion as a public health issue. The women's groups calling for change, such as Friends of Women and Foundation for Women, are often depicted by the anti-abortion lobby as radical feminists who support free abortion (*tham thaeng seri*) and give an image of this as completely unregulated access to abortion at any stage of pregnancy. Although they attempt to distance themselves from such a construction, this remains a common conception of their position on the issue.

Women' s experiences of abortion

Women's reproductive decisions are thus the centre of a debate about the nature of Thai society, the role of Buddhism in Thai society, the role of women and the leadership of the state. Little space is given to the women's experiences, their reasons or their pain. Images of women lying on hospital beds, or arrested by police, do little to explain the lived experience of abortion and the complexity of women's reproductive decision-making. Yet from a survey I conducted in 1997, unplanned pregnancies are a common dilemma for women. Of the 164 rural women surveyed between the ages of 15 and 45 years, 41 (24 per cent) had had unplanned pregnancies and 11 per cent had an unplanned pregnancy while using a contraceptive. Of the 41 women who had unplanned pregnancies, 23 (56 per cent) took no action, and the remaining 18 women (44 per cent) attempted abortions through various means, some successfully, some not. The survey sample was predominated by married women (98 per cent had ever been married and 92 per cent were currently married) with an average age of 31 years. Similarly, all the additional twenty women with whom I conducted taped in-depth interviews about their abortions were married village women. Thus the cases presented in this chapter do not coincide with popular notions of abortion depicted in the Thai media as a problem of unmarried students, prostitutes and promiscuous adolescents. In stark contrast to public discourse about abortion, the following case studies reflect more accurately the experiences of the majority of clients seeking abortions, who are married, rural women. Recent studies of abortion in Thailand reports that 75 per cent of women who seek abortions are married, seeking abortion for economic or family reasons (Koetsawang 1993). The following stories of some of these women highlight the contradictions between the present legislation in Thailand and the realities of abortion experiences.

The cases presented here cover a range of experiences of illegal abortions. Their stories allow us to understand the apparent inconsistencies frequently expressed between morality, ideology and practice. They also raise issues of the cultural definitions of personhood, situational ethics used by people in their decision-making, and how women negotiate the pressures of poverty and demands placed upon them to fulfil traditional ideas of motherhood and female nurturance within the modern economic realities.

Mrs Nang

Mrs Nang sits underneath her wooden house, sifting through the rice for the evening's meal, her little son playing with some straw beside her. She is 39 years-old, married with three children. She has four years of education. Her husband, who is 40 years-old, also has four years of education and works as a labourer in a brick factory in a nearby town. They own 7 rai of rice land on which they barely grow enough sticky rice for their own consumption. She approximates that they make around 20 000 baht income a year and they have 10 000 baht debt.

Mrs Nang has had six pregnancies. Her first child is her daughter now 13 years-old. Twelve years ago her second child died at one month old. Her third pregnancy resulted in her first son, 8 years-old. She aborted her fourth pregnancy at two months gestation. Her fifth pregnancy resulted in her last son, now 4 years-old, who is sitting beside her. She aborted her sixth pregnancy last year.

> [On my fourth pregnancy] I went to a house where they massage. They massage and press it out, but the first time it didn't come out. On the third time it came out. [The first time] the bleeding started at her house. I returned home and it stopped . . . I waited for a week and then went again . . . [The second time] the bleeding started there and by the time I had returned home it stopped so I waited another three days and then went again and this time it did come out . . . At first she [the abortionist] pressed the *sen* [ligaments]to make them loose before massaging them . . . Then she pressed after she got me to lie down with my legs bent up. She got me to sit like that and she got her fingers and pressed down to the lower abdomen. She would press until I said it hurt . . .

The abortionist is a middle-aged woman. She works from her home which is on a major road leading to a provincial town, hence women are able to catch a bus for 7 baht from their village to visit her. She has a beauty salon at the front of her house and conducts abortions in a small bathroom at the back of the house, with a mat and a pillow for women to rest on. Mrs Nang said that her practice was common knowledge in the village.

It was a lump of blood [*gon lu'at*]—as big as my big toe. It came out and then stopped. The lump of blood came out and then it pulled free. After it all came out the bleeding stopped and then I went to have an injection. The blood had stopped coming. When the blood came the stomach stopped hurting.

Massage abortion is the most common method used in the North-east. In a 1980 survey of abortion in the North-eastern province of Chaiyaphum, according to clients interviewed, 60 per cent of abortions were induced by massage, 23 per cent by uterine injection and 11 per cent by the use of an emmenagogue. Self-massage and intramuscular injections were reported by only a few (Narkavonnakit & Benett 1981:60). There is variation between different practitioners but, as described above, generally the client lies down with knees raised and often a rolled towel or pillow is placed underneath the woman's lower back. The fetal mass is located by external palpation. Some practitioners raise the uterus by pushing with their heel below the vagina. Then the fetal mass is dislodged by a pressing and pulling motion with the fingers. The area above the fetal mass is massaged in a rotating motion using either the base of the palm or the thumb. The whole procedure may take around 20 to 30 minutes, with pauses when the client complains of pain. This procedure is continued until the client begins to bleed. As in the case of Mrs Nang, many women return after seven days if the procedure is unsuccessful on the first attempt. Abortionists usually charge per month gestation. Sometimes an abortion in the first three months is charged at a set rate with prices rising steeply after the first three months as abortion becomes more difficult and more dangerous. Mrs Nang was charged 300 baht per month gestation.

When she discovered she was pregnant for the sixth time last year Mrs Nang went to an injectionist.

I got two injections. The first time he injected into my vagina it didn't work. The second time a lot came out. It came out as a lump of blood. In four or five days it came out . . .

In this technique, either a large syringe, urine catheter or a plastic tube containing a liquid is inserted into the uterus. In my study, women described a variety of liquids differing in colour and smell. Few could state what solution was used. Nurse informants suggested that the disinfectant 'Lysol', saline, or a variety of acidic or alkaline solutions were commonly used. A 1979 study found that abortionists used saline, distilled water, cumin mixed with water, glucose, Dettol, alcohol, gasoline, Piton-S (an oxytocin drug) and Duogynon-

Forte (Narkavonnakit 1979a; Narkavonnakit 1979b). Many practitioners in this study also prescribed antibiotics after the procedure; however, few injection abortionists described in my sample gave any medication to women.

Injection abortions are over-represented in figures of hospitalised abortion cases, suggesting that this practice is one of the most harmful techniques used to procure abortions (Narkavonnakit & Benett 1981). Like Mrs Nang, Twi also went to an injectionist to abort her third pregnancy, but with dangerous consequences. She is twenty-eight years-old and has two children. She and her husband both had six years of education and are rice farmers, supplementing their income through occasional hired labouring. Her first child is a 10 year-old boy. Her second pregnancy was unwanted and at that time she attempted an abortion through drinking *ya khap luat* and *ya dong lao*, 'hot' medicines in whisky used by women to bring the blood down. Her attempts were unsuccessful and she gave birth to her daughter, now six years-old. After her second pregnancy, Mrs Twi used Norplant for four years. At first she felt Norplant was 'correct' for her body, but in the fourth year she felt it was no longer good for her body as she felt abnormal and cold so she had it removed (see Chapter 5). She then tried the contraceptive pill, but fell pregnant six months ago after forgetting to take the pill. She took a pregnancy test at the local health station which confirmed her pregnancy. The nurse there advised her to keep the child. She did not want another child and so sought an abortion when she was two months pregnant. Twi hired a car and went with her elder sister to an old man who does abortions in Suwannaphum. He usually charges 500 baht per month gestation. Twi confided that she lied and stated her pregnancy was only one month gestation when it was really two; so the abortion only cost her 500 baht. The bleeding started immediately after the injection.

> It was a syringe and they injected me, but it was long, as long as this string for the chicken [indicates] about as long as from your arm to your elbow. He put it into my vagina, the medicine that he injected was from a little bottle, just like a *krathing daeng* bottle [a popular tonic], but it had a strong smell . . . And he injected it into my vagina. He got me to sit like this and then injected it. I felt pain in my lower abdomen right away. Like period pain. And then I sat and there was pain just like when I gave birth, at the time it came out. And after that, for two weeks afterwards I lost blood; it didn't stop.

> There was a lump of blood that came out as big as this egg here . . . It came out in two days after he did it and then it [the blood] came a little bit for two days and then after those two days it came for two weeks, it came out a lot for two weeks. I changed my sanitary pads so much [I used up] three packets. There was so much, it was not normal.

[AW] Why didn't you go to see a doctor earlier?

Because I thought that it would come out the same as it was coming out already and that soon it would stop and so I listened to my mother and father and they thought it would stop, and so I thought it would stop, but it didn't stop. It would have been about two or three weeks before I went to find a doctor.

After weeks with continued bleeding, Twi left for Bangkok with her elder sister to meet up with her husband, who was working there at the time, and to seek help from a Bangkok hospital.

The doctor said that my uterus had been all destroyed, [it had] destroyed my womb. The medicine that had been injected into me had been very strong and it destroyed my womb. The doctor had me go for an ultrasound . . . They examined me and then they asked me what I had done to get like this and so I told them everything truthfully. I said I had gone to have an abortion.

Twi spent five nights in the hospital and received intravenous antibiotics, a curette and sterilisation through tubal resection. Her stay cost her 2000 baht.

Always when other people had come back from abortions they were fine. I didn't think anything of it, normally my body was strong . . .

[AW] Before you went did you know what would happen to you?

He [the injectionist] said what would happen but said if anything happened to us it was our responsibility . . . But he said he had done lots of women and that they hadn't haemorrhaged like that and that some people would still go and do it at four months when it [the foetus] was a body already. Mrs Bun went and had one, people went and had them done and didn't lose blood. I went when the lump of blood was still small, but I went and got injected and it ruined my womb. The doctor said I got an infection. The doctor [at the hospital] said that if I had waited another five days, the germs would have risen and then anything could have happened and I might have died because of the dirt and germs . . . As it [the pregnancy] was only two months I didn't think it would be serious. But it turned out to be serious for me... My feelings now is that I don't want it. I don't want anyone to go and do it. I feel that it is dangerous, I am scared of it. If someone is pregnant I wouldn't let them go and do it. I would tell them about my own experience. It was torture. I wouldn't risk it again.

The most common complications that women may suffer after an unsafe induced abortion include immediate complications of uterine perforation, haemorrhage and infection (manifested by fever). The most common delayed complications which may occur within thirty days include damage to the cervix, Rh sensitisation (a blood sensitivity condition which can affect future pregnancies) or sterility due to infection (Population Council 1981). A recent study of 968 illegal abortions in five provincial hospitals across Thailand found 13 (1 per cent) of 968 women died due to complications after their abortion. Heavy bleeding was reported in 13 per cent of the total cases. Hysterectomy to remove a severely infected or perforated uterus was performed in 22 women and a blood transfusion was required in 104 women (Koetsawang 1993). Thai Ministry of Public Health Statistics state that in 1991 there were 40 deaths from abortion across the country (1993:147). In 1992 there were 28 maternal deaths classified as caused by abortion and in 1994 there were 14 deaths from abortions.[73] 'Pregnancy with abortive outcome' ranked thirteenth overall in the top twenty groups of illness for the total population of patients admitted to hospitals in Thailand in 1994 with 51 497 cases (96.9 per 1000 population) (Alpha Research 1994; 1997:61).[74] There are no deaths reported for medically induced abortions by competent trained practitioners in public hospitals or modern medical clinics in Bangkok. A 1980 survey in Chaiyaphoom province in the North-east found that one tenth of the total cases of induced abortion experienced complications serious enough to require hospitalisation, while 25 per cent of women experienced some form of complication and morbidity but did not seek hospital care (Narkavonnakit & Benett 1981:60).

Why do women such as Mrs Nang and Twi risk their lives by going to untrained abortionists? As both noted, many women in their community go to such practitioners and the majority do not require hospitalisation. Women know it can be dangerous and cite the case of one woman in the village who died seven years earlier from an illegal abortion and talked in hushed tones of another woman in a nearby community who had a severe haemorrhage last year. Knowledge of local abortionists is shared between women as secret and shameful information whispered between kin and close friends through networks that extend across districts. For example, Mrs Laem, thirty-six years-old and married with two children, had an injection abortion last year with a local woman in a nearby district. She knew about her through other people in the village who have been to see her for abortions:

> They said not to talk about it as they were afraid of gossip, but it [the abortion] was no problem, and it was effective, no problem. . . [The abortionist] said that if I died or anything she wouldn't take responsibility, and I said that I needed it and accepted that. But lots of people go, lots of people from our village, and they don't have any problems.

Mrs Laem has since had many women come and ask her about her experience and has referred them to the same abortionist. Likewise, one massage abortionist we spoke with stated she refers clients to other practitioners if her techniques do not succeed.

Other techniques

Apart from massage and injections, a range of other techniques are used by women to procure abortions. For women with money it is possible to have abortions induced by trained medical staff in private clinics using vacuum aspiration or dilatation and curettage. Their costs vary but are in the range of 5000 to 6000 baht for the first three months, with an additional 1000 baht per month after that. The fee can be as high as 15 000 baht for late terminations (Simmons 1996). But poor rural women rarely have such money, neither are they likely to have knowledge of or access to such practitioners, although several women spoke of their abortions in private hospitals in Bangkok, obtained while seeking work there. Such private clinics are also technically illegal and frequently subject to police raids. The illegality forces prices to be high, treatment to be rushed, stressful and of poor quality, and means clinics offer little follow-up care for women.

Other techniques used for inducing abortions by village practitioners include the insertion of herbs or roots into the vagina, often with incantations to supplement the action of the vegetation. This technique is reported to be more common in the south of Thailand (Narkavonnakit 1979a).

> I was pregnant and so I bought herbs from a travelling doctor, some herbs which I put inside me. This worked and I aborted but afterwards I had *mat khaw* [discharge] for twenty-one days, very heavy. I still haven't healed. I bought some medicine at the shop, *ya satri phen pa* [a brand of 'women's medicine'], and I had *ya tom* [a medicine from boiled herbs], but I still haven't healed (Aunt Thii).

The insertion of hard objects or rubber catheter into the vagina to puncture the amniotic sack is used in some areas. In addition, one case I encountered involved a trained nurse who inserts IUDs into women in early pregnancy. When this insertion causes a miscarriage, the women present to hospital.

More common, however, is the consumption of drugs, often in combination with traditional emmenagogues. Medications such as *Kano* (500 mg tetracycline) or the contraceptive pill, which specifically state that they should not be taken by women who are pregnant are sometimes taken in the hope that they will produce an abortion:

> The second time after I knew I was three months pregnant I took the pill. I tried lots of medicines for taking out the baby; so I don't know what worked. I took them until nine months and when it [the baby] came out it was dead already. (Aunt Yii)

The use of the brand of aspirin called *Tamjai* (lit. to strengthen your resolve) is very commonly cited as an effective abortifacient. *Tamjai* formerly combined aspirin and caffeine although the use of caffeine in such aspirin combinations is now banned. Women described using *Tamjai* in a variety of ways. For example, one woman from my survey said she took a couple of envelopes of *Tamjai* every day for the first four months of her pregnancy until she eventually miscarried, requiring antibiotics and intravenous fluids in a private clinic in Ban Phai. Other women describe attempting to abort through mixing several *Tamjai* powders into whisky and drinking that. They joked that even when not effective, at least 'you get very drunk!'

Women's medicines: The ambiguities of emmenagogues / abortifacients

The most common action taken by women involves the consumption of emmenagogues known generically as *ya satri* (women's medicine) or *ya khap lu'at* (medicine to bring the blood down). Sixteen per cent of 164 women in the interview survey had used some form of 'hot medicine' at some time to bring on their periods. The practice of menstrual regulation is common cross-culturally (see Hull, Sarwono, & Widyantoro 1993; Newman 1985; Nichter & Nichter 1987; Nichter & Nichter 1996; Sobo 1996)[75] As noted in Chapter 4, regular menstruation is important to Isan women and the failure to menstruate is interpreted variously by women either as due to some form of blockage or humoural imbalance causing the blood to begin to rise dangerously within the body, or the possibility that a woman is in the process of becoming pregnant. The use of these hot medicines is not necessarily viewed as causing an abortion, rather, it is a form of menstrual regulation. When Isan women do not recognise themselves as pregnant, the labelling of these medicines as menstrual restorers rather than abortifacients does not necessarily represent a misrepresentation of women's 'true intentions'.

The use of these medicines entails what Nations et al. in their study of Brazil call 'women's hidden transcripts about abortion', in which notions of delayed menstruation, lumps of blood and the use of these medicines as 'tests' for pregnancy allow for enormous cognitive ambiguity (Nations, Misago, Fonesca, Correia, & Campbell 1997). As Sobo (1996) states, an ethnographer or reader cannot make judgements of the goals of women taking these medicines, as the definitions of conception and pregnancy and the status of a newly conceived foetus differ cross-culturally (see for example Morgan 1990; Scheper-Hughes 1992). Although some women do state that they used these medicines consciously in the knowledge that they were pregnant, many women describe inducing delayed menstruation or curing clogged up menses without accusations of abortion. They are described as prudent prophylactic health behaviours with no association with abortion. The later these medicines are taken in relation to the missed menses, the more likely it is that it is considered an abortion attempt rather than menstrual restoration.

Definitions of actions to bring menstrual blood down and those used to cause abortions allow for multiple interpretations, and highlight the disjuncture between emic (indigenous) and etic (scientific) understandings of embodied experiences such as pregnancy loss, menstrual regulation and abortion. As Sobo (1996:40) notes, the criteria for categorising experiences as conception, abortion or miscarriage, or even a birth, differ cross-culturally and we need to guard against the imposition of biomedical categories on divergent cross-cultural reproductive experiences of women.

Isan men and women refer to the early pregnancy as consisting of no more than a *gon lu'at,* a lump of blood (see Chapter 4). At this early stage intervention to induce menstruation is considered to expel the blood and reverse the process through which it gradually becomes flesh. Most informants agree that the *gon lu'at* becomes a *luk* (child, baby) at sometime in the fourth month. At that stage when women begin to feel the foetal movements they start to use the term *luk* to describe their pregnancy and speak of it as *mi tho/tua lew* (as having a body already). After this stage, actions to stop the pregnancy are considered definite abortions and more sinful that earlier acts.

Apart from the herbal decoctions, a range of pharmaceuticals are also consumed by women to regulate their menstruation. A range of menstrual regulators containing hormones are easily available at medicine stores. One example is Norterone, containing 5 mg norethisterone, which can be purchased for 40 baht. Its packaging indicates its use for the 'treatment of abnormal menstruation, dysfunctional uterine bleeding, postponement of menstruation, premenstrual tension syndrome and mastopathy'. Another common and popular medicine is Mary Capsules. Its pink packaging states it is counterindicated for use in pregnancy and that it is for 'women with irregular menstruation'. It is readily available for 45 baht. Each capsule contains 100 mg Ethisterone, 100 mcg Cyanocobalamin and 0.05 mg Ethinyl Estradiol.[76] In addition, post-coital contraceptives, such as Postinor, are readily available across the counter in Thailand in most district towns. Postinor contains the hormone d-Norgestrel (0.75 mg). Its packaging contains a red diagram with a baby and a hand signal below it indicating a barrier or 'time out signal' which could be easily interpreted as indicating abortifacient action. The use of these medicines is ambiguous. Women may purchase these in the belief that, if taken in large enough doses, they may act as abortifacients.

The case of Mrs Wii demonstrates the subtlety of definitions used by some women to speak about their actions without defining them as attempted abortions. Mrs Wii is twenty-five years-old with two children, a son aged five and another son aged one year and four months. Speaking of her medical history she stated that she miscarried her first pregnancy at two months. She said her first pregnancy was unwanted when she was nineteen years-old. When her menstruation did not come she took *ya khap lu'at* (medicine to bring the blood down). She says she didn't know that she was pregnant at that time, although she felt like eating *som* (sour) foods. She said she bought the medicine and drank two bottles and then blood came heavily. So she went to the *sathani anamai* and was told that she had been two months pregnant. In conclusion she said: '*Siaday* [shame]. If I had known I was pregnant I would have kept it.'

Similarly, other women also spoke of unwanted pregnancies which resisted the effects of 'hot' medicines but later miscarried due to a 'fall'. Many narratives of women attempting abortions describe a series of failed attempts followed by increasing desperation. For example, 31 years-old Sen fell pregnant while still breastfeeding her son who was not yet one year old. She did not feel that she could look after another baby so soon. At first she bought a packet of *ya seua sipet tua* (eleven tiger brand medicine), which is a type of *ya dong lao*, a 'hot' herbal formula added to whisky and drunk. She tried two bottles of this mixture but this did not succeed. She also bought four envelopes of *ya tamjai* (at that time a combination pain killer containing aspirin and caffeine) and took those together but this also did not succeed in bringing on a miscarriage. By this time she was four months pregnant. Finally, she went to a *mor tam yae* (a traditional midwife) and paid 300 baht for her to massage out the foetus. Although she bled a lot after this procedure, she did not abort and carried the pregnancy to term.

Disabled babies and stillbirths often get labelled in village gossip as proof of their mothers' attempts to abort them. Physical deformities or congenital blindness or deafness are said to derive from attempts to press out the foetus, or due to the insertion of herbs or injections into the womb. For example, Mrs Daeng, 36 years-old, has three sons. Her third child is severely physically and mentally disabled to the extent that she must spend all her time caring for him. People gossip about her and her son, saying that he is disabled because she tried to abort him. Mrs Daeng contended that she had made no such attempt, even though she acknowledged that her third pregnancy was unwanted, as she fell pregnant due to failure of an IUD. She blames the doctors at the local hospital for her son's disabilities stating that she was prescribed antihypertensives early in her pregnancy, even though these were contra-indicated for pregnant women.

Making the decision: socially embedded morality

While most women and men interviewed are aware of the illegality of abortion in Thailand or may believe that abortion is immoral, nevertheless the social and economic realities of their lives are salient factors in their decision-making. Georges (1996) describes this as 'socially embedded morality'. It provides a justification for abortion that is congruent with broader social goals and expectations, allowing women and men to reconcile their Buddhist beliefs and culturally valued ideals of motherhood, female nurturance and family, with their experience of abortion. The reasons given by women for their abortions highlight issues such as the nature of relationships between men and women, and how the organisation of labour and class position influences their decisions.

In each interview women spoke of the difficulty of making the decision and the fears which accompanied it. In Mrs Laem's case, the divination of cooked rice provided the reassurance necessary for her to go ahead with the procedure:

[AW] What did you think before you went?

I thought a great deal. I thought and thought again. And I steamed the rice in the morning and spoke to the rice and water. I said, 'If the rice is red then something [bad] will happen.' But the rice was normal, and so I had the courage to go. If you want to do something you should ask the rice beforehand, and so there will be no problem. If it [a sign] had been in the rice or the water [then] I wouldn't have had the courage to go. I truly believe that if the rice was red [there would be a problem]. But the rice was normal; so I was confident and decided to just go and do it. My child was still breastfeeding so I wasn't ready [for another], and so I decided . . . I spoke with my friends and I decided we lacked any other path. So I forced myself to do it. We weren't ready [to have another child] and so what can you do? We didn't have any money and so it was a necessity.

The primary reason spoken about by women in this study was that of poverty and the inability to provide for more children. Mrs Nang referred to her decision to abort in these terms:

As soon as it [the pregnancy] came I didn't want it at all. I had enough [children] already. It was a big problem. A lot of children already and we are dreadfully poor [*yak jon*]. The economy was poor and everything's expensive—100 baht is nothing. We couldn't stand it any more and everything was terrible . . . My husband has to work to buy rice to eat. One bag of rice costs a lot.

Likewise, Twi spoke of her abortion in terms of the economic burden of having another child as the most salient factor in her decision-making:

My problem was that it was hard to find work. And so we didn't have any money. I couldn't stand the burden. There was only my husband working, one person only. I tried to find work. There was never enough money. We had two [children] at home and we didn't want to have any more.

[AW] Before you went, did you think hard about it?

Yes I did. I thought about different people [who had had abortions] and I
went to talk with people, but I really didn't want the child. I didn't. This
person and that person said this was no good and that was no good. It was
no good if I went, and no good if I kept it. I had a problem, we were so
poor [*yak jon*]. I looked at my two children. I saw the burden that they
give their mother already, isn't that so? Many children—and we rented
land. I had to be responsible for them and so I didn't want another. Two
children was enough. I didn't ask for another child and I would have to
look after it all the time.

By evoking the social idiom of poverty, *yak jon*, these narratives appeal to
common representations of the hardships of rural farming lives in Isan without
needing to resort to descriptions of the actual economic circumstances of their
speakers. To speak of *yak jon* is not necessarily to speak of absolute poverty,
although it is true that in many cases women are describing the absolute
deprivation of their material circumstances. For many, *yak jon* has come to
signal the relative deprivation another child would bring, the missed
opportunities for economic advancement and social mobility for the parents
and their existing children. As Muecke (1984) describes in Northern Thailand,
the prospects for most women from lower socio-economic backgrounds to
achieve social mobility is dependent upon their education and the
accumulation of wealth through labour migration. As in the north, Isan women
are also making rational choices to 'make money, not babies', utilising
abortion when necessary to restrict their family size and remove the barrier of
heavy child-care and household work responsibilities to allow them to engage
in wage labour and better provide for their existing children.

Given the idealised and celebrated status of motherhood (discussed in
Chapter 2 and 6), how do women negotiate the moral tensions inherent in their
identities as Buddhist mothers who nevertheless abort? Twi's description
evokes the values of motherhood and nurturance as the very reason why
abortion is necessary. By referring to her two children, and the need to ensure
that she can provide adequately for them without the extra burden and expense
of another child, Twi depicts her decision to abort as necessary in order to be a
good mother. In this way, somewhat paradoxically abortion is regarded by
many villagers as fully compatible with Thai ideals of the 'good mother'. With
economic pressures and the necessity of labour migration, bringing up children
has come to be seen as a task requiring far more intensive investments in time,
attention, energy, responsibility and money. This view of motherhood reflects
the changing view of children and a separation between fertility and
motherhood and nurturing. This emphasis on the quality of motherhood is
promoted by the Thai family planning program. Indeed, Twi makes a direct
reference to the state family planning campaign in her statements of 'Two
children are enough'. This demonstrates an active appropriation of state
discourse to justify and exonerate abortion. By this logic, being a good mother

necessarily entails bearing fewer children. When women find themselves undesirably pregnant due to contraceptive failure, or failure to use contraceptives, abortion is an option to be considered.

Like pregnancy, abortion has a variety of meanings depending on the context of the relationship within which it is undertaken. The decision to abort may be a joint decision, but this is by no means always the case. As Hardacre (1997:103) suggests, like contraception and intercourse, abortion is saturated with meanings for the couple. It can be withheld or coerced, it can be undertaken with positive purpose or with fear and reluctance. Discussions with women about their decisions to abort or not reveal the complexity of their lives and relationships which all impinge upon their decisions. The unwanted pregnancies occur at a time of stress or transition in the relationship or when there is a deterioration in their relationships with their male partners. Women speak of their financial hardship, the stress of work and the difficulties of balancing the physical and emotional burdens of domestic life with minimal support from their husbands. Each woman has her own story.

Aunty Sen who is 33 years-old, described the conditions under which her decision to abort was made. Her first child had Down's Syndrome and died when he was thirteen years-old. Aunty Sen spoke of her severe depression after the death of her son with Down's syndrome. Around the time of his death she fell pregnant for the second time and was around two to three months pregnant when she decided to abort.

> At that time my husband and I lived in separate houses. He could only come and see me in the evenings because we had problems with parents on both sides . . . My parents and his parents didn't approve of us. He had just come back from Bangkok and I had so many problems. I lived with my mother. At first I thought I would keep it, but I was scared of the problems and at that time me and my husband didn't get on well together . . . It took me a long time to decide whether to have it out or keep it. If I kept it, how was I to look after it, as my husband and I had problems and so I decided to have it out. I was scared that I wouldn't be able to live together with my husband. So I had it out. And he told me to have the abortion, as his parents didn't like me. So I had it out. I had it out. I decided to have it out.

Aunt Sen's ambivalence is evident in her verbal repetition of her act: 'I had it out'. Eventually she later gave birth to another healthy boy.

In Twi's story described earlier, she blames herself for her pregnancy and complications. She feels guilty for expecting her husband to use contraception 'for her convenience' and feels sorry for him when he finds her in the hospital in Bangkok with the infection.

> On my third pregnancy I didn't want it at all, but it was my mistake, my own mistake. I didn't take contraceptives. I wanted my husband to use

contraception 'cause I liked the convenience for myself, and so it was my own mistake that I did it [the abortion] and the pain and all of that.

[AW] When you went did you ask for advice from your husband?

I asked the advice of my husband. And he said he didn't want any more [children]. The mistake [in falling pregnant] was mine. And I saw that other people who went and had it done didn't have any problems. My husband said, 'So go and have it out. We don't need it at all.' So my husband agreed with me to go and do it. Afterwards I saw my husband come into the hospital and I felt sorry for him. I didn't think that it would turn out like this.

Twi feels she has wronged her husband in not using contraception and then in suffering the expensive complications.

As most interviews about abortion were held with women, what is presented here are women's representations of their decisions. Unlike the cases presented above, it is notable that in their representations of their actions, many women make no or little reference to their husbands and partners in their decision to abort. As with decisions about family planning described in Chapter 5, decisions to abort are represented as largely the responsibility of women (*nathi phuying*). Many women present their decision as an autonomous act, presented to their partners as a *fait accompli*, either before the abortion is carried out or after the act. In making her decision, Mrs Laem talked to other women who had had abortions and makes no reference to her husband in her narrative about her abortion. Likewise, Uan, who is 31 years-old made the decision to abort her third pregnancy in consultation with her husband's sister and did not talk to her husband, as he was in Bangkok working at the time. The ultimate demonstration of a woman's autonomy enacted through abortion is vividly referred to in Mrs Nang's description of her massage abortionist who had learned how to abort by practicing the massage technique on herself. She had one child and did not want another within an abusive relationship:

She [the abortionist] said she learned how to massage because she massaged out her own [pregnancies]. Aborted by herself. She only wanted one child. Because she only wanted one child she pressed the others out. Her husband was no good. He would beat her. After drinking whisky he would come and fight and beat up his wife. So, because of this she only wanted one child.

Buddhist sin and women's private rituals

Buddhism defines abortion as *bap* (sin), as it is considered a life-destroying act, *panatibat* (Pali). The people who perform this act must accept the karmic consequences of their actions. At the same time however, Buddhism teaches that there are different levels of sin depending on the intention of the individual. Hence someone who commits an act with bad intentions or purely for their own comfort and convenience is said to have the sin increased, whereas those who do something with a sense of responsibility and good intention still have sinned, but to a lesser degree. An example commonly used by Buddhist commentators is that of soldiers who must kill for the protection of society. In this case they still have committed *bap*, but the karmic consequences of this action will be less than for another person who kills for no reason (Payutto 1993).

Fear of *bap* is a reason given by many women as to why they did not attempt to terminate their unplanned pregnancies. Although the economic logic women describe dovetails nicely with the dominant discourses on the need for population control and quality in the family planning program, it provides little solace within a Buddhist context which equates abortion with murder. All women agreed to definitions of abortion as *bap* and many expressed fears of the karmic consequences of their actions in their later incarnations. Mrs Laem said that her abortionist reminded her it was a sin: 'She said it was *bap*, but only a small sin and not really a problem.' However, women spoke of their own private rituals to mitigate the sin they were about to commit. They prayed to their ancestors as they poured water to the ground at the end of the temple service, asking for forgiveness and explaining the neccessity of their actions. After this they felt less guilty about the abortion and felt that the sin could be repaid by lots of good acts in this life, such as attending temple services and feeding monks, which would accrue merit to counter the *bap*. For example, Aunty Sai described her actions:

> As I was leaving the house to go [for the abortion] I collected some
> flowers to venerate the good protective spirits and the spirits of my
> ancestors and I spoke to them. I said, 'Now your child isn't ready [to have
> another child] I don't have the things to be able to nurture [*liang*] it. If it
> was born it would be a hardship and so if it is ready to be born, allow it to
> be born to someone who is ready for it, allow it to be born to another
> mother. That's what I said. I told them to let it be born to another mother,
> that I wasn't ready now because if it was born things would be so hard.
> My ancestors, the benevolent deity, I told them all. After I said all of that I
> just went [to have the abortion].

In contrast, in focus group discussions men stated that the *bap* a woman accrued through an abortion could never be lessened in this life, as it was one of the worst possible sins. Thus they felt a woman was condemned to the karmic consequences no matter what actions she took in this life to accrue merit. Interestingly, in the focus group discussions men were divided as to whether the male partner of a woman who aborts also shares the *bap* of the abortion. Some stated that only if a man knew of the abortion or encouraged it would he share in the sin. In contrast, women agreed that men do share the sin of abortion.

While most Isan women agree that abortion is a sin, not fulfilling one's obligations as a mother and consigning a future child and one's existing children to relative deprivation is explained as perhaps a greater sin. In this way women posit an alternative 'morality of praxis' (Petchesky 1990) in which accountability to their existing children takes precedence over spiritual concerns. It is a morality that affirms themselves as good mothers forced to undergo suffering to ensure better lives for their children.

Obtaining legal abortions

To obtain a legal abortion the pregnancy must represent a serious threat to the woman's health or else she must prove that the pregnancy is the result of rape or unlawful sexual contact and have presented her case to the police. In practice, as members of women's NGOs testify, many women do not report their rape to police or suffer bureaucratic obfuscation and refusal from hospitals even when they fulfil the criteria for a legal termination (Simmons 1996). While some doctors operate on a broad definition of health and are willing to assist women on the grounds of their mental health or social problems, the ambiguity of the law means that such doctors are vulnerable to prosecution. This was highlighted in April 1997 when seven clinics of the Population and Development Association, one of Thailand's most famous family planning NGOs, were raided and forced to close. The clinics were said to have offered menstrual regulation services and abortions in addition to their family planning services. While there are hospitals and clinics in Bangkok at which a woman may obtain a safe abortion, for rural women the options are very limited. Rural district hospitals in Khon Kaen and Roi Et conduct very few abortions or menstrual regulation services, with services wholly dependent on the decisions of the lone doctor at each hospital. Most district hospital doctors I interviewed stated that they would not do an abortion under any circumstances and instead referred women to the Regional Maternal and Child Health Centre in Khon Kaen, where their case would be assessed by the staff there. It is very difficult to obtain any figures about legal abortions conducted in government hospitals.

The difficulty in obtaining an abortion from medical doctors was described by Aunt Uay, whose story highlights the linkages between class and wealth and access to a safe abortion:

I wanted to have the abortion because my husband wasn't here and I didn't think that I could look after the baby. I had it when I was four months pregnant. I had an injection from the *mor phu'n ban* [local untrained doctor]. I was very sick and thin and couldn't eat any food. After it was out it was very painful . . . I did the abortion at home because at the hospital they ask lots of questions and you have got to have enough reasons not to keep your baby. If you're in the city [working] having a baby will cause lots of problems for you and the doctor might do it [an abortion] for you, but for people in the village they try to force you to keep the baby even though you don't have lots of money. The pain was worse than when you give birth, not the same at all. . .

The pressure placed upon women not to have abortions became evident in an abortion counselling session I witnessed at a major teaching hospital in Khon Kaen in 1992:[77]

I enter the room where the intern counsellor, a nurses' aide and a patient are sitting. On the wall of the room, which doubles at other times as an examination room, are several posters. One depicts a man and woman in a pink heart promoting a two-child family. There are several baby posters showing cute, chubby, fair-skinned babies, and one photograph, placed strategically at eye level next to where the patient sits, showing a woman on a stretcher with an intravenous drip with the caption 'This is a woman who self-aborted at four months. It is very dangerous and leads to shock and death'.

A young woman in her second year of high school sits facing the doctor with her head lowered. Her mother sits behind her. She is two months pregnant after attending a birthday party with a girlfriend and five young men. She says she drank five or six drinks and can't remember with whom she had sex. She says it was her first time. The counsellor speaks accusingly, asking for all details of the night. 'You went to this party? With how many girls? How many boys? And drinking?' Tears well in the girl's eyes.
The intern asks, 'And what will you do about contraception? Or this will happen again, won't it? If you take the pill you will just forget to take it, you should have an IUD or maybe the new drug that goes into your arm [Norplant] that works for five years.'
She asks the girl if she has slept with this boy before.
'No. I never have,' the young woman replies.
The intern doesn't believe her and keeps questioning her. The intern suggests that the mother should find out who the father is and they should ask him about the baby's fate. The doctor goes to consult with another doctor. The nurses' aide says to the mother, 'We see cases like this all the time of young girls who go out riding the back of their boyfriends'

motorbike'. . . The intern comes back and says, 'There are no indications for an abortion.'

Another woman comes and explains that she had been having Depo Provera injections and has fallen pregnant. When she did not menstruate she saw a doctor, who told her she was not pregnant and gave her another injection of Depo Provera. Now she is four months pregnant and wants an abortion. The doctor replies that it is unfortunate that her contraceptive failed, but that there are no indications for an abortion and as she is four months pregnant it is too dangerous. The nurses' aide goes to call in the woman's husband, who explains that he doesn't want the child as they have three children already.
'How are your other children?' the counsellor asks.
'We have two girls and a boy,' he replies.
'Why don't you want another child just as lovely? The doctor said that you should think of the two lives [the baby and the mother].' The couple remains silent.
'In another five months you will have another baby! It's just too dangerous to abort.'
The husband expresses the fear that the child might be deformed because of the Depo Provera injection: 'It might have six fingers or something.'
'That's nothing, we'll just cut it off!' the counsellor replied jokingly.
Finally, the intern says to the nurses' aide, 'Go and show the couple the pictures of a four-month-old foetus. You'll see what you have inside you, it's a little baby already. Go and get the model.'

Despite the first case being a probable date rape, and the second late gestational case apparently caused by contraceptive failure, neither woman was granted an abortion. Another woman who attended was mute and intellectually disabled, and four months pregnant to an unknown father. Through a village friend who accompanied her, she indicated that she did not want the child. The doctor showed her the photograph of the woman who died from a late abortion and told the interpreter to tell her that if she died that way she would become a terrible *phi* (spirit).[78] The friend signed to her that if she did anything to herself she would die or else the police would take her away. In the end the doctor suggested that when she saw the baby her natural maternal desire would make her accept it.

Through a heavy use of moralistic discourse on motherhood and Buddhist values of not taking a life, the counselling I witnessed offered few choices to the women. It did not empower women to make a decision nor support them if their pregnancy was too advanced for a safe abortion. 'Responsible' control over one's fertility through contraception was contrasted with 'irresponsible' desire to control fertility through abortion, even when contraception had failed. The sanctity of motherhood and maternal desire and the authority of the husband/father, supported by appeals to religious and social tradition, were placed in discursive opposition to imagery of sexually wanton young women and evil female spirits. Even when granted access to a safe abortion, the moral opprobrium against women remains. Medical students and nurses told me that when women are granted an abortion at the hospital some doctors perform the procedure with no anaesthetic or pain relief, so as to discourage women from seeking an abortion again.

Conclusions: resistance or pragmatism?

Abortion poses questions concerning the relationship between structured power relations and women's agency. It is clear that in the Thai context there is both a direct exercise of power in the form of legal sanctions against abortion, police raids of clinics, media humiliation of women who have aborted and anti-abortion lobbying by institutional religion. There is also a more subtle relation of power which reinforces the idea of abortion as moral evil, as un-Thai and un-Buddhist behaviour, that characterises women who fall pregnant through not using contraceptives or using them incorrectly as irresponsible. Motherhood and nurturance are understood as naturally desired states for women. Blame and responsibility for abortion is placed solely upon women, who are seen as deviant. Women's bodies are at the centre of debates about the nature of Thai society, concepts of the nation and the role of Buddhism, conflicts over women's roles in society and the changing nature of motherhood. The state disciplines women's bodies through the promotion of family planning to limit fertility, and punishes women who are defined as having failed to comply appropriately.

As foreshadowed in the beginning of this chapter, the issue of abortion within Thailand thus highlights the need for more nuanced notions of agency and resistance. Publicly, women's groups, such as Foundation for Women and Friends for Women, along with members of the Thai medical profession are clearly contesting the existing social order in their demands for changes to the present abortion legislation. Similarly, the women portrayed in this chapter are not passive, although the restraints under which they must make choices are often narrow. But the decisions of women to defy legal sanctions, and the existing moral order to obtain clandestine abortions are more than a purely pragmatic response to their situation. Women are aware of the legal and moral status of their activities. Yet the question of consciousness is problematic, as women both consent to the dominant ideologies regarding abortion and motherhood even as they negate them through their action. It is impossible to place an unproblematic label upon their intention. Rather, it is necessary to recognise that few people conform to a romantic version of outright resistance but rather, the subtleties and pragmatics of people's lived experience defy simple characterisation.

As this chapter demonstrates, the decisions about whether or not to terminate a pregnancy are not simple exercises of 'choice'. Women both challenge the existing social and moral order and conform to it. When in doubt about their reproductive status, women can use ambiguous traditions concerning the curative, prophylactic and even fertility-enhancing qualities of 'women's medicines' to their benefit. Through these medicines women attempt to restore missed periods, without recourse to the anti-social act of abortion.

When abortions are deemed necessary, women justify them through an inversion of the state family planning discourses about ensuring a good quality life for one's children through limiting family size and their need to be 'good mothers'. Abortion is described as pragmatic action helping women control their lives, avoiding the burdens of large families that they can't afford, and allowing them and their children better lives. They also evoke discourses about the nature of poverty in Isan to explain the necessity of their action. But while reaffirming social discourses of motherhood, in procuring abortions in defiance of the law women directly challenge the state. By seeking abortions from local practitioners and through self-medication they contest the medical profession's dominance of gynaecological matters. In devising personal rituals to mitigate the sin abortion represents they defy the male dominance over institutional religious ritual. They are acutely aware of their subordination and powerlessness as women with unwanted pregnancies and reflect critically upon their relationships with their partners, their position as poor rural farmers, and the constraints of motherhood. But their form of resistance is not a glorious empowered decision as other forms of resistance might be portrayed, but one filled with dread, shame and pain.

Appendix 1

Data Collection Methods Used

Method	Number/Duration	Type of Data Collected
1991 Focus groups	7 groups in 2 village locations	Women's health and ethnogynecology
Ethnographic fieldwork 1991-93	18 months	11 months resident in Ban Srisaket
Village Household Survey 1992	96 households, Ban Srisaket	Morbidity/treatment data, socio-economic data, migration, household structure
Village Household Survey 1993	60 households, Ban Srisaket	Morbidity/treatment data, agricultural production/income, debt, migration
Birthing Survey, 1993	67 women, Ban Srisaket	birth location, birth attendant practices
Survey of women who gave birth in previous 12 months, 1993	57 women, Ban Srisaket	Place of birth, birth/postpartum practice
Semi-structured interviews,1992-93	89 interviews, Ban Srisaket	Traditional healers, traditional birth attendants, village health volunteers, health station staff, district hospital staff, doctors at teaching hospital, elder men and women, Temple abbots, village heads, migrant women
In-depth interviews with mothers, 1993	36 women, Ban Srisaket	Birth experience, post-partum practice, breastfeeding, quality of service
Birthing Observation, 1992	11 births	Provincial Hospital, District Hospital
Store Medicine Survey, 1993	6 village stores, Ban Srisaket	Drugs available to be purchased in village
Health/Socio-Economic Data collection, 1991-93, 1997	Documents	Provincial, District and Village authorities, Village Health Station

Observations, 1991-93, 1997	Roi Et, Khon Kaen provinces	Village Health Stations, District Hospitals, Provincial Hospital, Ante-natal Outpatient Clinic, Gynaecology Outpatient Clinic, Labor/Post-partum Wards, Provincial Public Health Centre
1997 structured interview survey	173 women in four rural districts	Reproductive history, contraception, abortion,
In-depth case study interviews, 1997	20 women	Illegal abortion experience
In-depth case study interviews, 1997	20 women	Experience with Norplant
1997 focus groups	7 groups in 2 village locations	Abortion, situationai ethics

Appendix 2

Survey of medicines available for sale in six general stores in Ban Srisaket, Roi Et, 1992.

The medicines with no entries for the active ingredient had no labels indicating their contents. In addition to the medicines listed here there were various *ya chut* available for numerous other conditions.

Brand name	Active Component	Use	Cost
BOMCIN	Tetracycline 250mg	Infections	2B/tab
PLOCAMMAD	Sulfamethoxazole/ Trimethoprim has a toxic reaction warning	Anti-bacterial, diarrhoea	
PENICILLIN	Penicillin	Infections	1B/tab
TREX-250	Tetracycline 250mg	"	
PIOMYCIN	Tetracycline 50mg	"	
GANO	Tetracycline 500mg	"	
SUL B.C.O.	Sulfadiazine VSP 325mg	Swellings, infections	
CHANKIT	Tetracycline HCl 250mg		
ROTEXCIN	Tetracycline HCl 250mg		
THEOPLEX	"		
PIRACAM	Piroxicam	Rheumatoid arthritis, gout	3B/tab
TAMJAI	Acetysalicylic acid		2B/3tab
LOD BHUAD	Aspirin		2B/3tab
BHUAD HAI	Aspirin 650mg	pain, headache	1B/tab
PYRANA		Pain	1B/tab
PARACETAMOL	Paracetamol	Analgesic	2B/6tab
PARACETAMOL SYRUP		Analgesic	10B/ bottle
5 RUA KRUNG THAI BRAND		for toothache with applicator	10B/5cc
TUA TONG BUN THAW PUAD	Aspirin 325mg, caffeine 30mg	Fever, headache, pain	1B/4tab
JIA KIM IEW			
YA PRADONG 101		skin diseases	

YA PRADONG MENBIN		"	
TIFFY		Cold tablet	5B/4tab
TIFFY SYRUP		Children's colds	
LEURA	aspirin 325mg		
NUTA	Paracetamol, chlorpheniramine maleate, phenylpromalamine HCl		5B/4 tab
CARE LIN		Anti-inflamatory for oral-mucous membrane	5B/pkt
ANTACIN	Mg tricylicate, kaolin aluminium hydroxide,	Peptic ulcer, dyspepsia	.5B/tab
ANTACIN GEL	"	"	25B/ 240cc
ALUGAS	Aluminium hydroxide gel	Antacid	
MET 77	Aluminium hydroxide	Antacid	
YA THATU NAM KHAW		Stomach pain, indigestion	
TUA TONG		Dyspepsia	
WINN		Pain, tiredness	1B/tab
DIMONATE		Travel sickness	3B/tab
BOY IN GOLDEN TRAY BRAND YA HOM		Nausea, tiredness, fainting, vertigo	
YA SUNFA		Diarrhoea	
OISONIC	Niclosamide phenolphthalein	Anti-helminthic	22B/tab
WORM TABLETS		"	1.5B/tab
BENDA 500	Mebendazole	"	26B/tab
SARAMIDE		"	
BOMPAR		For tapeworms	26B/tab
YA THAY		Anti-helminthic	26B/4 tab
ENTERMID	Loperamide HCl 2 mg	"	
PIPCIN 30CC		"	
NANAPIN		Round worms, threadworms	15B/ 30cc
BROWN MIXTURE	Camphorated opium tincture	Cough mixture	
THATU NAM DAENG	sodium bicarbonate, menthol peppermint oil, camphor water	Antacid	
WAY KHUN DEK		children's colds and headaches	

WAY KHUN DEK		children's colds and headaches	
BEBIDOL		Flatulence and hyperclorhydria in infants	25B/ 120ml
SNAKE BRAND YA KAE KHAY DEK		children's antipyretic	
SNAKE BRAND YA KAE AI DEK		children's cough mixture	
PANVIT		vitamin tablet	18B/bott
LECIN		vitamin tablet	
CYSTBLADD		Cystitis	17B/bott
HIPEX			10B/bott
ANT SYRUP		Colds	8B/bott
MERBROMIN 100ml		"	
SKINA	Salicylic acid		
KHI PHING NO. 37	Salicylic acid, benzoic acid		
ZENA LOTION		Dermatitis	12B/tube
PHONG PISET	Sulphur powder	pimples, infected wounds, ulcers, navels of babies	
CHLORAM OINTMENT		external use on wounds	30B/tube
THIOCIN	Acetylsalicylic acid 325mg		
TIGER BRAND YA DONG		pickled medicine for weakness and tiredness	
PAENG HOM		for pimples	
YA SATRI PHEN PA	patent formula	Irregular menstruation, vaginal discharge, prolapse	30B/bott
POH LEAF MEDICINE	patent formula	Fevers	
PAX- NOX		Inhalant	6B/bott
TUA TONG BRAND YA MONG		Inhalant	3B/pkt
YA KAE RON NAI		to correct internal heat, fever	3B/pkt
PURMOLAX	Phenolphthalein	Laxative	
DICOTIL	Loperamide HCl		
VIKOOLDEG	Acetosalicylic acid		
VICKS VAPORUB		colds, chest infections	7B/tin
LIPOVITAN		Tonic	

Notes

1 Transcription of local Thai and Lao words throughout this book follows a modified version of the Royal Thai transcription system. Under this system tones and long vowels are not indicated. Exceptions include place names, famous people's names and authors' names where the transcription follows that customarily used. For consistency in the bibliography, Thai authors are listed alphabetically according to their last names, but their first names are indicated where available.

2 Post-structuralists and feminists approach the study of the body in slightly different ways, both of which have influenced this book but can not be explored in great detail here. Turner (1991, 1992) provides excellent overviews of theories of the body. The series of essays in Featherstone, Hepworth and Turner (1991) exemplify the different approaches used to analyse the body. The edited volume by Csordas (1994) places emphasis upon a phenomenological reading. Ramazanoglu (1993) also explores the different approaches of feminism to Foucault's work.

3 Csordas describes embodiment as 'being-in-the-world, a term from phenomenology that captures the sense of lived experience defined by our perceptions and engagement with the world (1994). As Leder writes (1992:25) 'We cannot understand the meaning and form of objects without reference to the bodily powers through which we engage them—our senses, motility, language, desires. The lived body is not just one thing in the world, but a way in which the world comes to be.'

4 See for example the works of Dixon-Mueller and Wasserheit 1991, Jacobson 1991, Gray and Underwood 1991, and Germain 1987.

5 Hantrakul (1988) gives an estimate of the numbers of prostitutes as 500 000 to 700 000 women. Viravaidya suggests there are 700 000 women involved in prostitution (1990). Ungphakorn suggests a figure of 200 000 to 500 000 women (1990). The Thai Red Cross gives an estimate of 120 000 to 150 000 prostitutes (Sittitrai 1990a).

6 Matsui (1989) gives a description of prostitution in Chinese teahouses. Several studies of prostitution in establishments catering for local clients exist (Muecke 1992, Santasombat, 1992). A number of authors have also described the relationships between international tourism and the growth of the sex industry in Thailand (Heyzer 1986; Manderson 1990; Phongpaichit 1982b; Sereewat-Srisang 1987), as well as the global trade in Thai women and children (Skrobanek 1990; Truong 1990). The advent of HIV/AIDS in Thailand spurred a huge increase in academic studies on prostitution (for eg. Havanon, Knodel, & Bennett 1992; Van Esterik 1992).

7 These works for the most part concentrate upon women and only recently have there been studies exploring the construction of masculinity and the existence of a third gender category, the *katoey* a term which is generally applied to biological males, and more rarely with biological females (Jackson 1989). Jackson also documents the emergence of 'gay' male identity, a third identity in the previously binary structure of Thai male sex/gender identities of the demasculinised *katoey* and fully masculine

phu chai (Jackson 1996). Gay female identity is even more marginal in Thai studies and as yet studies of lesbian identity are predominantly urban with little work done within rural communities (Thongthiraj 1994).

[8] One baht weight of gold refers to a measurement of weight of gold that had a market price of approximately 4000 baht (A$250) at the time of this research.

[9] Giddens suggests that modernity be understood as a particular manner of experiencing social life based upon certain types of arrangements of political and economic power characteristic of nation-states and capitalism (Giddens 1990). Up until 1893, the Northeast consisted of semi-independent principalities under indirect Siamese rule. In 1893, the Lao-speaking territories were split when the French forced Siam to give up territories east of the Mekhong in the Franco-Siamese Treaty of 1893 (Keyes 1989). This spurred the implementation of a series of provincial administrative reforms to assure Siamese authority over the outlying provinces, along with the economic development of a capitalist market economy. The achievement of the status of Thailand as a newly industrialising country (NID) marks the capitalist modernisation of the Thai state.

[10] Agricultural incomes calculated from my household survey data ranged from no income, in cases where the family produced only enough rice and other crops for their own consumption, to 37 610 baht/annum, for a household of eight people who farmed 29 rai of sticky rice and 5 rai of ordinary rice, 5 rai of cassava and grew tobacco and lucerne seed in addition. They owned two motorcycles and had borrowed 45 000 baht from the BAAC to buy a ploughing machine. Village statistics estimate household income for the entire *tambon* (all twelve villages which constitute the administrative district) to be 13 400 baht/year (Thailand, Dept of Rural Development 1989b). It is uncertain how this is calculated and whether this includes debts and income received from migratory labour.

[11] The association of water with masculine fertility is central in many Isan rituals (Tambiah 1970:351-66,52). Tai-speaking people across the region believe there is an inherent link between the nurturing qualities of women, earth and rice complemented by maleness as potency, 'manifest in the power men have to plant the seed in women and the seed of rice in the earth' (Davis 1984a:77; Hanks 1972; Keyes 1986:123). This association is also found in other parts of Asia, where water is associated with male gods who impregnate the female earth to give birth to rice (Blanchet 1984: 42-43,47; Manderson 1986b).

[12] In this sense, the word *hoi* carries another nuance of meaning as it may describe the 'hanging or suspension' of an object but also 'to follow behind' (Phintong 1989:880).

[13] *Lap* is a meat dish consisting of beef, buffalo, pork, fish or chicken, finely chopped and combined with coriander, mint, shallots, fish sauce, lime juice, chillies and crushed roasted sticky rice. When made with beef, buffalo or fish meat, it may be prepared with raw meat with bile added for flavour.

[14] *Bun bang fai* is the rocket festival held in the sixth month of the Lao calender. It is notable for its drunken bawdiness and the use of wooden phalluses in mock sexual acts to incite the sky to release the rain upon the earth. Gender inversions are notable with many transvestites dancing in the procession around the village. Similarly,

ordination processions in Ban Srisaket were rowdy affairs featuring behaviours not normally acceptable in normal situations such as men and women touching, women drinking, dancing *kathoey* and open flirtation.

[15] As *mae chi*, women wear white robes, shave their heads and observe extra precepts as lay devotees but are not allowed to be ordained and generally have a low status in Thailand, although this is changing (Kabilsingh 1991; Muecke 1989; Van Esterik 1982b). The popular image of *mae chi* is of old women who are misfits or without family support, or young women escaping unhappy love affairs or too ill to bear normal life. Although there were no *mae chi* in either temple at Ban Srisaket, there were some at the temple of a village thirteen kilometres away where they were responsible for cleaning and cooking for the monks. While women cannot ordain, female meditators predominate clerical and lay circles (Van Esterik 1982a). Thitsa sees this as 'indicative . . . of women taking advantage in an area of Buddhism still relatively free of state control and male authority structures' (Thitsa 1983:26).

[16] Keyes noted as early as 1963 that in his field-site village 72 per cent of men between the ages of 20 and 40 had worked in Bangkok or Vientiane (Keyes 1975:291). Parnwell (1986:103) states that in the Isan village he studied, 53.4 per cent of people under the age of 51 had migrated at some time. At the time of his survey, 53 per cent of all the villagers then aged between 15-29 had migrated, of which 78 per cent had left for urban settings. Lightfoot, Fuller and Kamnuansilpa (1983) found that 46 per cent of people between 15-29 years who are normally resident in the study villages had been in Bangkok for a least part of the year. Larson et al (1993) report that in three villages they studied, 92 per cent of individuals aged between 15 to 29 had migrated at least once in their life for no less than a month, 80 per cent had migrated in the previous year and 39 per cent expected to migrate the following year.

[17] Data from Tirasawat (1985:481) suggests 60-62 percent of migrants are male. A study by Onchan showed 62 percent of migrants are male (1985:458). The sex distributions reported here also reflect the large numbers of men who migrate from Ban Srisaket for cane-cutting work.

[18] I am unable to give a sex distribution for people under age 20 in the 1993 data.

[19] Increasingly, women from Ban Srisaket live with men they have met in Bangkok without the approval of kin, eventually returning to the village to seek permission to marry. As Grandmother Thong noted, the traditional involvement of elder kin in marriage negotiations is being ignored: "Nowadays, young women, they all just go to find husbands from *thang thai* (the Thai region)". Now increasingly women are the mobile ones, choosing their partners without the advice of their kin and crossing ethnic boundaries to marry Central Thai outsiders who they have met in the city.

[20] *Meng sap* refers both to a cockroach and also to a rank smelling vine.

[21] The concept of pluralism developed through its use by Kleinman (1976; 1980), Janzen (1978) and Leslie (1977).

[22] More recently, a number of authors use the terms 'local' and 'global' for descriptions of medical practice. Here 'global' is a substitute for Western biomedical practices now institutionlised in most countries, and local is used for 'other' practice. Yet implicit in these terms is a spatial metaphor for what is really a

statement about relative power. Such a geographical metaphor is deceptive, leading us to forget the market across the world for indigenous medicinal recipes and approaches to care. One only has to consider the ubiquity of Chinese medicinal treatments to see the dangers in spatial compartmentalising between the local and global.

[23] As Irvine notes, institutionalised forms of Thai traditional medicine make further distinctions between forty-two 'bodily constituents' (1982:120). My informants however, only described the importance of the balance between four *that:* fire, wind, earth, and water.

[24] Manderson (1981b; 1986a) provides an extensive description of humoral food classifications and medicine in Malaysia. I found ordinary villagers in Ban Srisaket largely unable to name which food were 'hot' and which were 'cold' except for some common foods, although many used dietary restrictions for certain ailments and dietary prophylaxis when ill. In those contexts they were able to state that such a food was 'hot' or 'cold' or 'itchy'. Mulholland states that within Thai traditional pharmacy there are three principal tastes, hot tasting drugs, cool tasting drugs and mild tasting drugs and nine medicinal tastes: astringent, sweet, *mau bu'a* (intoxicating/poisonous), bitter, hot and spicy, cool and fragrant, salty, sour and bland (1979:107-108).

[25] Eating rice, especially the symbolically laden sticky rice, marks the socialisation of a child into the Lao community. Before they can walk, young children are encouraged by adults to sit politely in a circle on a mat and place their hands together in a *wai* of respect to their elders each time they are passed a small ball of sticky rice. Adults derive enormous delight when the child begins to reach for the sticky rice basket themselves. Women say that rice is the only truly satisfying food for infants and introduce pre-chewed rice to babies when they are only a few weeks old. They say that if a baby cries it indicates that it is hungry for rice.

[26] *Mor waen khwan* use a small net as used to collect prawns and small fish to capture a lost soul at the scene of an accident or misfortune. I witnessed one such ritual take place at the scene of a motorcycle accident where the soul of the young man involved was said to have been jolted out by the shock and force of the accident.

[27] *Mor oen khwan* literally call the soul back to the person's body as in the ritual described at the beginning of this chapter.

[28] Tambiah provides a detailed description of *su khwan* ceremonies at marriage, pregnancy and ordination (1970:230-237) as does Heinze (1982).

[29] See Halpern (1963) for a description of *phi* beliefs in Laos, and Westermeyer (1988) for a summary of the lowland Lao conceptual system for understanding health which is in agreement with that of the ethnic Lao in North-east Thailand.

[30] These are a series of monthly rituals, many of which are specific to Northeast Thailand and lowland Laos, that follow the older Lao calender whereby the first month, *du'an ai*, is December. They were listed by Grandfather On as follows: 1st month *bun khaw kam*, 2nd month *bun kam khaw yai*, 3rd month *bun khaw ji*, 4th month *bun phawet*, 5th month *torn khun pi mai*, 6th month *bun bang fai*, 7th month *bun phasaphu'ng*, 8th month *khaw phansa*, 9th month *bun khaw pradap din*, 10th month *bun khaw sak,* 11th month *ok phansa*, 12th month *bun tord khatin*.

[31] Bamber (1987:188) describes how a number of illnesses in Thailand are understood to be caused by the entry of worms into the body, such as *sang*, a category of children's illnesses, and illness with symptoms that are consistent with nematodes and other parasitic infections. He also mentions dental caries which are commonly described as caused by worms or insects. In a conversation I had with one villager whose nephew had many dental caries, he asked, '*Maeng yang gin fan?*' ('What insects eat teeth?') to which a friend replied, '*Maeng gin khanom lai!*' ('The eat-sweets-a-lot insects!').

[32] In 1992, of the 21 deaths in Baan Srisaket, 14 were officially reported as from liver-related diseases, most likely due to cholangiocarcinomas (Haswell-Elkins 1992, pers. comm.). Liver fluke infection remains a major public health problem in many parts of Asia and has been a target of a public health campaign since 1953 (Sadun 1955).

[33] Fever and itchiness (puritis) is a common symptom of people with liver cancer as excess amounts of bilirubin are stored underneath the skin due to the poor functioning of the liver. Fevers may be caused as a result of the breakdown of homeostasis. See Pungpak (1985) on the clinical features of severe infection with liver flukes.

[34] Non-government organisations have also been involved in supporting indigenous medicinal practices through such organisations as the Herbal Medicine for Self-Reliance Project, the Project for the Revival of Thai Massage, the Cultural Centre for the Development of the North-eastern Villages and the Khorat Primary Health Care Group among others. These organisations emphasise community self-reliance and participation but have difficulty in negotiating an un-supportive political climate (see Cohen 1989a; Grand & Sri-ngernyuang 1989; Grand, Sri-ngernyuang & Streefland 1993).

[35] Nurse Silaa is a nurse/midwife who has completed tenth grade at school and then underwent an eighteen month course in midwifery training. Nurse Thong is a technical nurse who has undergone a two-year post secondary school certificate. It is possible for technical nurses to complete a further 2.5 years of training to become professional nurses.

[36] One of these, "Pirana" contains pyrazalone which has been banned in numerous countries in simple pain killers (Grand & Sri-ngernyuang 1989:57). Such combination analgesics are addictive, and there is a national lobby group which wants them banned from sale. Their regular use is associated with a high incidence of dyspepsia and peptic ulceration (Klinsong 1993).

[37] In 1991 the national expenditure on medication was estimated to be 60 000 million baht, 60 percent of the total health budget. According to the Drug Study Group, there are 30 000 formulas sold in Thailand ranking Thailand second in the world after India for the number of registered drugs (Klinsong 1993). Many traditional formulas sold are not registered on this list.

[38] See Nichter (1980) for a similar discussion of the importance of mode of administration and characteristics of medicines in India.

[39] A National Essential Drugs List containing 402 items was introduced in 1981. However, it is only implemented in the government sector where its principles are

not strictly followed with many physicians continuing to prescribe tradename medicines. The Drug Study Group research showed that 50% of medicines prescribed by physicians were tradename medicines (DSG 1978 in Grand & Sringernyuang 1989).

[40] Hanks (1988) writes that 'if a Thai or Lao man walks under a woman's skirt hanging perhaps on a clothesline or even walks under a line on which a skirt may have once been hung, every one of his protective amulets, including the Buddha locket is negated' (see also Hanks & Hanks 1963).

[41] The assumption of similarity between male and female bodies in Western medicine has resulted in male bodies traditionally being the test subjects for medications, dosage and side-effects. Only very recently has this assumption been challenged by a variety of women's groups who suggest that many medications have differential effects on women and are demanding the use of female test subjects as well as male.

[42] See Manderson (1981b; 1986a) and Ngin (1985) for a discussion of humoral properties in Malaysia.

[43] It is also to these spirits that women make appeals when contemplating abortion (see Chapter 7).

[44] Poulsen makes the only other reference to this ceremony that I have found (Poulsen 1983:85). He translates *kha suang* as 'to kill the worm'.

[45] A *mahanagai* monk refers to one of the two orders of monks in Thailand, the *thammayut* and *mahanagai*. The different sects may be identified by the way in which the monks robes are worn. The Thammayuttika Sect was founded by King Rama IV (Mongkut) and is characterised by am emphasis upon scholarship and discipline. The Mahanagai sect is associated particularly with the North-east forest monasteries and is noted for its meditation practices and supernatural powers (see Tambiah 1970; Tambiah 1984).

[46] For example, *ya satri phen phak* states on its label: *pen ya bamrung lohet. Prajum du'an ma mai pokathi thong khu'n fer lae win wiang on-plia* (This is a body-strengthening medicine (for) irregular menstruation, rising excess wind in the stomach, dizziness, weakness).

[47] Traditional healers recognise many different forms of *kamlert* that occur in neonates, such as green, yellow and black *kamlert*. The symptoms typically involve a neonate usually three to five days after birth and are suggestive of a range of conditions including neonatal tetanus and jaundice. Typically the child is said to die unless treated quickly by a *mor pow*. It is said that *kamlert* is caused by the mother of the child from a previous incarnation wishing to make to child return to heaven to be with her, thus people sometimes speak of the *mae kaw mae lang* as the *mae kamlert* ('mother' or source of the *kamlert*) (Poulsen 1983). The ritual 'claiming' of the new born child on the third day after birth described in Chapter 6 marks the child as belonging to the parents and no longer to the spirit world.

[48] Apart from epidemiological studies, recent work on AIDS in Thailand cover issues of sexual behaviours and attitudes (Thongchai & Guest 1995), the impact on women (Shah et al. 1991; Ungphakorn 1990), and female sex workers (Pornsiripongse & Rawangpan 1996), masculinity (Fordham 1995; Vanlandingham, Somboon, Grandjean, & Werasit 1995), sexual networks (Havanon et al. 1992), homosexuality

and risk behaviours (de Lind van Wijngaarden 1995), adolescent sexuality (Soonthorndhada 1996); social responses to care of HIV positive people (Fordham 1993), and media coverage of AIDS and education messages (Fordham 1996; Lyttleton 1993). In addition several studies provide detailed ethnography of AIDS in the North and North-east (see Lyttleton 1993; 1994a; 1994b; Whittaker 1996a) and education interventions (Maticka Tyndale, Haswell Elkins, Kuyyakanond, Kiewying & Elkins 1994a).

[49] Intravenous drug use is more predominant within urban populations and is more widespread in the Northern provinces where it is associated with a very high prevalence of HIV infection (Ford & Koetsawang 1991).

[50] Other non-government organisations involved in family planning include the Planned Parenthood Association of Thailand, The Association for Strengthening Information on the National Family Planning Program and the Thailand Association for Voluntary Sterilisation.

[51] Approximately 560 condoms were distributed by the health station at Ban Srisaket in 1992. The low numbers of condoms being supplied through the health station may be due to a number of factors. People may use a different source for their condoms as social marketing of condoms is widespread in Thailand. However, the health station is the first source of free condoms at the village level. The low numbers of people being supplied condoms included some of the village health volunteers who were given up to thirty at a time to distribute and so actual usage of condoms may be slightly higher than the percentage of users indicates.

[52] This attitude is specifically targeted in a rare poster promoting vasectomies that I collected from the storage area in a Provincial Public Health Centre. In the text of the poster a doctor asks a farmer how he is after his vasectomy to which the farmer replies: 'Very well, doctor. Heavy work or light work, whether outside the mosquito net or within, I am as *su* (a colloquial expression conveying a sense of fighting/strength/potency) as before!'

[53] The accuracy of local government statistics is uncertain as there is no indication how they are derived. A more accurate picture of local patterns of contraceptive use by women in Ban Srisaket is presented in this chapter. It is derived from the family planning data I collected from the village health station for 1992 for the entire *tambon* (sub-district) consisting of twelve *muban* (administrative villages). As this data refers to people who used the local health station for their family planning services, it may not represent all people using contraception in the twelve villages, as these services are also available elsewhere in district and regional centres. It also does not include any people who have been sterilised, since sterilisations are not performed locally and do not appear in local records.

[54] 1985 data (Chintana 1986) shows that in the North-east 56.2 per cent of currently married women use contraception, with 32 per cent of these using the pill, 34 per cent using female sterilisation, 11 per cent using injections, 18 per cent using IUDs, 4 per cent having partners with vasectomies and 1 per cent using other means.

[55] The injectable contraceptive known as Depo Provera (Depo Medroxyprogesterone Acetate, or DMPA) has not been approved of by the Food and Drug Administration in the United States due to reports of higher incidence of breast cancer in beagles

and evidence of congenital malformations among infants if accidentally exposed to the drug early in pregnancy. However, after a review, the United States Agency for International Development (USAID) recommended that Depo Provera should be made available to other countries that request it. The international controversy over the use of injectables has centred around the questions of long-term cancer risks of DMPA, and the ethics of its use in developing countries. A review for Save the Children Fund (Archer 1985) concluded that any long-term cancer risks are outweighed by the hazards of uncontrolled fertility for women in developing countries and noted that such risks also exist for other hormonal contraceptives. With correct counselling and use, the study concluded that injectable contraceptives provided highly effective, simple to use, and undetectable contraception.

[56]Humoral notions underlie local descriptions of tubal ligations, as either 'wet' ligations or 'dry' ligations. 'Wet' ligations are those done very soon after birth and are said to be less painful, whereas 'dry' ligations are those performed at times other than after birth.

[57] As noted in Chapter 5, female sterilisation is the most used method of contraception in Thailand with 22.5 per cent of married women of reproductive age (MWRA) using sterilisation in 1992 (in the North-east 25.7 per cent of MWRA were sterilised in 1992) (Thailand 1993).

[58] Although *phae thorng* is most commonly thought of as similar to a form of allergy, Hanks (Hanks 1963:33-34) also translates *phae thorng* as 'defeated by her pregnancy'. *Phae* may have this meaning within the imagery of pregnancy and childbirth as a battle in traditional texts (Rajadhon 1968).

[59] For further detail, see descriptions of this ceremony that follows the pattern of the *su khwan* ceremony described earlier in Poulsen (1983:97) and Tambiah (1970:239-251).

[60] Pitaktepsombati and Wongboonsin (1989) found that 73 per cent of rural women went to see trained medical personnel for prenatal care compared to 95 per cent of urban mothers.

[61] In 1992 the women who gave birth at home, or were given the placenta by hospital staff, buried the placentas of male children under a window, under stairs, under the eaves of the house, and under the eaves of the *horng phra* (the room in which the Buddha images are kept). The placentas of female babies were buried under a window of the house.

[62] See for example the work of Camey, Barrios, Guerrero et al (1996), Cominsky (1976), and Sesia (1996).

[63] See discussion in Chapter 3. Davis (1984b), Halpern (1963), Irvine (1982), and Poulsen (1983:266-267) provide further description of the dangers of these spirits.

[64] *Phi tai thang kom* is the name given to the spirit that arises from a death in childbirth when both mother and child die. Irvine suggests that this word is also associated with a similar word for circle and thus signifies the binding of the mother and child in a circle of life and death (Irvine 1982:266). In such cases the bodies of mother and child are separated and buried immediately to ensure that the aggrieved souls cannot leave the corpses and remain amongst the living. After a period of time, three to five years, the remains will be disinterred and given a Buddhist cremation.

[65] Post-partum warming is practiced in rural Korea, (Sich 1981), Bangladesh (Blanchet 1984), Taiwan (Chu 1996; Pillsbury 1982) Cambodia (Townsend & Rice 1996), and Malaysia (Laderman 1982; Manderson 1981a). It remains common practice amongst refugee and migrant groups in Western countries (Chu 1993; Mathews & Manderson 1981; Rice 1993; Rice 1994; Sargent, Marcucci, & Elliston 1983).

[66] The term *kam* is translated by Poulsen (1983) as meaning 'trouble' in the local Lao dialect. In contrast, Mougne (1978:77) gives the meaning, 'to observe restrictions'. The word *kam* is spelled as in karma and Phintong (1989:12) lists a number of translations such as 'work/action, kharma/fate, misfortune, things that happen as a result of one's kharma, to die/pass away'. As will be discussed in the text, Keyes also equates the use of the term *yu kam* with 'living in karma' and the symbolic role that this time has as marking the attainment of full maturity for women (Keyes 1986). The phrase *yu kam* is multivalent and probably encompasses all of the meanings described by various authors. *Yu fai* is a Central Thai term meaning simply to stay by the fire and is also used sometimes in Ban Srisaket.

[67] This medicine is called *ya tom* 'boiled medicine' and in Ban Srisaket usually consists of *phak kha* (galangal, *Languas Galanga*), *mak thaek* (unknown), bark of *mak fu'ang* (starfruit tree or *Averrhoa carambola L.*), *mai phi* (bamboos shoots, *Bambusa arundinacea* and other *Bambusa spp.*) that have withered, *makham*, (tamarind bark, *Tamarindus Indica L.*), and the outer peel of a tuber of *ya hua* (scientific name unknown). *Ton fang* (sappan wood, *Caesalpinia sappan L.*) is also used by some people.

[68] Mougne describes foods encouraged and forbidden during the post-partum period for women in the North of Thailand (1978:77-79). She argues that the colour of foods symbolically guides/determines those able to be eaten. 'White' foods are permitted because of a symbolic association with breast milk. No such pattern emerges from my data. Laderman explores the reasons why some foods are forbidden in Malaysia (1983:71). She finds that fish with inconsistent characteristics or disturbing colouration are considered dangerous because of their ambiguity or symbolic associations, and others are forbidden because they may be toxic.

[69] The data about the incidence of the custom is varied. In Northern Thailand, Mougne (1978:80) and Muecke (1976) describe the practice as one no longer practised or unlikely to continue, while Chirawatkul (1993; 1996) states that it is no longer practised in the North-eastern village she studied near to Khon Kaen. Poulsen (1983) describes the continuation of the practice in a North-eastern village and my observations and conversations with women in villages in Khon Kaen and Roi Et provinces in 1996 and 1997 confirm the continuation of this practice.

[70] The generic names of Floxacillan is flucloxacillan and is prescribed to treat any aerobic infections. Bactrim is trimethroprim/sulphamethoxazole and is given also to treat aerobic infections that may be resistant to the other antibiotics and to treat urinary tract infections. Metronidazole is already a generic name and is given to treat possible anaerobic infection.

[71] See Chaturachinda et al. 1981; Cook & Leoprapai 1974; Koetsawang 1973; 1993; Koetsawang, Gordon, & Pachauri 1974; Koetsawang, Saha, & Pachauri 1975; Koetsawang et al. 1978; Phuapradit, Sirivongs, & Chaturachinda 1985; Pinchun &

Chullapram 1993; Pongthai, Phuapradit, & Chaturachinda 1984; Rattakul 1971; Toongsuwan, Bhadrakom, & Usavajindawatn 1973; Population Council 1981; Narkavonnakit & Benett 1981; Thailand 1984; Narkavonnakit 1979a; Narkavonnakit 1979b; Rauyajin 1979; Burnight & Leoprapai 1977; Rauyajin 1979; Soonthorndhada 1996; Institute of Population Studies 1982; Varakamin, Devaphalin, Narkavonkit, & Wright 1977.

[72] See Burnight & Leoprapai 1977; Phuapradit, Sirivongs, & Chaturachinda 1986; Rauyajin 1979; Soonthorndhada 1996; Institute of Population Studies 1982; Varakamin, Devaphalin, Narkavonkit, & Wright 1977.

[73] These figures are based upon definitions under the International Classification of Disease (ICD) (Alpha Research 1994; 1997). Between the 1992 and 1994 figures the (ICD) underwent a revision and so the definitions may have been altered slightly.

[74] Under the ICD definition, this figure may include spontaneous natural abortions/ miscarriages as well as induced abortions, but it is likely that a large proportion of these women have had induced abortions.

[75] In Columbia the notion of a delayed menstruation *atrazo* is understood as a blocked menstrual flow which is a sign of ill health. The belief in Columbia that equates delayed menstruation with poor health allows for covert fertility regulation to take place in the guise for treating minor health disturbances (Browner 1985). In the Malaysian Chinese community Ngin notes that irregular menstruation is considered unclean and bad for a woman's health and remedies are taken to correct this (Ngin 1985). In Jamaica, Brody reports the use of bush teas to bring down a period (Brody 1985:170) as does Sobo (1996).

[76] I have a collection of similar capsules purchased at various rural drug stores, all stating they are for irregular menstruation or 'recent cases of amenorrhoea' and all containing warnings against their use by pregnant women. They include the wonderfully named 'Pregnoneforte' costing 39 baht for 3 capsules, each containing Ethistherone, 50mg, Ethinyl Estradiol 150 mg and Cyanocobalamin, 100mg. 'K.B Estracap' and Sibbon Forte' sell for 32 baht and both contain 2 capsules of Ethistherone, 100mg, and Ethinyl Estradiol, 0.05mg. 'Sibbon Forte' also includes added advice not to drink iced water or coconut milk which as explained in Chapter 4 is understood humourally to prevent menstrual blood from flowing out. Finally, each capsule of Duoton T.P contains Ethistherone, 75mg, and Ethinyl Estradiol 0.05mg and is sold for 25 baht for 2 capsules.

[77] In contrast to the women attending the outpatients' antenatal clinic who wore pregnancy dresses even in the first trimester, women who were seeking abortions were all dressed in pants, even those who were already four months pregnant. The signification of the clothing of these women was striking.

[78] Women who die in childbirth or in unnatural circumstances are said to become *phi tai hong*, fierce spirits.

Bibliography

AbouZahr, Carla, Vlassoff, Carol, & Kumar, Anuradha 1996 'Quality Health Care for Women: A Global Challenge', *Health Care for Women International,* vol. 17, no. 5, pp. 449-68.

Abu-Lughod, Lila 1990 'The romance of resistence: tracing transformations of power through Bedouin women', *American Ethnologist,* vol. 17, pp. 41-55.

Adams, Vincanne 1992 'The Production of Self and Body in Sherpa-Tibetan Society', *Anthropological Approaches to the Study of Ethnomedicine,* ed. M. Nichter, Gordon and Breach, Amsterdam, pp. 149-90.

Alpha Research 1994 *Pocket Thailand Public Health 1995,* Alpha Research Company Ltd & Manager Information Services, Bangkok.

Alpha Research 1997 *Pocket Thailand Public Health 1997,* Alpha Research Company Ltd, Bangkok.

Anonymous 1981a 'Chamlong lashes Abortion Bill'. *Bangkok Post,* Friday, 2 October, p. 1.

Anonymous 1981b 'Chamlong quits over abortion controversy'. *Bangkok Post*, Wednesday, 21 October, p. 1.

Anonymous 1981c 'House Passes Abortion Bill'. *Bangkok Post*, Wednesday, 30 September, p. 3.

Anonymous 1981d 'Senate rejects Abortion Bill'. *Bangkok Post,* Saturday, 19 December, p. 1.

Anonymous 1996 'Abortion Law Amendment to be Considered'. *Bangkok Post,* Friday, 9 February, p. 1.

Anonymous 2524 (1981a) *'Khwam kor mor tham thaeng. Wuthi samachig mai yomrap rang phor ror por duay khanaen 147 tor 1* (Abortion law overturned. Senate members don't accept bill 147 votes to 1)'. *Dailynews,* Saturday, 19 December, p. 1.

Anonymous 2524 (1981b) *Phor ror por luk mai mi phor phan sapha riaproi thong mai thongklua toklong tham thaeng day* ('Fatherless child' bill passes through parliament. Don't fear pregnancy, you may have an abortion)'. *Thairat,* Wednesday, 30 September, p. 1.

Anonymous 2524 (1981c) *'Wutisapha khwam rang kor mor tham thaeng athiprai khan thang thi prachum* (Senate overturns draft abortion law. All the meeting opposes the debate)'. *Siamrat,* Saturday, 19 December, p. 1.

Anuman, Phya Rajadhon 1961 'Customs Connected with Birth and the Rearing of Children', *Life and Ritual in Old Siam. Three Studies of Thai Life and Customs,* ed. W. J. Gedney, HRAF Press, New Haven.

Archer, E. 1985 *Injectable Contraceptives. The Role of Long-Acting Progestagens in Contraception in Developing Countries,* Save the Children Fund, London.

Bailey, M. E. 1993 'Foucauldian Feminism: Contesting Bodies, Sexuality and Identity', *Up Against Foucault: Explorations of Some Tensions Between Foucault and Feminism,* ed. C. Ramazanoglu, Routledge, London, pp. 99-122.

Bamber, Scott 1987 'Metaphor and Illness Classification in Traditional Thai Medicine', *Asian Folklore Studies,* vol. XLVI, no. 2, pp. 179-95.

Bell, Peter 1992 'Gender and Economic Development in Thailand', *Gender and Development in Southeast Asia: Proceedings of the Twentieth Meeting of the Canadian Council for Southeast Asian Studies,* eds. P. V. Esterik & J. V. Esterik, Canadian Asian Studies Association, York University, Montreal.

Bhattachary-ya, Deborah P 1983 'Psychiatric Pluralism in Bengal, India', *Social Science and Medicine,* vol. 17, no. 14, pp. 947-56.

Bhiromrut, Patama no date *Report. A study of the Acceptability of Norplant Implant in Thailand to Improve Product Introduction Effort (Use of Group Discussion Research)* Thailand, Family Health Division, National Family Planning Program.

Blanchet, Therese 1984 *Women, Pollution and Marginality: Meanings and Rituals of Birth in Rural Bangladesh,* University Press, Dhaka.

Boonmongkon, Pimpawun 1997 'Living Through Infertility: From Loss to Resolution Over the Life Course of Thai Women', *Women, Gender Relations and Development in Thai Society,* eds. V. Somswasdi & S. Theobald, Vol. 2, Women Studies Center, Faculty of Social Sciences, Chiang Mai University, Chiang Mai, pp. 499-516.

Boonmongkon, Pimpawun, Nichter, Mark, Pylypa, Jennifer, & Chantapasa, Kornkaew 1998 *Understanding Women's Experience of Gynecological Problems: An Ethnographic Case Study from Northeast Thailand,* Center for Health Policy Studies, Faculty of Social Science and Humanities, Mahidol University, Bangkok.

Bordo, Susan 1993 'Feminism, Foucault and the Politics of the Body', *Up Against Foucault. Explorations of Some Tensions Between Foucault and Feminism,* ed. C. Ramazanoglu, Routledge, London, pp. 179-202.

Bourdieu, Pierre 1977 *Outline of a Theory of Practice,* (Richard Nice, Trans.) Cambridge University Press, Cambridge.

Bourdieu, Pierre, & Passeron, Jean Claude 1977 *Reproduction in Education, Society and Culture,* Routledge & Kegan Paul, London.

Brodwin, Paul 1996 *Medicine and morality in Haiti: The contest for healing power,* Cambridge University Press, Cambridge.

Brody, Eugene B. 1985 'Everyday Knowledge of Jamaican Women', *Women's Medicine. A Cross-Cultural Study of Indigenous Fertility Regulation,* ed. L. F. Newman, Rutgers University Press, New Brunswick, New Jersey, pp. 161-78.

Brown, D. 1994 'Thailand: Internal colonialism and ethnic rebellion', *The State and Ethnic Politics in Southeast Asia,* Routledge, New York, pp. 158-205.

Brown, Tim, & Sittitrai, Werasit 1993 *Estimates of Recent HIV Infection Levels in Thailand,* Bangkok, Program on AIDS, Thai Red Cross Society.

Browner, C. H. 1985 'Traditional Techniques for Diagnosis, Treatment, and Control of pregnancy in Cali, Colombia', *Women's Medicine. A Cross-Cultural Study of Indigenous Fertility Regulation,* ed. L. F. Newman, Rutgers University Press, New Brunswick, New Jersey, pp. 99-123.

Bruce, Judith 1990 'Fundamental elements of the quality of care: A simple framework', *Studies in Family Planning,* vol. 21, pp. 61-91.

Brun, Viggo, & Shumacher, Trond 1994 *Traditional Herbal Medicine in Northern Thailand,* White Lotus, Bangkok.

Buckley, Thomas, & Gottlieb, Alma (eds.) 1988 *Blood Magic: The Anthropology of Menstruation,* University of California Press, Berkeley.

Burnight, Robert G. & Leoprapai, Boonlert 1977 'Attitudes of Rural Thai Women Towards Induced Abortions', *Journal of Biosocial Science,* vol. 9, no. 1, pp. 61-72.

Camey, Xochitl Castaneda, Barrios, Cecilia Garcia, Guerrero, Xochitl Romero, Nunez-Urquiza, Rosa Maria, Hernandez, et al 1996 'Traditional Birth Attendants in Mexico: Advantages and Inadequacies of Care for Normal Deliveries', *Social Science and Medicine,* vol. 43, no. 2, pp. 199-207.

Carter, Anthony T. 1995 'Agency and fertility: For an ethnography of practice', *Situating fertility: Anthropology and demographic inquiry,* ed. S. Greenhalgh, Cambridge University Press, Cambridge, pp. 55-85.

Cecil, Roseanne (ed.) 1996 *The Anthropology of Pregnancy Loss: Comparative Studies in Miscarriage, Stillbirth and Neonatal Death,* Berg, Oxford.

Chaturachinda, K., Tangtrakul, S., Pongthai, S., Phuapradit, W., Phausopone, A., Benchakan, V., & Clinton, J. J. 1981 'Abortion: an epidemiologic study at Ramathibodi hospital', *Studies In Family Planning,* vol. 12, no. 6/7, pp. 257-62.

Chayovan, Napaporn, Kamnuansilpa, Peerasit, & Knodel, John 1988 *Thailand Demographic and Health Survey, 1987,* Institute of Population Studies, Chulalongkorn University, Bangkok.

Chintana, Pejaranonda 1986 *Contraceptive Method Choice in Thailand,* National Statistical Office of the Prime Minister, Bangkok.

Chirawatkul, Siriporn 1993 'Sud Lyad, Sud Luuk, The Social Construction of Menopause in Northeastern Thailand' Unpublished PhD, University of Queensland, Brisbane.

_____ 1996 'Blood beliefs in a transitional culture in Northeast Thailand', *Maternity and Reproductive Health in Asian Societies,* eds. P. Liamputtong Rice & L. Manderson, Harwood Academic Publishers, Amsterdam, pp. 247-60.

Chirawatkul, Siriporn, & Manderson, Lenore 1994 'Perceptions of Menopause in Northeast Thailand: Contested Meaning and Practice', *Social Science and Medicine,* vol. 39, no. 11, pp. 1545-54.

Chu, Cordia 1993 *Reproductive Health Beliefs and Practices of Chinese and Australian Women,* Women's Research Program, Population Studies Center, National Taiwan University, Taipei, Taiwan.

_____ 1996 '*Tio Yueh-tzu* (sitting the month) in contemporary Taiwan', *Maternity and Reproductive Health in Asian Societies,* eds. P. Liamputtong Rice & L. Manderson, Harwood Academic Publishers, Amsterdam, pp. 191-204.

Cohen, Paul T. 1989 'The Politics of Primary Health Care in Thailand, with special reference to Non-Government Organizations', *The Political Economy of Primary Health Care in Southeast Asia,* eds. P. T. Cohen & J. Purcal, Australian Development Studies Network, ASEAN Training Centre for Primary Health Care Development, Canberra, pp. 159-76.

Cominsky, Susan 1976 'Cross-cultural Perspectives on Midwifery', *Medical Anthropology,* eds. F. Grollig & H. Haley, Mouton, The Hague.

Cook, M. J., & Leoprapai, B. 1974 'Some observations on abortion in Thailand', *Paper presented at the Asian Regional Research Seminar on Psychosocial Aspects of Abortion, Kathmandu, Nepal, November.*

Cook, Rebecca J. 1993 'International Human Rights and Women's Reproductive Health', *Studies in Family Planning,* vol. 24, no. 2, pp. 73-86.

Correa, Sonia 1994 *Population and Reproductive Rights: Feminist Perspectives from the South,* Zed Books Ltd, DAWN, London.

Csordas, Thomas J. 1994 'Introduction: the body as representation and being-in-the-world', *Embodiment and Experience: the existential ground of culture and self,* ed. T. J. Csordas, Cambridge University Press, Cambridge, pp. 1-24.

Cunningham, C. E. 1970 'Thai "Injection Doctors" Antibiotic Mediators', *Social Science and Medicine,* vol. 4, pp. 1-24.

Davis, Richard 1984a 'Muang Matrifocality', *Mankind,* vol. 14, no. 4, suppl. 3, pp. 263-271.

_____ 1984b *Muang metaphysics: a study of Northern Thai myth and ritual,* Pandora, Bangkok.

de Lind van Wijngaarden, Jan W. 1995 'The Variety of Homosexual Experience in the Context of HIV/AIDS', Paper presented at the conference on Gender and Sexuality in Modern Thailand, 11-12 July, 1995, Australian National University, Canberra.

Demaine, Harvey 1986 'Kanpatthana: Thai Views of Development', *Context, Meaning and Power in Southeast Asia,* eds. M. Hobart & R. H. Taylor, Southeast Asia Program, Cornell University, Ithaca, New York, pp. 93-114.

Devisch, Rene 1998 'Treating the affect by remodelling the body in a Yaka healing cult', *Bodies and persons: Comparative perspectives from Africa and Melanesia,* eds. M. Lambek & A. Strathern, Cambridge University Press, Cambridge, pp. 127-57.

Dixon-Mueller, Ruth 1993 *Population Policy and Women's Rights: Transforming Reproductive Choice,* Praeger, Westport.

Dixon-Mueller, Ruth, & Wasserheit, Jan 1991 *The Culture of Silence: Reproductive Tract Infections Among Women in the Third World,* International Women's Health Coalition, New York.

Donabedian, A. 1988 'The quality of care: How can it be assessed?' *Journal of the American Medical Association,* vol. 260, pp. 1743-48.

Douglas, Mary 1966 *Purity and Danger: an analysis of concepts of pollution and taboo,* Routledge and Kegan Paul, London.

Eberhardt, Nancy 1988 'Introduction', *Gender, Power, and the Construction of the Moral Order: Studies from the Thai Periphery,* ed. N. Eberhardt, Centre for Southeast Asian Studies, University of Wisconsin, Madison, pp. 3-13.

Elson, Diane, & Pearson, Ruth 1981 'The Subordination of Women and the Internationalisation of Factory Production', *Of Marriage and the Market: Women's Subordination in International Perspective,* eds. K. Young, C. Wolkowitz, & R. McCullagh, CSE Books, London, pp. 144-66.

Farmer, Paul 1992 *AIDS and Accusation: Haiti and the Geography of Blame,* University of California Press, Berkeley.

Fiedler, Deborah Cordero 1996 'Authoritative Knowledge and Birth Territories in Contemporary Japan', *Medical Anthropology Quarterly,* vol. 10, no. 2, pp. 195-212.

Fongkaew, Warunee 1997 'Female Sexuality and Reproductive Health in a Northern Thai Suburb', *Women, Gender Relations and Development in Thai Society,* eds. V. Somswasdi & S. Theobald, Vol. 2, Women Studies Center, Faculty of Social Sciences, Chiang Mai University, Chiang Mai, pp. 577-620.

Ford, N. & Koetsawang, Suporn 1991 'The Socio-Cultural Context of the Transmission of HIV in Thailand', *Social Science and Medicine,* vol. 33, no. 4, pp. 405-414.

Ford, N. & Saiprasert, S. 1993 *Destinations Unknown: The Gender Construction and Changing Nature of the Sexual Lifestyles of Thai Youth,* Paper presented at The 5th International Conference on Thai Studies, 5-10 July, SOAS, London.

Fordham, Graham 1993 'The Northern Thai Response to the AIDS Pandemic: A Cultural Analysis', Paper presented at The 5th International Conference on Thai Studies, 5-10 July, SOAS, London.

_____ 1995 'Whisky, Women and Song: Men, Alcohol and AIDS in Northern Thailand', *Australian Journal of Anthropology,* vol. 6, no. 3, pp. 154-77.

_____ 1996 'The Construction of HIV/AIDS as a Disease Threat in the Northern Thai (Print) Media', Paper presented at The 6th International Conference on Thai Studies, 1-17 October, Chiang Mai, Thailand.

Foucault, Michel 1973 *The Birth of the Clinic,* Tavistock, London.

_____ 1977 *Discipline and Punish: The Birth of the Prison,* Penguin, London.

_____ 1980 *Power/Knowledge: selected interviews and other writings, 1972-1977,* Pantheon, New York.

_____ 1984 *The History of Sexuality: An Introduction,* Penguin, London.

Frank, Arthur W. 1991 'For a Sociology of the Body: an Analytical Review', *The Body: Social Process and Cultural Theory,* eds. M. Featherstone, M. Hepworth, & B. S. Turner, Sage Publications, London, pp. 36-5.

Georges, Eugenia 1996 'Abortion Policy and Practice in Greece', *Social Science and Medicine,* vol. 42, no. 4, pp. 509-20.

Germain, Adrienne 1989 'The Christopher Tietze International Symposium: An Overview', *International Journal of Gynecology and Obstetrics,* suppl. 3, pp. 1-8.

Giddens, Anthony 1990 *The Consequences of Modernity,* Polity Press, Cambridge.

Ginsburg, Faye D. 1989 *Contested lives: the abortion debate in an American community,* University of California Press, Berkeley.

Ginsburg, Faye. & Rapp, Rayna. 1991 'The Politics of Reproduction', *Annual Review of Anthropology,* vol. 20, pp. 311-43.

_____ (eds.) 1995a *Conceiving the New World Order: The Global Politics of Reproduction,* University of California Press, Berkeley.

_____ 1995b 'Introduction: Conceiving the New World Order', *Conceiving the New World Order: The Global Politics of Reproduction,* eds. F. D. Ginsburg & R. Rapp, University of California Press, Berkeley, pp. 1-17.

Gordon, Alec & Sirisambhand, Napat (eds.) 1987 *Thai Rural Women and Agricultural Change: Approaches and a Case Study,* Women's Studies Programme, Chulalongkorn University, Bangkok.

Grand, Amanda Le & Sri-ngernyuang, Luechai 1989 *Herbal Drugs in Primary Health Care. Thailand: The Impact of Promotional Activities on Drug Consumption, Drug Provision and Self-Reliance,* Mahidol University, Bangkok.

Grand, Amanda Le, Sri-ngernyuang, Luechai, & Streefland, Pieter H. 1993 'Enhancing Appropriate Drug Use: The Contribution of Herbal Medicine Promotion: A Case Study in Rural Thailand', *Social Science and Medicine,* vol. 36, no. 8, pp. 1023-35.

Gray, Jennifer 1990 'The Road to the City: Young Women and Transition in Northern Thailand' Unpublished PhD Thesis, Macquarie University, Sydney.

Greenhalgh, Susan 1995a 'Afterword: (Re)capturing reproduction for anthropology', *Situating fertility: Anthropology and demographic inquiry,* ed. S. Greenhalgh, Cambridge University Press, Cambridge, pp. 259-63 .

_____ 1995b 'Anthropology theorises reproduction: Integrating practice, political, economic, and feminist perspectives', *Situating fertility: Anthropology and demographic inquiry,* ed. S. Greenhalgh, Cambridge University Press, Cambridge, pp. 3-28.

_____ (ed.) 1995c *Situating fertility: Anthropology and demographic inquiry,* Cambridge University Press, Cambridge.

Hale, Ann 1979 'A Reassessment of Northern Thai Matrilineages', *Mankind,* vol. 12, pp. 138-50.

_____ 1984 'The Search for a Jural Rule: Women in Southeast Asia - the Northern Thai Cults in Perspective', *Mankind,* vol. 14, no. 4, suppl. 3, pp. 330-38.

Halpern, Joel M. 1963 'Traditional Medicine and the Role of the Phii in Laos', *Eastern Anthropologist,* vol. 16, pp. 191-200.

Handwerker, W. Penn 1990 'Politics and Reproduction: A Window on Social Change', *Births and Power: Social Change and the Politics of Reproduction,* ed. W. P. Handwerker, Westview Press, Boulder, pp. 1-38.

Hanks, Jane Richardson 1963 *Maternity and Its Rituals in Bang Chan,* Cornell Thailand Project, Cornell University, Ithaca.

_____ 1988 'The Power of Akha Women', *Gender, Power, and the Construction of the Moral Order: Studies from the Thai Periphery*, ed. N. Eberhardt, Center for Southeast Asian Studies, University of Wisconsin, Madison, pp. 13-31.

Hanks, Lucien M 1972 *Rice and Man: Agricultural Ecology in Southeast Asia*, Aldine Atherton Inc, Chicago.

Hanks, Lucien M, & Hanks, Jane Richardson 1963 'Thailand: Equality Between the Sexes', *Women in the New Asia*, ed. B. E. Ward, UNESCO, Geneva, pp. 424-51.

Hantrakul, Sukanya 1988 'Prostitution in Thailand', *Development and Displacement: Women in Southeast Asia*, eds. G. Chandler, N. Sullivan, & J. Branson, Centre for Southeast Asian Studies, Monash University, Melbourne, pp. 115-36.

Hardacre, Helen 1997 *Marketing the Menacing Fetus in Japan*, University of California Press, Berkeley and Los Angeles.

Havanon, Napaporn, Knodel, John, & Bennett, Tony 1992 *Sexual Networking in a Provincial Thai Setting*, AIDSCAP, Bangkok, Thailand.

Heinze, Ruth-Inge 1982 *Tham Khwam: How to Contain the Essence of Life*, Singapore University Press, Singapore.

Heyzer, Noeleen 1986 'The Trade in Female Sexuality', *Working Women in South-East Asia*, ed. N. Heyzer, Open University Press, Philadelphia, pp. 52-63.

Hobart, Mark 1993 'Introduction: the growth of ignorance?', *An Anthropological Critique of Development: The Growth of Ignorance*, ed. M. Hobart, Routledge, London, pp. 1-30.

Hull, Terence H, Sarwono, Sarsanto W, & Widyantoro, Ninuk 1993 'Induced Abortion in Indonesia', *Studies in Family Planning*, vol. 24, no. 4, pp. 241-51.

Hull, Valerie, & Simpson, M (eds.) 1985 *Breastfeeding, Child Health and Birth Spacing: Cross-cultural Perspectives*, vol. 24, Croom Helm, London, pp. 241-51.

Hull, Valerie J. 1996 'Improving quality of care in family planning: how far have we come?', South and East Asia Regional Working Papers 5, The Population Council, Jakarta.

Hunter, Cynthia L. 1996 'Women as "Good Citizens": Maternal and Child Health in a Sasak Village', *Maternity and Reproductive Health in Asian Societies*, eds. P. Liamputtong Rice & L. Manderson, Harwood Academic Publishers, Amsterdam, pp. 169-89.

Institute of Population Studies 1982 *Knowledge and Attitudes Concerning Abortion Practice in Urban and Rural Areas of Thailand*. Bangkok, Institute of Population Studies, Chulalongkorn University.

Irvine, Walter 1982 'The Thai- Yuan "Madman" and the "Modernising, Developing Thai Nation" as Bounded Entities Under Threat: A Study in the Replication of a Single Image' Unpublished PhD, University of London, London.

Jackson, Peter 1989 *Male Homosexuality in Thailand*, Global Academic Publishers, Elmhurst, New York.

_____ 1996 '*Kathoey* >< Gay>< Man: The Historical Emergence of Gay Male Identity in Thailand', *Sites of Desire, Economies of Pleasure: Sexualities in Asia and the Pacific*, eds. L. Manderson & M. Jolly, The University of Chicago Press, Chicago, pp. 166-90.

Janzen, John M 1978 'The Comparative Study of Medical Systems as Changing Social Systems', *Social Science and Medicine*, vol. 12, pp. 121-29.

Jeffery, Patricia, Jeffery, Roger, & Lyon, Andrew 1989 *Labour pains and labour power*, Zed Books, London.

Jeffery, Roger, & Jeffery, Patricia M. 1993 'Traditional Birth Attendants in Rural North India', *Knowledge, Power and Practice: The Anthropology of Medicine and Everyday Life*, eds. S. Lindenbaum & M. Lock, University of California Press, Berkeley, pp. 7-31.

JICA 1992 'Public Health Service System Development Project at the District Level, Khon Kaen Province', Unpublished paper, Provincial Health Office, Japan International Cooperation Agency (JICA) Project, Khon Kaen.

Jirojwong, Sansnee 1996 'Health beliefs and the use of antenatal care among pregnant women in southern Thailand', *Maternity and Reproductive Health in Asian Societies,* eds. P. Liamputtong Rice & L. Manderson, Harwood Academic Publishers, Amsterdam, pp. 61-82.

Johnson, Stanley Patrick 1995 *The politics of population: the International Conference on Population and Development, Cairo 1994,* Earthscan Publications, London.

Jolly, Margaret 1998 'Introduction. Colonial and postcolonial plots in histories of maternities and modernities', *Maternities and Modernities: Colonial and postcolonial experiences in Asia and the Pacific,* eds. K. Ram & M. Jolly, Cambridge University Press, Cambridge, pp. 114-43.

_____ 1998b *What borders? Whose being? The sexuality and fertility of states,* Unpublished m.s.

Jordan, Brigitte 1993 [1978] *Birth in Four Cultures: A Cross-Cultural Investigation of Childbirth in Yucatan, Holland, Sweden and the United States,* 4th ed., Waveland Press, Prospect Heights, Illinois.

Jordan, Glenn, & Weedon, Chris 1995 *Cultural Politics: Class, Gender, Race and the Postmodern World,* Blackwell, Oxford.

Kabeer, Naila 1992 *From Fertility Reduction to Reproductive Choice: Gender Perspectives on Family Planning. Institute of Development Studies Discussion Paper no. 299, March 1992,* IDS Publications, Brighton, England.

Kabilsingh, Chatsumarn 1991 *Thai Women in Buddhism,* Parallax Press, Berkeley, California.

Kanchanaraksa, S. 1987 *Review of the Health Situation in Thailand: Priority Ranking of Diseases,* National Epidemiology Board of Thailand, Bangkok.

Kay, Margarita 1982 *The Anthropology of Human Birth,* F A Davis Co, Philadelphia.

Kendall, Laurel 1987 'Cold Wombs in Balmy Honolulu: Ethnomedicine among Korean Immigrants', *Social Science and Medicine,* vol. 25, no. 4, pp. 367-76.

Keyes, Charles F. 1975 'The Northeastern Thai Village: Stable Order and Changing World', *Journal of the Siam Society,* vol. 63, pp. 177-207.

_____ 1984 'Mother or mistress but never a monk: Buddhist notions of female gender in rural Thailand', *American Ethnologist,* vol. 11, no. 2, pp. 223-41.

_____ 1986 'Ambiguous Gender: Male Initiation in a Northern Thai Buddhist Society', *Gender and Religion: On the Complexity of Symbols,* eds. C. Walker Bynum, S. Harrell, & P. Richman, Beacon Press, Boston.

_____ 1989 *Thailand: Buddhist Kingdom as Modern Nation-State,* Editions Duang Kamol, Bangkok.

Kielmann, Karina 1998 'Barren ground: contesting identities of infertile women in Pemba, Tanzania', *Pragmatic women and body politics,* eds. M. Lock & P. A. Kaufert, Cambridge University Press, Cambridge, pp. 127-63.

Kirsch, A Thomas 1975 'Economy, Polity and Religion in Thailand', *Change and Perspective in Thai Society: Essays in Honour of Lauriston Sharp,* eds. G. W. Skinner & A. T. Kirsch, Cornell University Press, Ithaca, New York.

_____ 1982 'Buddhism, Sex-Roles and the Thai Economy', *Women of Southeast Asia,* ed. P. V. Esterik, Northern Illinois University, Wyoming, pp. 16-41.

Kleinman, Arthur 1976 *Medicine in Chinese Cultures: Comparative Studies of Health Care in Chinese and Other Populations,* U.S. Government Printing Office, Washington D.C.

_____ 1980 *Patients and Healers in the Context of Culture: An exploration of the Borderland between Anthropology, Medicine and Psychiatry,* University of California, Berkeley.

Klinsong, Patima 1993, 'Prescription for Danger'. *The Nation,* Thursday, 4 March, p. C1.

Knodel, John, Chamratrithirong, Aphichat, & Debavalya, Nibhon 1987 *Thailand's Reproductive Revolution. Rapid Fertility Decline in a Third World Setting,* The University of Wisconsin Press, Madison, Wisconsin.

Knodel, J. & Chayovan, Napaporn 1989 'Contraceptive Initiation Patterns in Thailand', *Health and Population Studies based on the 1987 Thailand Demographic and Health Survey*, Institute of Population Studies, Chulalongkorn University, Bangkok, pp. 99-121.

Knodel, John, Havanon, Napaporn, & Pramualratana, Anthony 1983 *A Tale of Two Generations: A Qualitative Analysis of Fertility Transition in Thailand. Publication No. 80*, Institute of Population and Social Research, Mahidol University, Bangkok.

Knodel, John, Havanon, Napaporn, & Sittitrai, Werasit 1990 *Family Size and the Education of Children in the Context of Rapid Fertility Decline. Report No.2 January 1990*, Bangkok, Project on Socio-economic Consequences of Fertility Decline for the Thai Family, Institute of Population Studies, Chulalongkorn University.

Koblinsky, Marge, Timyan, Judith, & Gay, Jill (eds.) 1993 *The Health of Woman: A global perspective*, Westview Press, Boulder.

Koetsawang, Suporn 1973 'Induced abortion in Bangkok', *Abortion Research Notes*, vol. 2, no. 2, Suppl. 5.

_____ 1993 'Illegally Induced Abortion in Thailand', Paper presented at Paper presented at the IPPF SEAO Regional Programme Advisory Panel Meeting on Abortion, 29-30 October, Bali, Indonesia.

Koetsawang, Suporn, Gordon, J. & Pachauri, S. 1974 'Spontaneous and illegally induced abortions at Siriraj Hospital, Bangkok', *Paper presented at the First Scientific Congress in Family Planning*, January, *Colombo, Sri Lanka*.

Koetsawang, Suporn., Saha, A., & Pachauri, S. 1975 'Study of abortion in Thailand', *Paper presented at All India Congress in Obstetrics and Gynecology*, December, *Jamshedpur, India.*

_____ 1978 'Study of "spontaneous" abortion in Thailand', *International Journal of Gynaecology and Obstetrics*, vol. 15, no. 4, pp. 361-68.

Koetsawang, S., Varakamin, S., Satayapan, S. & Dusitsin, N. 1984 'NORPLANT clinical study in Thailand', *Long Acting Contraceptive Delivery Systems*, eds. G. Zatuchni, A. Goldsmith, J. Shelton, & S. Harper and Row, Philadelphia.

Komonkitiskun, Jiranan 1992 *Research Report. Analysis of Women's Role and Status from Esarn Proverbs*, Department of Foreign Languages, Khon Kaen University, Khon Kaen.

Kong-thap tham mulanithi 1981 *Tham thaeng...khong sut-thai haeng haiyanatham (Abortion: The Last Curve on the road to Moral Catastrophe)*, 3 ed., *Kong-thap tham mulanithi*, Bangkok.

Krannich, L, & Krannich, C. R. 1983 *The Politics of Family Planning Policy: Thailand - A Case of Successful Implementation*, University Press of America, Lanham, Madison.

Krongkaew, Medhi 1980 'The Distribution of and Access to Basic Health Services in Thailand', no. 82, Faculty of Economics, Thammasat University, Bangkok.

_____ 1993 'Poverty and Income Distribution', *The Thai Economy in Transition*, ed. P. G. Warr, Cambridge University Press, Melbourne, pp. 401-37.

Kundstadter, Peter 1978 'The Comparative Anthropological Study of Medical Systems in Society', *Culture and Healing in Asian Societies: Anthropological, Psychiatric, and Public Health Services*, eds. A. Kleinman, P. Kundstadter, E. R. Alexander, & J. L. Gale, Schenkman Publishing Company, Cambridge, MA, pp. 393-406.

Laderman, Carol 1982 'Giving Birth in a Malay Village', *Anthropology of Human Birth*, ed. M. A. Kay, F.A. Davis Company, Philadelphia, pp. 81-100.

_____ 1983 *Wives and Midwives: Childbirth and Nutrition in Rural Malaysia*, University of California Press, Berkeley.

_____ 1992 'Malay Medicine, Malay Person', *Anthropological Approaches to the Study of Ethnomedicine*, ed. M. Nichter, Gordon and Breach, Amsterdam, pp. 191-205.

Ladipo, Oladipo A. 1989 'Preventing and Managing Complications of Induced Abortion in Third World Countries', *International Journal of Gynecology and Obstetrics,* suppl. 3, pp. 21-8.

Larson, Ann, Elkins, David B., Maticka-Tyndale, Eleanor, Sithithaworn, Paiboon, Thongkrajai, Pramote, et al 1993 'Migration and Sexually Transmitted Infections in Rural Northeast Thailand', 5-9 December, Annecy, France.

Leder, Drew 1992 'A Tale of Two Bodies: The Cartesian Corpse and the Lived Body', *The Body in Medical Thought and Practice* ed. D. Leder, Kluwer Academic Publishers, Dordrecht, pp. 17-35.

Leslie, Charles M. 1977 'Pluralism and Integration in the Indian and Chinese Medial Systems', *Culture, Disease and Healing: Studies in Medical Anthropology,* ed. D. Landy, Macmillan Publishing Co. Inc, New York, pp. 511-18.

Lewin, Ellen 1998 'Wives, mothers and lesbians: rethinking resistance in the US', *Pragmatic women and body politics,* eds. M. Lock & P. A. Kaufert, Cambridge University Press, Cambridge, pp. 164-77.

Lightfoot, Paul, Fuller, Theodore, & Peerasit, Kamnuansilpa 1983 'Circulation and Interpersonal Networks Linking Rural and Urban Areas: The Case of Roi-Et, Northeastern Thailand', Papers of the East-West Population Institute, East-West Population Institute, Honolulu, Hawaii.

Lock, Margaret 1998 'Perfecting society: reproductive technologies, genetic testing, and the planned family in Japan', *Pragmatic women and body politics,* eds. M. Lock & P. A. Kaufert, Cambridge University Press, Cambridge, pp. 206-39.

Lock, Margaret, & Kaufert, Patricia A 1998 'Introduction', *Pragmatic women and body politics,* eds. M. Lock & P. A. Kaufert, Cambridge University Press, Cambridge, pp. 1-27.

London, Bruce 1980 *Metropolis and Nation in Thailand: The Political Economy of Uneven Development,* Westview Press, Boulder.

Luker, Kristin 1975 *Taking Chances: Abortion and the Decision Not to Contracept,* University of California Press, Berkeley.

_____ 1984 *Abortion and the Politics of Motherhood,* University of California Press, Berkeley.

Lyttleton, Chris 1993 'Knowledge and Meaning: The AIDS Education Campaign in Rural Northeast Thailand', *Social Science and Medicine* vol. 38, no. 1, pp. 135-46.

_____ 1994a 'The Good People of Isan: Commercial Sex in Northeast Thailand', *The Australian Journal of Anthropology,* vol. 5, no. 3, pp. 257-79.

_____ 1994b 'The Love-Your-Wife Disease: HIV/AIDS Education and the Construction of Meaning in Northeast Thailand' Unpublished PhD thesis, University of Sydney, Sydney.

MacCormack, Carol P (ed.) 1982 *Ethnography of Fertility and Birth,* Academic Press, London.

Mallett, Shelley 1997 'Conceiving Cultures: Person, Health and Place on Nua'ata, Papua New Guinea' Unpublished PhD thesis, La Trobe University, Bundoora, Victoria.

_____ forthcoming 'Colonial Impregnations: reconceptions of Maternal Health practice on Nua'ata, Papua New Guinea', *The Contemporary Pacific,* Special Issue: Mothering in the Contemporary Pacific: Fertility, Birthing and Family Planning.

Manderson, Lenore 1981a 'Roasting, Smoking and Dieting in Response to Birth: Malay Confinement in Cross-Cultural Perspective', *Social Science and Medicine,* vol. 15B, pp. 509-20.

_____ 1981b 'Traditional Food Classifications and Humoral Medical Theory in Peninsula Malaysia', *Ecology of Food and Nutrition,* vol. 11, pp. 81-93.

_____ 1986a 'Food Classification and Restriction in Peninsular Malaysia: Nature, Culture, Hot and Cold?', *Shared Wealth and Symbol: Food, Culture, and Society in Oceania and Southeast Asia*, ed. L. Manderson, Cambridge University Press, Cambridge, pp. 127-43 .

_____ 1986b 'Introduction: The Anthropology of Food in Oceania and Southeast Asia', *Shared Wealth and Symbol: Food, Culture, and Society in Oceania and Southeast Asia*, ed. L. Manderson, Cambridge University Press, Cambridge, pp. 1-25.

_____ 1990 'Patpong and Explorations of the Edges of Imagination', Paper presented at The International Conference on Gender and Sexuality in East and Southeast Asia, 9-11 December, Los Angeles.

Martin, Emily 1987 *The Woman in the Body: A Cultural Analysis of Reproduction*, Beacon Press, Boston.

Mathews, M. & Manderson, Lenore 1981 'Vietnamese behavioral and dietary precautions during confinement', *Ecology of Food and Nutrition*, vol. 11, pp. 9-16.

Maticka Tyndale, Eleanor, Haswell Elkins, Melissa, Kuyyakanond, Thicumporn, Kiewying, Monthira, & Elkins, David 1994a 'A research-based HIV intervention in Northeastern Thailand', *Health Transition Review*, vol. 4, pp. 349-67.

Maticka Tyndale, Eleanor, Kiewying, Monthira, Haswell Elkins, Melissa, Kuyyakanond, Thicumporn, Anursornteerakul, Soiy, et al 1994b 'Knowledge, Attitudes and Beliefs about HIV/AIDS among Women in Northeastern Thailand', *AIDS Education and Prevention*, vol. 6, no. 3, pp. 205-18.

Matsui, Yayori 1989 'Sexual Exploitation of Women: Child Prostitution and the Expanding Sex Industry', *Women's Asia*, Zed Books, London, pp. 62-74.

McDonnell, Etain, & Sukpanich, Tunya 1996 'Abortion: Damned If You Do, Damned If You Don't'. *Bangkok Post*, 5 June, Outlook Section.

Mies, Maria 1986 *Patriarchy and Accumulation on a World Scale: Women in the International Division of Labor*, Zed Books, London.

Mills, Mary Beth 1996 'Working for Wages in Bangkok, Reworking Gender and Family in the Countryside', Paper presented at The 6th International Conference on Thai Studies, 1-17 October, Chiang Mai, Thailand.

_____ 1997 'Contesting the margins of modernity: women, migration, and consumption in Thailand', *American Ethnologist*, vol. 24, no. 1, pp. 37-61.

_____ 1993 '"We are Not Like Our Mothers": Migrants, Modernity and Identity in Northeast Thailand' Unpublished PhD thesis, Graduate Division of the University of California, Berkeley.

_____ 1995 'Attack of the Widow Ghosts: Gender, Death, and Modernity in Northeast Thailand', *Bewitching Women, Pious Men: Gender and Body Politics in Southeast Asia*, eds. A. Ong & M. G. Peletz, University of California Press, Berkeley, pp. 244-273.

Moerman, Michael 1968 *Agricultural Change and Peasant Choice in a Thai village*, University of California Press, Berkeley.

Morgan, Lynn M. 1990 'When Does Life Begin? A Cross-Cultural Perspective on the Personhood of Fetuses and Young Children', *Abortion Rights and Fetal 'Personhood'*, eds. E. Doerr & J. W. Prescott, 2nd ed., Centerline Press, Long Beach, California, pp. 89-107.

Mougne, Christine M 1978 'An Ethnography of Reproduction: Changing Patterns of Fertility in a Northern Thai village', *Nature and Man in South East Asia*, ed. P. A. Stott, SOAS, University of London, London, pp. 68-106.

Muecke, Marjorie 1976 'Health Care Systems as Socialising Agents: Childbearing the Northern Thai and Western Ways', *Social Science and Medicine*, vol. 10, pp. 377-83.

_____ 1979 'An explanation of "wind illness" in Northern Thailand', *Culture, Medicine and Psychiatry*, vol. 3, pp. 267-300.

_____ 1981 'Changes in Women's Status Associated with Modernisation in Northern Thailand', *Southeast Asia: Women, Changing Social Structure and Cultural Continuity*, eds. G. B. Hainsworth, H. E. Jacobson, T. G. McGee, & J. Placzek, University of Ottawa Press, Ottawa, pp. 53-65.

_____ 1984 'Make Money Not Babies. Changing Status Markers of Northern Thai Women', *Anthropology Today*, vol. 26, no. 4, pp. 459-70.

_____ 1989 'The New Thai "Nun": A Paradigm Shift From Buddha to Chamatevi', Annual Meeting of the American Anthropological Association, 15-19 November, Washington D C.

_____ 1992 'Mother Sold Food, Daughter Sells Her Body: The Cultural Continuity of Prostitution', *Social Science and Medicine*, vol. 35, no. 7, pp. 891-901.

Mulholland, Jean 1979 'Thai Traditional Medicine: Ancient Thought and Practice in a Thai Context', *Journal of the Siam Society*, vol. 67, pp. 80-115.

_____ 1989 *Herbal Medicine in Paediatrics. Translation of a Thai Book of Genesis*, Faculty of Asian Studies, Australian National University, Canberra.

Narkavonnakit, Tongplaew 1979a 'Abortion in Rural Thailand: A Survey of Practitioners', *Studies in Family Planning*, vol. 10, no. 8/9, pp. 223-29.

_____ 1979b *Rural abortion in Thailand: a National Survey of Practitioners*. Bangkok, Research and Evaluation, National Family Planning Program.

Narkavonnakit, Tongplaew, & Bennett, Anthony 1981 'Health Consequences of Induced Abortion in Rural Northeast Thailand', *Studies in Family Planning*, vol. 12, no. 2, pp. 58-65.

Nations, Marilyn K., Misago, Chizuru, Fonesca, Walter, Correia, Luciano L. & Campbell, Oona M.R. 1997 'Women's Hidden Transcripts About Abortion in Brazil', *Social Science and Medicine*, vol. 44, no. 12, pp. 1833-45.

Newman, Lucile F. 1981 'Midwives and Modernization', *Medical Anthropology*, vol. 5, no. 1, pp. 1-12.

_____ (ed.) 1985 *Women's Medicine. A Cross-Cultural Study of Indigenous Fertility Regulation*, Rutgers University Press, New Brunswick, New Jersey.

Ngin, Chor-Swang 1985 'Indigenous Fertility Regulating Methods Among Two Chinese Communities in Malaysia', *Women's Medicine. A Cross-Cultural Study of Indigenous Fertility Regulation*, ed. L. F. Newman, Rutgers University Press, New Brunswick, New Jersey, pp. 25-42.

Nichter, Mark 1980 'The Layperson's Perception of Medicine as Perspective into the Utilization of Multiple Therapy Systems in the Indian Context', *Social Science and Medicine*, vol. 14B, pp. 225-33.

_____ 1996 'Self-medication and STD prevention', *Sexually Transmitted Diseases*, vol. Sept/Oct, pp. 353-56.

Nichter, Mark, & Nichter, Mimi 1987 'Cultural Notions of Fertility in South Asia and Their Impact on Sri Lankan Family Planning Practices', *Human Organization*, vol. 46, no. 1, pp. 18-28.

_____ 1996 *Anthropology and International Health: Asian Case Studies*, Gordon and Breach Publishers, Amsterdam.

Onchan, Tongroj 1985 'Migration and Characteristics of Migrants in Selected Areas of Thailand', *Urbanisation and Migration in Asean Development*, eds. P. M. Hauser, D. B. Suits, & N. Ogawa, National Institute for Research Advancement, Tokyo, pp. 455-74.

Osaka, Ryoko, & Nanakorn, Somsong 1995a 'Health Care of Villagers in Northeast Thailand - A Health Diary Study', *The Kurume Medical Journal*, vol. 43, pp. 49-54.

Osaka, Ryoko, & Nanakorn, Somsong 1995b 'Health Diary Study on Illness in Rural Northeast Thailand', *The Kurume Medical Journal*, vol. 42, pp. 269-74.

Parnwell, Mike 1986 'Rural Development in North-East Thailand', *Rural Development in North-East Thailand: Case Studies in Migration, Irrigation, and Rural Credit,* ed. M. Parnwell, Centre for South EAst Asian Studies, Univerity of Hull, Hull, pp. 1-12.

Payutto, Phra Thepwethi Prayut 1993 *Tham thaeng: tatsinjai yangrai chiwit rerm ton mu'arai kan tham thaeng nai thatna khong phraphuthasasana (Abortion: How to decide? When does life begin? A Buddhist view of abortion),* Mulnithi phuthatham (Phuthatham Foundation), Bangkok.

Pedersen, Lise R. 1968 'Aspects of Women's Life in Rural Thailand', *Folk,* vol. 10, pp. 136-49.

Pengsaa, P., Udomthavornsuk, B., Vatanasapt, W., Pesi, M., Tungvorapongchai, V. & Shibata, Y 1989 'Survival Analysis of Cervical Cancer Patients at Srinagarind Hospital 1976-1987', *Journal of the Medical Association of Thailand,* vol. 72, no. 6, pp. 346-50.

Petchesky, Rosalind 1990 *Abortion and Woman's Choice: The State, Sexuality and Reproductive Freedom,* revised ed., Northeastern University Press, Boston.

Petersen, Alan R. 1993 'Re-Defining the Subject?: The Influence of Foucault on the Sociology of Health and Illness', *Annual Review of Health Social Science,* vol. 3, pp. 119-31.

Phintong, Preecha 1989 *Isan-Thai-English Dictionary,* 1st ed., Siritham Press, Ubolratchathani, Thailand.

Phongpaichit, Pasuk 1980 'The Open Economy and Its Friends: The 'Development' of Thailand', *Pacific Affairs,* vol. 53, no. 3, pp. 440-60.

_____ 1982a *Employment, Income and the Mobilisation of Local Resources in Three Thai Villages,* Asian Employment Programme, Bangkok.

_____ 1982b *From Peasant Girls to Bangkok Masseuses,* International Labour Office, Geneva.

Phuapradit, W., Sirivongs, B., & Chaturachinda, K. 1985 'Maternal mortality in Ramathibodi Hospital: a 14-year review', *Journal of the Medical Association of Thailand,* vol. 68, no. 12, pp. 654-58.

_____ 1986 'Abortion: an attitude study of professional staff at Ramathibodi Hospital', *Journal of the Medical Association of Thailand,* vol. 69, no. 1, pp. 22-7.

Pikaktepsombati, Pichit, & Wongboonsin, Kua 1989 'Maternal Health Care: Recent trends, Differentials and Correlates', *Health and Population Studies Based on the 1987 Thailand Demographic and Health Survey,* Institute of Population Studies, Chulalongkorn University, Bangkok, pp. 85-97.

Pillsbury, B. 1982 'Doing the month: confinement and convalescence of Chinese women after childbirth', *Anthropology of Human Birth,* ed. M. Kay, F.A. Davis Company, Philadelphia, pp. 119-46.

Pinchun, P., & Chullapram, T. 1993 'A 10-year review of maternal mortality in Chon Buri Hospital, Thailand', *Journal of the Medical Association of Thailand,* vol. 76, no. 6, pp. 308-13.

Pittman, Patricia, & Hartigan, Pamela 1996 'Gender Inequality: An Issue for Quality Assessment Researchers and Managers', *Health Care for Women International,* vol. 17, no. 5, pp. 469-86.

Pongthai, S., Phuapradit, W., & Chaturachinda, K. 1984 'Illegally induced abortion: observation at Ramathibodi Hospital', *Journal of the Medical Association of Thailand,* vol. 67, no. Suppl 2, pp. 50-3.

Population Council 1981 *Abortion in Thailand: A Review of the Literature,* The Population Council, Bangkok.

Pornsiripongse, Saowapa, & Rawangpan, Nittaya 1996 'High Risk Behaviours among Female Commercial Sex Workers and Male Clients on Transmission Routes in Thailand', The

Third Asia and Pacific Conference on Social Science and Medicine, 11-16 February, Edith Cowen University, Perth.

Potter, Sulamith Heins 1977 *Family Life in a Northern Thai Village: A Study in the Structural Significance of Women,* University of California Press, Berkeley.

Poulsen, Anders 1983 *Pregnancy and Childbirth - its Customs and Rites in a North-eastern Thai Village,* Danish International Development Agency, Copenhagen.

Prasartkul, Pramote, & Sethaput, Chanya 1982 'Women's Role and Status in Family Planning', *Women in Development: Implications for Population Dynamics in Thailand,* eds. S. Prasith-rathsint & S. Piampiti, The National Institute of Development Administration, Bangkok, pp. 234-53.

Prukpongsawalee, Malee 1982 'Women and the Law', *Women in Development: Implications for Population Dynamics in Thailand,* eds. S. Prasith-rathsint & S. Piampiti, The National Institute of Development Administration, Bangkok, pp. 144-76.

Pungpak, S, Riganti, M, Bunnag, D, & Harinasuta, T 1985 'Clinical Features of Severe Opisthorciasis Viverrini', *Southeast Asian Journal of Tropical Medicine and Public Health,* vol. 16, pp. 405-9.

Rajadhon, Phya Anuman 1968 *Essays on Thai Folklore,* The Social Science Association Press of Thailand, Bangkok.

Ram, Kalpana 1998 'Maternity and the Story of Enlightenment in the Colonies: Tamil Coastal Women, South India', *Maternities and Modernities: Colonial and postcolonial experiences in Asia and the Pacific,* eds. K. Ram & M. Jolly, Cambridge University Press, Cambridge, pp. 114-43.

Ram, Kalpana, & Jolly, Margaret (eds.) 1998 *Maternities and Modernities: Colonial and postcolonial experiences in Asia and the Pacific,* Cambridge University Press, Cambridge.

Rathanamongkolmas, Abhinya Charoanborn 1983 'Developmental Stances of Thai Women Elites: A Study of Socialisation, Social Roles and Social Policy Prescriptions' Unpublished PhD, Indiana University, Bloomington.

Rattakul, P. 1971 'Septic abortion: the scourge of modern obstetrics', *Journal of the Medical Association of Thailand,* vol. 54, no. 5, pp. 312-19.

Rauyajin, Oratai 1979 'Induced Abortion: Facts and Prospect in Thailand', Mahidol University, Bangkok.

Reeler, A. V. 1990 'Injections: A Fatal Attraction', *Social Science and Medicine,* vol. 31, no. 10, pp. 1119-25.

Rice, Pranee Liamputtong 1993 *My Forty Days,* The Vietnamese Antenatal/Postnatal Support Project, Melbourne.

_____ (ed.) 1994 *Asian Mothers, Australian Birth. Pregnancy, childbirth and childrearing: the Asian experience in an English speaking country,* Ausmed Publications, Melbourne.

Rice, Pranee Liamputtong, & Manderson, Lenore (eds.) 1996 *Maternity and Reproductive Health in Asian Societies,* Harwood Academic Publishers, Sydney.

Riley, James N, & Sermsri, Santhat 1974 'The Variegated Thai Medical System as a Context for Birth Control Services', Institute for Population and Social Research, Mahidol University, Bangkok.

Ringheim, K 1993 'Factors that Determine Prevalence of Use of Contraceptive Methods for Men', *Studies in Family Planning,* vol. 24, no. 2, pp. 87-99.

Rodman, Margaret 1992 'Empowering Place: Multilocality and Multivocality', *American Anthropologist,* vol. 94, pp. 640-56.

Rozario, Shanti 1998 'The dai and the doctor: discourses on women's reproductive health in rural Bangladesh', *Maternities and Modernities: Colonial and postcolonial experiences in Asia and the Pacific,* eds. K. Ram & M. Jolly, Cambridge University Press, Cambridge, pp. 144-76.

Rylko-Bauer, Barbara 1996 'Abortion from a Cross-Cultural Perspective: An Introduction', *Social Science and Medicine,* vol. 42, no. 4, pp. 479-82.

Sadun, E. H. 1955 'Studies on *Opisthorcis viverrini* in Thailand', *American Journal of Hygiene,* vol. 62, pp. 81-115.

Santasombat, Yos 1992 *Mae Ying Si Khai Tua (Woman, Sell Yourself),* Institute of Local Community Development, Bangkok.

Sargent, Carolyn, & Bascope, Grace 1996 'Ways of Knowing about Birth in Three Cultures', *Medical Anthropology Quarterly,* vol. 10, no. 2, pp. 213-36.

Sargent, Carol, Marcucci, J., & Elliston, E. 1983 'Tiger bones, fire and wine: maternity care in a Kampuchean refugee community', *Medical Anthropology,* vol. 7, no. 4, pp. 67-79.

Scheper-Hughes, Nancy 1992 *Death Without Weeping: The Violence of Everyday Life in Brazil,* University of California Press, Berkeley.

Scheper-Hughes, N., & Lock, M. 1987 'The Mindful Body: A Prolegomenon to Future Work in Medical Anthropology', *Medical Anthropology Quarterly,* vol. 1, no. 1, pp. 6-41.

Scott, James 1985 *Weapons of the Weak: Everyday Forms of Peasant Resistance,* Yale University Press, New Haven.

Sereewat-Srisang, Sudarat 1987 'Migration, Tourism and Women', Unpublished paper, Women's Study Program, Chiangmai University, Chiangmai.

Sermsri, Santhat 1988 'Utilisation of Traditional and Modern Health Care Services in Thailand', *Traditional and Modern Health Care Utilization in the Eighties: A Comparative Study of Selected Countries,* ed. S. R. Quah, The University of California Press, Berkeley.

Sesia, Paola M. 1996 '"Women Come Here on Their Own When They Need To": Prenatal Care, Authoritative Knowledge, and Maternal Health in Oaxaca', *Medical Anthropology Quarterly,* vol. 10, no. 2, pp. 121-40.

Shah, Iqbal, Thongthai, Varachai, Leoprapai, Boonlert, Mundigo, Axel I, Prasartkul, Pramote, & Chamratrithrong, Aphichat 1991 'Knowledge and Perceptions About AIDS Among Married Women in Bangkok', *Social Science and Medicine,* vol. 33, no. 11, pp. 1287-93.

Sich, Dorothea 1981 'Traditional Concepts and Customs on Pregnancy, Birth and Post Partum Period in Rural Korea', *Social Science and Medicine,* vol. 15B, pp. 65-9.

Simmons, Pam 1996 'Breaking the silence on abortion'. *The Nation,* Friday, 20 September, Opinion, A5.

Simmons, Ruth, & Elias, Christopher 1994 'The Study of Client-Provider Interactions: A Review of Methodological Issues', *Studies in Family Planning,* vol. 25, pp. 1-17.

Simmons, Ruth, Koenig, M. A., & Huque, Zahidul 1990 'Maternal-child health and family planning: User perspectives and service constraints in rural Bangladesh', *Studies in Family Planning,* vol. 21, pp. 187-96.

Sittitrai, Werasit 1988 'Rural transformation in Northern Thailand' Unpublished PhD, University of Hawaii, Honolulu, Hawaii.

_____ 1990a 'HIV Transmission and Interventions in Thailand: Socio-Economic and Cultural Issues', Paper presented at AIDS in Asia and the Pacific Conference, 5-8 August, Canberra.

_____ 1990b 'Multi-Stage Interventions for Sex Workers', Paper presented at AIDS in Asia and the Pacific Conference, 5-8 August, Canberra.

Sittitrai, Werasit, Wolff, B., Knodel, J., Havanon, Napaporn, & Podhista, Chai 1991 *Family Size and Family Well-Being: The Views of Thai Villagers,* Institue of Population Studies, Chulalongkorn University, Bangkok.

Sivin, I., Robertson, D. N., & Stern, J. 1980 'Norplant: reversible implant contraception', *Studies in Family Planning,* vol. 11, no. 7/8, pp. 227-35.

Skrobanek, Siripon 1990 'Child Prostitution in Thailand', *Voices of Thai Women,* vol. 4, pp. 10-17.

Skultans, Vieda 1988 'Menstrual Symbolism in South Wales', *Blood Magic: The Anthropology of Menstruation,* eds. T. Buckley & A. Gottlieb, University of California Press, Berkeley, pp. 137-60.

Sobo, E.J. 1993 *One Blood: The Jamaican Body,* State University of New York Press, Albany, NY.

_____ 1996 'Abortion Traditions in Rural Jamaica', *Social Science and Medicine,* vol. 42, no. 4, pp. 495-508.

Somswasdi, Virada 1987 'Women in the Constitutions of Thailand: Far-fetched Hope for Equality', Paper presented at Women's Global Perspectives: Bridging the Gap in their Constitutions, 19-23 July, Philadelphia.

Soonthorndhada, Amara 1996 *Sexual Attitiudes and Behaviours and Contraceptive Use of Late Female Adolescents in Bangkok: A Comparative Study of Students and Factory Workers,* Institute for Population and Social Research, Mahidol University, Salaya, Nakornpathom.

Sparkes, Stephen 1995 'Taming Nature - Controlling Fertility. Concepts of Nature and Gender among the Isan of Northeast Thailand', *Asian Perceptions of Nature: A Critical Approach,* eds. O. Bruun & A. Kalland, Curzon Press, Surrey, pp. 63-87.

Stein, Dorothy 1995 *People Who Count: Population and Politics, Women and Children,* Earthscan, London.

Steinberg, Susan 1996 'Childbearing Research: A Transcultural Review', *Social Science and Medicine,* vol. 43, no. 12, pp. 1765-84.

Strathern, Andrew J 1996 *Body Thoughts,* The University of Michigan Press, Ann Arbor.

Tambiah, Stanley Jeyaraja 1970 *Buddhism and the Spirit Cults in North-East Thailand,* Cambridge University Press, Cambridge.

_____ 1984 *The Buddhist Saints of the Forest and the Cult of Amulets,* Cambridge University Press, Cambridge.

Tansubhapol, Kulcharee 1997 'The right to choose'. *Bangkok Post,* September 20, Outlook Section.

Tantiwiramonond, Darunee, & Pandey, Ranjan Shashi 1997 'New Opportunities or New Inequalities: Development Issues and Women's Lives in Thailand', *Women, Gender Relations and Development in Thai Society,* eds. V. Somswasdi & S. Theobald, Vol. 1, Women Studies Center, Faculty of Social Sciences, Chiang Mai University, Chiang Mai, pp. 83-135.

_____ 1987 'The Status and Role of Thai Women in the Pre-Modern Period: A Historical and Cultural Perspective', *Sojourn,* vol. 2, no. 1, pp. 125-49.

Thailand, Department of Rural Development 1989a '*Baep Sorptham khormun phu'nthan radap muban. Muban 1,5,8,9,10,11* (Village Survey Data, Ban Srisaket)'in Thai, Unpublished report.

_____ 1989b '*Baep Sorptham khormun phu'nthan radap muban. Muban 1,5,8,9,10,11* (Village Survey Data, Ban Srisaket)' in Thai, Unpublished report.

Thailand, Ministry of Public Health 1977 *Village Health Communicator and Village Health Volunteer Scheme, Thailand 1977-1981.* Bangkok, Health Training Division, The Office of the Under-Secretary of State for Public Health.

_____ 1984 *Intensive study of rural traditional abortion in Thailand,* Ministry of Public Health. Special Projects Section, Family Health Division, Department of Health, Bangkok.

_____ 1988 *Norplant acceptability in Thailand. Report on a survey of acceptors in clinical trial,* Research and Evaluation Unit, Family Health Division, Department of Health, Ministry of Public Health, Bangkok.

_____ 1993 *Sathiti prachagon lae kan anamai khrop khrua lem 3. Selected Population and Family Health Statistics, 1992,* Thai Population Information Centre, Family Health Division, Department of Health, Ministry of Public Health, Bangkok.

_____ no date *A New Contraceptive Technology for Thailand: A Finding (sic) Proposal for a Feasibility Study. Report of Client Continuation of Norplant, Bangkok, Thailand,* National Family Planning Program, Ministry of Public Health, Bangkok.

Thailand, Ministry of Public Health, & World Health Organisation 1994 *Follow up Study of 1986 Norplant Acceptors.* Nonthaburi, Family Health Division, Ministry of Public Health.

Thailand, NESDB 1992 *The Seventh National Economic and Social Development Plan (1992-1996),* National Economic and Social Development Board, Office of the Prime Minister, Bangkok.

Thailand, National Statistical Office 1990 *Preliminary Report of the 1990 Household Socio-Economic Survey,* Office of the Prime Minister, Bangkok.

Thailand, Roi Et Provincial Health Office 1992 'AIDS situation as of 27 February, 1992, Roi Et', in Thai, Unpublished report, Roi Et Provincial Health Office, AIDS Division, Roi Et.

Thitsa, Khin 1980 *Providence and Prostitution: Women in Buddhist Thailand,* Change International Reports, London.

_____ 1983 'Nuns, Mediums and Prostitutes in Chiengmai: A Study of Some Marginal Categories of Women', *Women and Development in South-East Asia,* eds. K. Thitsa & S. Howell, University of Kent, Canterbury, pp. 4-45.

Thomson, Suteera 1990 *Gender Issues in Thailand Development: A Paper Prepared for the UN Development Programme.* Bangkok, Gender and Development Research Institute.

Thongchai, Varachai, & Guest, Philip 1995 'Thai Sexual Attitudes and Behaviour: Results from a Recent National Survey', Paper presented at conference on Gender and Sexuality in Modern Thailand, 11-12 July, 1995, Australian National University, Canberra.

Thongkrajai, Earporn, Thongkrajai, Pramote, & Stoeckl, Jeffrey n.d. *Socioeconomic and Health Program Effects Upon the Behavioural Management of Diarrhoeal Disease in Northeast Thailand,* The Population Council, Bangkok.

Thongthiraj, Took Took 1994 'Toward a Struggle against Invisibility: Love between Women in Thailand', *Amerasia Journal,* vol. 20, no. 1, pp. 45-58.

Thorbek, Susan 1987 *Voices from the City,* Zed Books Ltd, London.

Tirasawat, Penporn 1985 'The Impact of Migration on Conditions at the Origin: A Study of Selcted Villages in Thailand', *Urbanisation and Migration in Asean Development,* eds. P. M. Hauser, D. B. Suits, & N. Ogawa, National Institute for Research Advancement, Tokyo, pp. 475-96.

Toongsuwan, S., Bhadrakom, C., & Usavajindawatn, C. 1973 'Therapeutic abortions in Siriraj Hospital', *Journal of the Medical Association of Thailand,* vol. 56, no. 4, pp. 237-40.

Townsend, Kimberley, & Rice, Pranee Liamputtong 1996 'A baby is born in Site 2 Camp: pregnancy, birth and confinement among Cambodian refugee women', *Maternity and Reproductive Health in Asian Societies,* eds. P. Liamputtong Rice & L. Manderson, Harwood Academic Publishers, Amsterdam, pp. 125-44.

Truong, Thanh-Dam 1990 *Sex, Money and Morality: Prostitution and Tourism in Southeast Asia,* Zed Books, London.

Turton, Andrew 1972 'Matrilineal Descent Groups and Spirit Cults of the Thai-Yuan in Northern Thailand', *Journal of the Siam Society,* vol. 60, pp. 217-56.

_____ 1978 'The Current Situation in the Thai Countryside', *Thailand: Roots of Conflict,* eds. A. Turton, J. Fast, & M. Caldwell, Spokesman, Nottingham, pp. 143-57.

Ungphakorn, Jon 1990 'The Impact of AIDS on Women in Thailand', Paper presented at AIDS in Asia and the Pacific Conference, 5-8 August 1990, Canberra.

Van Esterik, John 1982a 'Women Meditation Teachers in Thailand', *Women of Southeast Asia*, ed. P. V. Esterik, Northern Illinois University, Wyoming, pp. 42-54.

Van Esterik, Penny 1982b 'Laywomen in Theravada Buddhism', *Women of Southeast Asia*, ed. P. V. Esterik, Northern Illinois University, Wyoming, pp. 55-78.

_____ 1985 'The Cultural Context of Breastfeeding in Rural Thailand', *Breastfeeding, Child Health and Child Spacing: Cross-Cultural Perspectives*, eds. V. Hull & M. Simpson, Croom Helm, London, pp. 139-61.

_____ 1986 'Feeding their Faith: Recipe Knowledge Among Thai Buddhist Women', *Food and Foodways*, vol. 1, pp. 197-215.

_____ 1988 'To Strengthen and Refresh: Herbal Therapy in South-East Asia', *Social Science and Medicine*, vol. 27, no. 8, pp. 761-68.

_____ 1992 'Thai Prostitution and the Medical Gaze', *Gender and Development in Southeast Asia. Proceedings of the Twentieth Meetings of the Canadian Council for Southeast Asian Studies, York University, October 18-20, 1991*, eds. P. V. Esterik & J. V. Esterik, Canadian Asian Studies Association, Montreal.

Van Esterik, Penny, & Van Esterik, John (eds.) 1992 *Gender and Development in Southeast Asia. Proceedings of the Twentieth Meetings of the Canadian Council for Southeast Asian Studies, York University, October 18-20, 1991*, Canadian Asian Studies Association, Montreal.

Vanlandingham, Mark, Knodel, John, Saengtienchai, Chanpen & Pramualratana, Anthony 1998 'In the company of friends: peer influence on Thai male extramarital sex', *Social Science and Medicine*, vol. 47, no.12, pp. 1993-2011.

Vanlandingham, Mark, Somboon, Suprasert, Grandjean, Nancy, & Werasit, Sittitrai 1995 'Two views of risky sexual practices among northern Thai males: the health belief model and the theory of reasoned action', *Journal of Health and Social Behavior*, vol. 36, pp. 195-212.

Varakamin, S., Devaphalin, V., Narkavonkit, T., & Wright, N. H. 1977 'Attitudes toward abortion in Thailand: a survey of senior medical students', *Studies in Family Planning*, vol. 8, no. 11, pp. 288-293.

Vera, H. 1993 'The client's view of high quality care in Santiago, Chile', *Studies in Family Planning*, vol. 24, pp. 40-9.

Verderese, M. & Turnball, L. 1975 *The Traditional Birth Attendant in Maternal and Child Health and Family Planning*, World Health Organisation (WHO), Geneva.

Viravaidya, Mechai 1990 'Confronting a Culture at Risk: A Curbside View of AIDS Education and Prevention in Thailand', Paper presented at AIDS in Asia and the Pacific Conference, 5-8 August, Canberra.

Viravaidya, Mechai, Obremskey, Stasia A, & Myers, Charles 1992 'The Economic Impact of AIDS on Thailand', Working paper series No. 4, Harvard School of Public Health, Boston.

Waitzkin, H. 1991 *The politics of medical encounters*, Yale University Press, New Haven.

Weisberg, Daniel H. 1982 'Northern Thai Health Care Alternatives: Patient Control and the Structure of Medical Pluralism', *Social Science and Medicine*, vol. 16, pp. 1507-17.

_____ 1984 'The Practice of 'Dr' Paep: Continuity and Change in Indigenous Healing in Northern Thailand', *Social Science and Medicine*, vol. 18, no. 2, pp. 117-28.

Westermeyer, John 1988 'Folk Medicine in Laos: A Comparison between Two Ethnic Groups', *Social Science and Medicine*, vol. 27, no. 8, pp. 769-78.

Whittaker, Andrea 1996a 'Silence and Susceptibility: Northeast Thai village women and HIV/AIDS', *Women, Sexuality, Culture: Cross-cultural Perspectives on Sexuality*, eds. M. Spongberg, J. Larbalestier, & M. Winn, Women's Studies Centre, University of Sydney, Sydney, pp. 104-14.

_____ 1996b 'Water Serpents and Staying by the Fire: Markers of Maturity in a Northeast Thai Village', Paper presented at 20th Anniversary conference of the Asian Studies Association of Australia, "Communications with Asia", 8-11 July, La Trobe University, Melbourne.

_____ 1996c 'White blood and falling wombs: ethnogynaecology in northeast Thailand', *Maternity and Reproductive Health in Asian Societies,* eds. P. Liamputtong Rice & L. Manderson, Harwood Academic Publishers, Amsterdam, pp. 207-25.

_____ 1996d 'Quality of Care for Women in Northeast Thailand: Intersections of Class, Gender and Ethnicity,' *Health Care for Women International,* vol. 17, no. 5, pp. 435-48.

_____ 1998 'Women's Desires and Burden: Family Planning in Northeast Thailand,' *Asian Studies Review,* vol. 22, no. 2, pp. 137-55.

_____ 1999a 'Women and Capitalist Transformation in a Northeastern Thai Village,' *Thai Sexuality and Modernity,* eds. P. Jackson & N. Cook, Silkworm Books, Chiang Mai.

_____ 1999b 'Birth and the Postpartum in Northeast Thailand: Contesting Modernity and Tradition,' *Medical Anthropology,* vol. 18, pp.1-29.

Whittaker, Maxine, Rezina Mita, Hossain, Bazle, & Koenig, Michael 1996 'Evaluating Rural Bangladeshi Women's Perspectives of Quality in Family Planning Services', *Health Care for Women International,* vol. 17, no. 5, pp. 393-412.

Widyantoro, Ninuk 1993 'The Story of Norplant Implants in Indonesia', *Reproductive Health Matters,* vol. 3, May, pp. 20-29.

Wijeyewardene, Gehan 1984 'Northern Thai Succession and the Search for Matriliny', *Mankind,* vol. 14, no. 4, supplement 3, pp. 286-92.

Winikoff, Beverly 1988 'Women's Health: An Alternative Perspective for Choosing Interventions', *Studies in Family Planning,* vol. 19, no. 4, pp. 197-213.

World Health Organization 1994 Creating Common Ground in Asia: Women's Perspectives on the Selection and Introduction of fertility Regulation Technologies. Report of a meeting between women's health advocates, researchers, providers and policy makers. Manila, 5-8 October, 1992, Special Programme of Research, Development and Research Training in Human Reproduction, World Health Organization, Geneva.

Index

abortion, 18, 137, 150-176;
complications of, 151, 160-161;
legislation, 154-155; abortion
rhetoric, 155-156; techniques of,
159, 163-164; definitions of, 163-4;
decision-making, 166-170; legal
abortions 172-175; *see also*
massage abortion, injection
abortion
agency, 9-10,102-103, 152-153, 175-
176
antenatal care, 126-130
antibiotics, 96-97; *see* self-
medication
authoritative knowledge,124-125,
137-138

Ban Srisaket, 25-27
biomedicine, 70; incorporation into
local medicine, 57-58; *see also*
government health services,
medical pluralism
bio-power, 7-8, 152; *see also* power
birth,12,18; in village 121, 131-132,
135-136; in hospital, 122, 133;
power relations in, 134; changing
patterns of, 125-126; the role of
men, 133-4; *see also* antenatal care,
maternity, traditional birth
attendants
blood, 73-76, 164; lochia, 141; *see
also* menstruation
body, 7-9, 49-58; women's bodies
70-74; sexual differentiation, 71
Bourdieu, Pierre, 124
Brodwin, Paul, 48,68
Buddhist sin (*bap*), 171-172

capitalist transformation, 27, 33
care-seeking, 94-95, 97-100; *see also*
self medication, medical pluralism
cervical cancer, 87-89
children, definitions of, 165; child
spacing, 107; social recognition of,
147-148
conception,74-76,
condom use, 106-7, 112; and
STD/HIV prevention, 93-94
contraception, delivery of services,
117-119; failure, 157, 174;
traditional means of, 104-105; side
effects of, 110-113; as
abortifacients, 165; *see also* family
planning, pill, IUD, condom,
sterilisation, vasectomies, Depo
Provera (DMPA), Norplant
cultural capital, 17, 124, 138

Depo Provera (DMPA), 106-7, 111-
112
diet 50-51; restrictions, 97, 142-144;
in pregnancy 127; *see also* humoral
elements
dirtiness, *see* ethnicity
disability, 166
discharge, 84-87; and cervical cancer,
87; *see also* gynecological
problems
discourses, 7
district hospitals, 61-62

embodiment, 7-9, 49-50; *see also*
body
emmenagogues, *see* menstrual
regulation